ANALYTICAL PHOTOGRAMMETRY

SECOND EDITION

Related Journals

Advances in Space Research

Space Technology (formerly Earth-Oriented
Applications of Space Technology)

ANALYTICAL PHOTOGRAMMETRY

SECOND EDITION

BY

SANJIB K. GHOSH

PERGAMON PRESS

NEW YORK · OXFORD · BEIJING · FRANKFURT
SÃO PAULO · SYDNEY · TOKYO · TORONTO

U.S.A.	Pergamon Press, Maxwell House, Fairview Park, Elmsford, New York 10523, U.S.A.
U.K.	Pergamon Press, Headington Hill Hall, Oxford OX3 0BW, England
PEOPLE'S REPUBLIC OF CHINA	Pergamon Press, Room 4037, Qianmen Hotel, Beijing, People's Republic of China
FEDERAL REPUBLIC OF GERMANY	Pergamon Press, Hammerweg 6, D-6242 Kronberg, Federal Republic of Germany
BRAZIL	Pergamon Editora, Rue Eça de Queiros, 346, CEP 04011, Paraiso, São Paulo, Brazil
AUSTRALIA	Pergamon Press Australia, P.O. Box 544, Potts Point, N.S.W. 2011, Australia
JAPAN	Pergamon Press, 8th Floor, Matsuoka Central Building, 1-7-1 Nishishinjuku, Shinjuku-ku, Tokyo 160, Japan
CANADA	Pergamon Press Canada, Suite No 271, 253 College Street, Toronto, Ontario, Canada M5T 1R5

Copyright © 1988 Pergamon Books Inc.

First edition 1979
Second edition 1988

Library of Congress Cataloging in Publication Data
Ghosh, Sanjib Kumar, 1925–
Analytical photogrammetry,
Bibliography: p.
Includes index.
I. Photogrammetry.   I. Title.
TR693.055   1988   526.9'82   87-29134

British Library Cataloguing in Publication Data
Ghosh, Sanjib K.
Analytical photogrammetry.—2nd ed.
I. Photogrammetry—Mathematics
I. Title
526.9'82'0151   TA593

ISBN 0-08-036103-X

Printed in Great Britain by A. Wheaton & Co. Ltd, Exeter

To

RANA and RAJA

My sons, my two legs to walk,
        My two wings to fly.
I wish I had all the answers
        To their 'how' and 'why'.

... Man is not travelling from error to truth, but
from truth to truth, from lower to higher truth ...

SWAMI VIVEKANANDA, 1893
Chicago Lectures

CONTENTS

LIST OF FIGURES

LIST OF TABLES

PREFACE

TO THE FIRST EDITION

The main purpose of this book is to establish aspects of analytical photogramme-tric concepts and procedures, the backbone of which consists of various *Mathematic-al Models*. In scientific usage, the word 'model' is often applied to physical or conceptual systems that are supposed to represent the involved chain of events in a phenomenon under study. A variety of languages is used in a conceptual model. The system can be expressed in ordinary English, in terms of the specialized scientific jargons, or through the abstract symbolic languages from the domain of Mathematics. Systems of the last type, called 'mathematical models', have been used in physical sciences for centuries.

A mathematical model provides insight into the underlying chain of events. There is, however, no mystery about the way in which this insight is achieved. Mathematical models have no scientific values until and unless they have been adequately va-lidated with factual data through experience or research.

Mathematical models are often, in a way, 'crippled' by a lack of informational backgrounds, and the task of making the connection to reality is difficult. In this respect, the involved people, both the scientist and the mathematician, strive for 'generality'. The mathematician is concerned with generality in the form of the statement, and the scientist with generality in its content. The former objective -- the generality of language, and the latter -- one of fact, can be incompatible in some cases. Such differences in the goals of mathematics and sciences may lead to differences in strategies of model-making. Traditionally, this task of model-making has been carried out by mathematically minded individuals, often yielding headway in unproductive directions.

The *strategy* for a productive direction is simple. Firstly, one seemingly cor-rect mathematical model is set up. Secondly, implications of the model are explo-red. Thirdly, outcomes due to the model are compared with reported results. If the theory fits the facts, it provides scientific validation. Whatever its mathematic-al virtues may be, the model has no specific value unless it has been validated.

Scientific validation is an open-ended process. As a mathematical model is suc-cessfully tested for repeated performances, it becomes established for all practi-cal uses. Otherwise, depending on its degree of failure, it stands to be changed, modified or simply rejected.

There is no mathematical-scientific approach that can guarantee fully successful

AP-B

xvii

results in the complex circumstances of major problems.   The user of ideas presented in this book must be aware of this reality of practical life.   In the   context of action, it is not easy to move from the abstract ideal of mathematical generality to the discrete goals of science-engineering generality.

Furthermore, in the science-engineering generality, it is the content and not the form of the mathematical statements that matters. The reader, therefore, often may benefit from modifying a mathematical model such that the form is adaptable to the circumstances without really changing its basic contents. Numerous suggestions in this direction are included in the text.

Modern analytical photogrammetry seems to be overwhelmed with the technique of *Adjustment Computations*.   A rigorous solution, even by using the method of Least-Squares, would not always justify the trouble expended.   This is because the data, observed or calculated, do not depend merely on errors of observation but also have their origin in the inequalities of the terrain, atmospheric conditions, measuring instrument, camera, etc. as well as the inadequacy of the mathematical models used for the purpose of processing, assessing and analyzing the data.

This book must be taken in these perspectives.

Intended for graduate students, researchers and practitioners in photogrammetry and remote sensing, this book presupposes a good background in physics and mathematics as generally required in undergraduate education at American or European universities. The author has made concerted efforts to present a self-contained book. Detailed derivations are given wherever feasible. Related relevant publications are cited in the text by the authors' names and years of publication. Bibliographies of such cited works (as well as others deemed useful for further studies) have been given at the end of each chapter. Although each and every symbol and notation has been explained when first introduced in the book, a list of symbols is separately appended in order to avoid possible confusions.

Observational and photographying techniques which are necessary in any practical job are deliberately omitted as being out of place in this theory oriented presentation. With similar justification, discussions on the basic tool of acquiring photographic or sensing information, viz., the camera or the sensing device, have been omitted also.   The reader would benefit in this respect by examining many other available publications such as the *Manual of Photogrammetry* published by the American Society of Photogrammetry. Although some computer programs would have enhanced the value of such a book to the uninitiated reader, they were not included in view of the bulk and associated cost for such a proposition.

Chapters are arranged in an order found most convenient by the author from his many years of teaching. Each chapter, however, is self-contained in order that any teacher using this book as a classroom text should find no difficulty in following any different order of the subject matter.   Moreover, considerable blending of details was made for presenting a logical and meaningful flow of the text.

The book is divided into ten chapters and two appendices. The decimal numbering system has been used for sections, figures, tables and equations according to chapters.

Perhaps some points in this book could have been more elaborated, some more derivations could have been added or some examples from actual cases could have been presented. This is a task for the future. Time and economics of publication could not permit these in some cases, while in others it was felt that the general flow of the text would have been disturbed.

PREFACE

TO THE SECOND EDITION

The science of photogrammetry has been rather dynamic in the recent years -- in that certain new data-reduction techniques and various new analytical instruments have been introduced in the world. Furthermore, the first edition of the book has almost been sold out. These two primary reasons prompted the publisher and the author to consider the second edition.

The published reviews on the first edition indicated that the philosophy of the approaches and the structuring of the book were on the correct track. Consequently, it was felt that there was no need to restructure the book. Hence, the Foreword to the first edition is retained (as the preceding Preface). There were, nevertheless, certain minor errors which were discovered after the book was in circulation.

In view of the above, the efforts are concentrated on updating the book; firstly, by correcting the discovered errors; secondly, by adding necessary elaborations regarding analytical instruments; thirdly, by adding or modifying discussions on the data-reduction techniques; and finally, by adding some worked out numerical examples and computer programs to enhance the worth of the book.

During the last seven years the author received numerous communications on the book suggesting various improvements, linguistic and technical. Those have all been duly considered. The greatest modifications are in Chapters 2, 4, 6, 7 and 10, as also in the Appendix. Chapter 2 is practically rewritten in view of the influx of new instruments on the market. A subsection on 'Polylateration' is added in Chapter 3. The section on 'Critical geometry' in Chapter 4 is rewritten with significant elaborations. A new subsection on 'Intersection with terrestrial photographs' is added, in view of its usefulness in engineering applications, in Chapter 6. The author's research studies made recently as a consultant to the United Nations Organization (on the status of mapping in the world) gave ideas to improve Chapter 7 with regard to planning and designing of projects. In view of recent research studies in unconventional technologies in photogrammetry (Note: The author continues to act as the Chairman of the Working Group on Unconventional Photogrammetry in the International Society for Photogrammetry and Remote Sensing), the section on 'Electron micrography' in Chapter 10 is rewritten and the rest fully updated.

A self-calibration program (on the photographic imaging system) developed under the author's guidance is added as Appendix C at the end of the book. This program would prove to be a unique addition. It is flexible enough to be used in conventional (aerial or satellite imaging) as well as unconventional (like X-ray or EM) systems as has already been used successfully in numerous projects.

The lists of abbreviations and of symbols are modified appropriately enough in view of the changes in the text. The style of presenting the text has been improved as much as possible without, however, sacrificing the correctness of the implied technical meanings.

Special appreciation is expressed for the generous and constructive contributing comments received from numerous colleagues around the world, the outstanding ones being from Dr. O. Ayeni, Dr. A.J. Brandenberger, Mr. D. Brown, Mr. G.B. Das, Dr. J. B. De Andrade, Dr. H.H. Deker, Dr. J. Hothmer, Dr. H.M. Karara, Dr. M. Leupin and Dr. T. Oshima. All of their comments have been considered in this edition. Mr. J. Dumas contributed with his excellent typing of the complex manuscript at the word-processor of Jean-Devin, enr. The author also thanks profusely the instrument manufacturers and individuals who provided many of the illustrations or diagrams or even ideas which have been assimilated in this edition. All these have been appropriately acknowledged in the text. The group directly involved in the publication and marketing of the book, i.e., all of the Pergamon Press, deserves special appreciation for their excellent cooperation.

Analytical photogrammetry is being applied now-a-days in numerous fields other than the conventional field of mapping,- topographic, cadastral or engineering,like biological, architectural, medical or industrial. It is universally recognized for having the inherent capability of non-contact and rapid spatial measurements. The fact, however, remains that this technique would not be accepted in all such applications unless it is cost-effective and provides enough economical and technical advantages over other existing measuring techniques suitable to their respective needs. Automobile construction, metal working, mining engineering, shipbuilding, traffic engineering and machine construction are certain industrial fields where adequate success has already been achieved.

It is hoped that this edition would serve its purpose and would encourage all readers further to develop the analytical photogrammetric procedures far beyond the current scopes presented here.

Laval University
Quebec, Canada

SANJIB K. GHOSH

August, 1987

LIST OF SYMBOLS

A   Coefficient matrix of observations (composed of partial derivatives of observations in condition equations, Chap 4)

a   Semi-major axis of an ellipsoid (Chap 3); Transformation coefficient; Format size of square frame photographs; Expansion coefficient of air due to temperature (Chap 5)

a_1 , a_2 Shifts due to decentering distortion (Chap 5)

B   Coefficient matrix of parameters (composed of partial derivatives of parameters in condition equations, Chap 4, 8, 9)

$\dot{B}$ Coefficient matrix of estimated orientation parameters (Chap 8, 9)

$\ddot{B}$ Coefficient matrix of estimated ground coordinates (Chap 8, 9)

B   Atmospheric pressure (Chap 5)

B_x, B_y, B_z X, Y and Z components, respectively, of base in model or ground

b   Semi-minor axis of an ellipsoid (Chap 3); Transformation coefficient; Photographic base

$\underline{b}$ Blur (of image)

$\vec{b}$ Vector representing base in a model

b_x, b_y, b_z X, Y and Z components, respectively, of base at photo-scale

C_f Differential film shrinkage constant (Chap 2)

C_x, C_y X and Y components, respectively, of the projection distance in view of scale-affinity

c   Camera constant; Half distance between images on film for a strip-photo (Chap 10); Fiducial center of photo

$\dot{c}, \ddot{c}$ Estimated unknowns for orientation parameters and ground coordinates, respectively; Contributions to normal equations

D   Object distance from camera perspective center

$\vec{D}$ Vector defining total parallax (Chap 4)

D_i Certain constants (Chap 3, 10)

d   Prefix indicating differentials; Scalar multiplier to parallax $\vec{D}$; Target diameter (Chap 7); Umbra diameter in X-ray imagery (Chap 10)

d'   Measuring mark diameter; Penumbra diameter in X-ray imagery (Chap 10)

d_i Certain constants (Chap 3); Distances of points from perspective center in strip photography (Chap 10)

dr   Radial distortion

dx,dy,dz   Translational constants; Coordinate errors

e e'   Ellipsoidal eccentricities, first and second, respectively (Chap 3)

e   Error (specifics identified with appropriate subscripts)

F, F_o Function and function evaluated with approximate values, respectively

f   Function; Camera focal length

H   Elevation in ground or in model (above specified datum)

h   Flying height; Elevation above geodetic ellipsoid (Chap 3)

h_o Elevation of Origin in Local Space Coordinate system

I   Identity matrix

i   Subscript indicating sequential numbering in a series; Angle of incidence (reflection or refraction case)

J_i Profile function coefficients in decentering lens distortion

j   Subscript indicating sequential numbering in a series

K   Constant factor in atmospheric refraction

K_{im} Image motion constant

k   Scale factor; Scalar multiplier (Chap 4); Distortion coefficients (Chap 5, 10)

k_i Atmospheric refraction coefficients (Chap 5)

L   Observations (Chap 8)

M   Rotation matrix (elements identified with appropriate subscripts); Coefficient matrix of Normal Equations

M   Row matrices corresponding to the general rotation matrix; Radius of curvature of geodetic meridian (Chap 3)

M_B Photo scale

$M_K, M_{K'}$ Map scales, of publication and of compilation, respectively

M_M Model scale

M_Ω, M_Φ, M_K Rotation matrices representing Ω, Φ and K rotations, respectively

m   Elements of rotation matrix (identified with appropriate subscripts); Standard error (or deviation); Subscript indicating influence of IMC

N   Normal equations matrix; Augmented rotation matrix (Chap 5)

N   Radius of curvature of geodetic prime vertical (Chap 3); Coefficients of Normal equations; Augmented rotation row matrices (Chap 5); Sub-matrices of Normal equations (identified with appropriate subscripts)

n   Number of observations; Atmospheric refractive index

O   Exterior orientation parameters

P   Weight matrix associated with observations (Chap 7, 8, 9)

P   Lens distortion coefficients (Chap 5); Point on ground or model; Y-parallax in model (identified with appropriate subscripts)

p   Subscript indicating panoramic effect (Chap 10); Point on photograph

Px,Py   X- and Y-parallaxes, respectively, in model

px,py   X- and Y-parallaxes, respectively, on photo

Q   Weight coefficient matrix (Chap 4)

q   Band width in recursive partitioning (Chap 8)

R   Radius of Earth-sphere (Chap 3, 5); Radius of Critical circle (Chap 4)

$\vec{R}$ Vector defining location of a point on ground (or in model) with regard to perspective center (identified with appropriate subscripts)

$\vec{R}_O$ Unit vector in object space

R_M Mean radius of Earth-sphere (Chap 3)

r   Radial distance of an image point (from fiducial center or principal point of symmetry); Border width in recursive partitioning (Chap 8)

$\vec{r}$ Vector defining location of an image point with regard to perspective center (identified with appropriate subscripts)

$\vec{r}_O$ Unit vector in camera space

S   Distance of a point on ground from Nadir point; Polylateration quantities (Chap 3); A parameter (Chap 9); Constants of Spiral distortion (Chap 10) -- all identified with appropriate subscripts

s   Distance of a point on photo from Nadir point

T   Thickness of film or plate; Resection coefficients (Chap 6) t   Temperature;   Third partition in recursive partitioning (Chap 8); A parameter (Chap 9);   Time (identified with appropriate subscripts)

U   Constant vector associated with Normal equations (Chap 4)

u   A parameter (Chap 9)

V   Vector of residuals (of photo coordinates)

v   Column vector composed of residuals to observations;   Ground speed of aircraft (Chap 5, 10);   Fundamental ellipsoidal quantity (Chap 3)

v,ν Error, deviation or alteration (identified with appropriate subscripts)

v_F, v_I Speed of movement of film and image, respectively (Chap 5, 10)

W   Weight matrix associated with observations (Chap 4)

W   Thickness of material in X-ray photography (Chap 10);   Fundamental ellipsoidal quantity

w   Slit width in Strip or Panoramic photography (Chap 10)

X   Solution vector associated with Normal equations; Coordinates' vector

X   Column vector of alterations (corrections) to parameter values (Chap 4)

X, Y, Z Ground or Model coordinates (three dimensions)

$\bar{X}$ Vector of coordinates before transformation

$\bar{X}, \bar{Y}, \bar{Z}$ Three dimensional coordinates before transformation;   Coordinates in Geocentric Universal system (Chap 3)

X_o, Y_o, Z_o Coordinates of the Origin   (perspective center in particular)

$\bar{X}_o, \bar{Y}_o, \bar{Z}_o$ Coordinates of the Origin of a Local system

x, y, z Photo coordinates (three dimensional, z being a constant)

x_o, y_o Photo coordinates of Principal point (in a Fiducial reference system)

$\dot{x}, \dot{y}$ Image velocities in X and Y directions, respectively (Chap 5)

x', y' Reseau point coordinates from calibration (Chap 5)

x', y'
x_1, y_1 Photo coordinates on the left-side photograph (of a pair)

x'', y''
x_2, y_2 Photo coordinates on the right-side photograph (of a pair)

α, β, γ Angles for Direction Cosines, with respect to X, Y and Z axes, respectively (Chap 4)

α Camera field angle;   Angle of deviation due to refraction (Chap 5); Local slope of terrain (Chap 7);   Angle at a station (Chap 7)

β View angle of incidence of a ray (Chap 5)

α,β Tangential offsets at Multilaterative comparator (Chap 2)

γ Angle of intersection;   Parallactic angle

Δ As prefix, diminutive error or deviation to a parameter;   Certain values used in Space Resection (Chap 6);   Column vector composed of corrections to parameters (Chap 4)

δ As prefix, diminutive correction to a parameter;   Correlation coefficient (Chap 8)

$\dot{\delta},\ddot{\delta}$ Corrections to estimated orientation parameters and ground coordinates, respectively (Chap 8, 9)

ε Function with estimated values of unknowns (Chap 8);   Discrepancy vector (Chap 9)

$\dot{\varepsilon},\ddot{\varepsilon}$ Discrepancy vectors for orientation parameters and ground coordinates, respectively (Chap 8, 9)

θ Angle of convergence;   Direction angle in Plane-polar system of coordinates (Chap 3);   Scan angle in Panoramic photography (Chap 10)

$\dot{\theta},\ddot{\theta},\dddot{\theta}$ Scan-rate, Scan-acceleration and Scan-jerk, respectively (Chap 10)

λ Geodetic Longitude (Chap 3);   Certain scalar multipliers (Chap 4)

ν Azimuth (Chap 7)

λ,μ,υ Certain constants used in transformation (Chap 3)

ρ Atmospheric density (Chap 5)

Σ Variance-covariance matrix;   Summation (Chap 4)

$\dot{\Sigma},\ddot{\Sigma}$ Variance-covariance matrix for orientation parameters and ground coordinates, respectively

σ Standard error (or deviation, identified with appropriate subscripts); Elements of a covariance matrix (Chap 9)

Φ Geodetic Latitude (Chap 3)

ϕ *   Direction angle for maximum tangential

Ω,Φ,K Model rotations around X, Y and Z axes, respectively

ω,ϕ,κ *   Photo (camera or projector) rotations around X, Y and Z axes, respectively

ω_o,ϕ_o,κ_o *   Rotations referred to calibrated positions

$\dot{\omega},\dot{\phi},\dot{\kappa}$ *   Angular velocities in ω, ϕ and κ, respectively

ℓ Distance between fiducial marks (Chap 5);   Dimensional indications of matrices (Chap 9)

∇   Angles at perspective center (identified with appropriate subscripts; Chap 4, 6); A substitute relating parallel and perspective projections (Chap 10)

ψ   Angular deviation of ray path in atmospheric refraction (Chap 5)

---

* Note: The symbol φ has been printed at the word processor as φ .

LIST OE ABBREVIATIONS

ACIC   Aeronautical Chart and Information Center (of the USA, in the DMA)

ACSM   American Congress on Surveying and Mapping

AMS   Army Map Service (of the USA, currently in the DMA)

ANOVA   Analysis of Variance (from Statistics)

APPS   Analytical Photogrammetric Positioning System

ARDC   Air-Force Rome Development Center (of the USA)

ARME   Automated Réseau Measuring Equipment

ASCE   American Society of Civil Engineers

ASP   American Society for Photogrammetry (currently ASPRS)

ASPRS   American Society for Photogrammetry and Remote Sensing

ATL   Army Topographical Laboratories (of the USA, also known as ETL)

BL   Bildmessung und Luftwildwesen (journal of the German Society of Photogrammetry)

BRATS   Bundle Refinement Aerial Triangulation Solution (of J.F. Kenefick)

BRL   Ballistic Research Laboratories (of the USA)

BSOR   Block Successive Over-Relaxation

C&GS   Coast and Geodetic Survey (of the USA, currently NOS, NOAA)

CRT   Cathode Ray Tube

DBA   Duane Brown Associates (a private organization)

DMA   Defense Mapping Agency (of the USA)

DOD   Department of Defense (of the USA)

DTM   Digital Terrain Model

EDM   Electronic Distance Measurement

ETL   Engineering Topographical Laboratories (US Army)

FORTBLOCK   Fortran Block Triangulation (program at the Ohio State Univ.)

ICAO   International Civil Aviation Organization

IEFP   Instantaneous Equivalent Frame Photograph

IEVP   Instantaneous Equivalent Vertical Photograph

IMC   Image Motion Compensation

ISP   International Society for Photogrammetry (currently ISPRS)

ISPRS   International Society for Photogrammetry and Remote Sensing

ITC   International Training Center (currently The International Institute
             for Aerial Surveying and Earth Sciences, Enschede, The Netherlands)

JEOL   Japan Electro Optical Laboratories

LFC   Large Format Camera (of NASA, USA)

MSS   Multispectral Scanner Subsystem

MUSAT   MUltiple Station Analytical Triangulation

NASA   National Aeronautics and Space Administration (of the USA)

NBS   National Bureau of Standards (of the USA)

NGS   National Geodetic Survey (branch of NOAA, USA)

NOAA   National Oceanic and Atmospheric Administration (of the USA)

NOS   National Oceanic Survey (branch of NOAA, USA)

NRC   National Research Council (of Canada)

OEEPE   Organisation Européenne d'Etudes Photogrammétriques Expérimentales
             (European Organization for Experimental Photogrammetric Research)

OLM   Optical Light Microscope

OS   Ordnance Survey (of the UK)

PE   Photogrammetric Engineering (currently PERS)

PERS   Photogrammetric Engineering and Remote Sensing (journal of ASPRS)

PR   Photogrammetric Record (journal of the Photogrammetric Society, UK)

RABATS Rapid Analytical Block Triangulation System (of J.F. Kenefick)

RBV Return Beam Vidicon

RMS Root Mean Square

SAPGO Simultaneous Adjustment of Photogrammetric and Geodetic Observations

SEM Scanning Electron Microscope

SI Système Internationale (International system of units)

SMAC Simultaneous Multiframe Analytical Calibration

SPOT Système Pour l'Observation de la Terre (French satellite imaging system)

TEM Transmission Electron Microscope

UNO United Nations Organization

USAF United States Air Force

USCGS United States Coast and Geodetic Survey (currently NOS, NOAA)

USGS United States Geological Survey

UTM Universal Transverse Mercator (Projection)

1

INTRODUCTION

Photogrammetry (Gk *phot* = light; Gk *gramma* = writing and Gk *metron* = to measure) is defined by the American Society for Photogrammetry and Remote Sensing (ASPRS) as "The art, science and technology of obtaining reliable information about physical objects and the environment by recording, measuring and interpreting photographic images".

1.1 BASIC PRINCIPLES

Included within the above definition are two distinct aspects of photogrammetry: (1) *Quantitative* (or metric), which involves precision dimensional measurements to obtain direct information related to size and shape of objects or derived information such as change- (like velocity or volume change), statistical- (like area distribution or time variation) or associated- (like stress or force) parameters; and (2) *Qualitative* (or interpretive), which deals with the recognition and interpretation of objects. Digital, graphic or visual representation of such information is almost always implied.

The latter (qualitative photogrammetry) does not fall within the scope of this book. The interested reader would benefit from reading the *Manual of Remote Sensing* (published in two volumes by the ASPRS in 1983) or other books in that subject area. Within the scope of the former (quantitative photogrammetry), *Analytical Photogrammetry* deals with the solution of problems by mathematical computations, by using measurement data obtained from the photograph (image) as input. Suitable mathematical models are used to represent relations between points in the object, their corresponding images and errors in the system.

1

Principles of perspective projective geometry are inherent in the object-to-image relationship. In conventional approaches of photogrammetry, the image on film (negative) is considered as central (perspective) projection of the photographed object, the perspective center of the camera lens being the projection center.

During recent developments of the analytical (computational) procedures, the interest of numerous photogrammetrists has been to somewhat duplicate the perform-ance of analog instruments, at least for standard mapping problems. For numerous such applications, analytical approaches have demonstrated efficiency (in terms of costs, accuracy and time), such as are comparable to the instrumental approaches without any great improvement, however.

The analytical photogrammetrists have tried to justify their efforts on the basis that they should be able to obtain more accurate results in less time than with the instrumental approaches. The application over which much discussion and effort have been made with not so much result is that of aerotriangulation. This is due to both the strength and weakness of the aerotriangulation procedures under the state of the art. The weakness lies in the fact that it frightens away a great majority of the practitioners and involves considerable cost, which causes the reluctance to make use of it. The strength lies in the freedom it permits in data reduction with a computer. The real strength of analytical photogrammetry, however, lies beyond this and justifies its continous application and growth.

The principal justification would be apparent in its recent applications on the tracking of ballistic missiles and satellites or numerous other applications which are completely outside the capabilities of the instruments of only optical-mechanical scopes. The second justification lies in those applications where the concept of a simple central perspective projection is no longer adequate. Pan-oramic and strip photographic systems, electron micrography and X-ray radiography are certain examples in this regard. Included in these are the applications in which the greatest accuracies are required in eliminating mensural errors due to influences like those of lens distortion, atmospheric refraction and film defor-mation, which are difficult or impossible to incoporate in optical-mechanical de-vices but are accomplished easily through mathematical models with a computer. The third justification lies in the inclusion of auxiliary information data and numerical adjustment procedures in a satisfactory manner. Such information may be obtained from various sources like electronic positioning or inertial navigation systems. Often, such information may not be directly enforced but may be con-sidered as adequately weighted parameters to reinforce rather than override the geometric strength of normal photogrammetric procedures.

The basic material used in all these are the photographs, negatives or diapositives of various types. The basic inputs are the photo coordinates in a x,y (rectangular two-dimensional) system. The outputs are of various types like X,Y,Z ground coordinates, orientation elements and even derived information on specific relations and conditions.

The working system (Fig. 1.1) involves, broadly speaking, the following: (a) the object (terrain or other), (b) the sensor (camera or other), (c) the environment (items like atmosphere), (d) the data acquisition tool (instrument or comparator), (e) the data processing mechanisms (computer, accessories and mathematical models), and (f) the human worker. Each, with its working limitations, contributes towards errors of various nature. A comprehensive knowledge of such limitations and error contributions is essential for an efficient job.

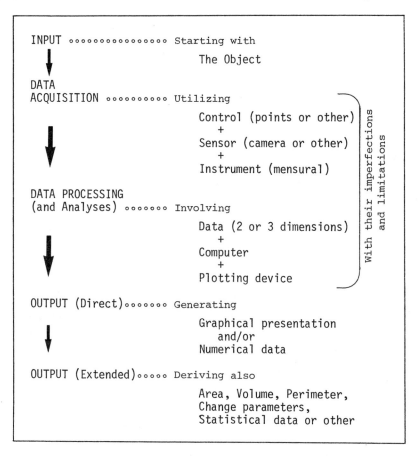

Fig. 1.1 The general working system in photogrammetry

Provision of control in the classical topographical sense may not be necessary or even be usable in some non-topographic applications. Furthermore, computer utilization may not be needed in many cases of data processing. Yet, one of the major trends in the development of photogrammetry during the past two decades has been in the increasing use of electronic computers for data processing and analyses. A computer can be used in photogrammetric operations for the following broad purposes:

Data acquisition:
1. Digitizing existing charts obtained by using analogical or graphical photogrammetric techniques;
2. Recording measured photo coordinates at a comparator or a stereoplotter; and
3. Digitizing spatial coordinates from a stereomodel at a stereoplotter.

Information required in various applications (output in Fig. 1.1):
1. Mensuration parameters like area, volume, curvature, gradient or perimeter;
2. Change parameters like velocity, acceleration, volume change or changes with regard to time or to parameters other than time;
3. Statistical parameters like area or volume distrubution, time variation or probabilistic inferences; and
4. Associated parameters like stress or force.

The software potentials throughout these are enormous. Generally speaking, one efficient and appropriate file handling and computer programming system is essential in most applications.

Analytical photogrammetry is, however, rapidly becoming more and more complex. Increased complexity does not necessarily mean increased worth. By being more complex, it may become less used because of the concern of the potential user. In this respect, it would be pertinent to emphasize that such situations call for wisest possible treatments of photogrammetric resources and all involved technologies with sensible innovations at all stages.

1.2 HISTORICAL DEVELOPMENTS

Development of mathematics as an organized, independent and logical discipline did not exist before about 1000 B.C.. The Greek philosopher Aristotle ($\approx$350 B.C.) referred to the process of optical projection of images. Leonardo da Vinci and other master minds of the *Renaissance* period published ideas on the laws of graphical perspective during the fifteenth century. In the mean time, mathematicians had developed the subject of projective geometry, which provides the foundation of photogrammetry. The problem of *Space Resection* was first discussed by J. H. Lambert in 1759 in his book, "Freie Perspektive". Wheatstone of England, in 1838, developed the stereoscope, one most important tool used in photogrammetry.

The actual practice of photogrammetry could, however, be started only after photography was developed by Daguerre and Niepce, as reported by the former in Paris in 1839. Thereafter, photogrammetry for general mapping and measurements was being used in Europe. The names of Arago, Laussedat and Nadar, among others, became well known through their contributions. A direct outcome of such mapping experiences with baloon -and kite- borne arial photography as well as with terrestrial photography was the work of two Germans, Sturm and Hauck (Doyle, 1964), where they established the relationship between projective geometry and photography.

The word *photogrammetry* is credited to Meydenbauer of Germany, who in 1867 published a paper on this subject. His work was continued by Jordan, Hauck, Koppe and many others in Germany (ASP Manual of Photogrammetry, 1980).

Sebastian Finsterwalder, in a series of papers during 1899 to 1932, established a very strong foundation for analytical photogrammetry. In these, he brought about the resection of single and double points in space as well as other principles like those of relative and absolute orientations. In view of the contributions made by him, Doyle (1964) very aptly comments, "There is little doubt that if Finsterwalder had possessed modern capabilities for extensive computations the course of aerial photogrammetry might have been quite defferent". Finsterwalder was probably one of the first ones to use vector terminology in photogrammetric articles.

Carl Pulfrich of the Zeiss Jena group announced the development of the first stereocomparator at the 73rd Conference of Natural Scientists and Physicians held at Hamburg in 1901. The Stereoautograph of von Orel (of Zeiss) and the Aerokartograph of Hugershoff were the outcomes of natural developments in photogrammetric instrumentation following the work of Pulfrich.

Another pioneer on the theoretical side was Otto von Gruber, whose contributions to the solution of the problem of single point resection in space and the development of the differential formulas for projective relations between planes have been applied by numerous photogrammetrists in their works. His lectures in the Vacation Courses on Photogrammetry at Jena, first published in 1930 (with English reprints published in 1942) were essential to the development of photogrammetry.

For about two decades, in the 1930s through the 1950s, some pioneering theoretical and practical developments were made in Switzerland through the efforts of Max Zeller and his associates, some of whom have made well earned names for themselves, like W. K. Bachmann and A. J. Brandenberger. Hugo Kasper, also in Switzerland, contributed considerably to the general concepts during the 1950s and later.

Earl Church in the USA, with the support of a Guggenheim Foundation grant, published a series of bulletins on computational photogrammetry in the 1930s. Church started a trend in the USA in which numerous scientists made significant contributions for solving the problems of space resection, orientation, intersection, etc. One of the approaches developed by Church, on the determination of the air station (perspective center) coordinates by utilizing an approximate position and an iterative solution, has virtually remained unchanged today (see Church, 1934). He later formalized his method with derivations in the direction cosine notation (see Church, 1948). In general, the approaches of Church were explicit and without any consideration of using redundant observations or data. Furthermore, he did not apply any error analysis to his solutions. Church created tremendous motivation towards applying photogrammetry for solving various engineering problems.

Great advancements were made in various countries during the post World War II days and through the 1950s. The British are generally credited with the development of the first operational system of analytical aerotriangulation (with a réseau camera and with the Cambridge stereocomparator) at the Ordnance Survey Organization (Shewell, 1953). The complete system was described by Arthur (1955). During this period and later, numerous contributions were made by E. H. Thompson and others.

Significant contributions were made in Canada by National Research Council much of which was due to the work of Schut (1959-60), who was the first to use the Condition of Coplanarity. Here he analysed the existing aerotriangulation methods, reduced them to a common notation and classified them according to various criteria.

The major thrust in analytical photogrammetry has been made in the USA. Merritt (1958) deserves the credit of publishing first (and the only other so far) book on analytical photogrammetry. His work shows a very strong influence of Church in all approaches. Hellmut Schmid, first with the US Ballistic Research Laboratories and later with the Coast and Geodetic Survey (C&GS), in a series of publications, outlined the principles of multi-station analytical photogrammetry by using the Condition of Collinearity. His work has been unique in view of the applications of the principles of Least Squares and complete studies of error propagations. His early works were by using the vector notations. His later works were expressed by using matrix notations, wich are now considered almost standard in analytical photogrammetry. Duane Brown, earlier an associate of Schmid, has made major contributions to the analytical principles as applicable to numerous engineering problems. Brown has made solid contributions in the following: (a) Treatment of all orientation parameters as either known or unknown; (b) Solution of Normal Equations achieved by partitioning the matrix to separate the orientation elements and ground points; (c) The method of introducing ground control points and the air-station parameters with appropriate weights, making it possible to include auxiliary data without disturbing the basic mathematical model; and (d) Development of a new mono-comparator.

James Case (1961) showed how a substitution of parameters may greatly reduce the order of the Normal Equation Matrix, while at the same time decreasing accumulation of errors by constrianing the parameters to known functions. He further demonstrated in 1967 how the standard collinearity equations can be modified to handle some unconventional photogrammetric systems.

The first analytical system to become operational in the USA was at the C&GS (currently NOS, NOAA), primary credit for which would go to M. Keller and G. C. Tewinkel (1967) for their work on aerotriangulation. Numerous other private and public organizations have since been deeply involved in analytical photogrammetry.

In the mean time, sincere efforts have been made in developing analytical procedures in various applications in many countries. The credit of doing outstanding work during the last two decades would go to numerous scientists like K.

Rinner of Austria; F. Ackermann and G. Konecny of FR Germany; U. Bartorelli and G. Inghilleri of Italy; K. Ryokichi and T. Oshima of Japan; A. N. Lobanov of the USSR; G. B. Das of India; and many others, omission of whose names here is due to lack of space and limitations of the author (thus, not·intentional).

Analytical photogrammetry is now on the way of a great expansion in its applications. This is indicated in the recent developments of several comparators as well as numerous analytical plotters, which utilize computers "on-line" to perform functions too numerous to list here. The last two decades have witnessed tremendous growths for analytical approaches. The technology continues to change with the digital computer having played a key role. All-digital systems are in their initial stages of development at this time. On-line analytical photogammetry is indeed preferred for various tasks.

The efforts of the International Society for Photogrammetry and Remote Sensing (ISPRS), through its seven commissions (service area related) and with considerable support from around eighty national societies and agencies (as members) have been greatly instrumental in helping develop the analytical approaches in photogrammetry to its present state. The greatest support in this regard has been provided by the American Society for Photogrammetry and Remote Sensing (ASPRS). International cooperation is essential for progressive developments to benefit all human beings.

BIBLIOGRAPHY

American Society of Photogrammetry; *Manual of Photogrammetry (4th Ed.)*, (ASPRS, Falls Church, Virginia 1980).

American Society of Photogrammetry; *Manual of Remote Sensing (2nd Ed.)*, (ASPRS, Falls Church, Virginia; 1983).

Arthur, D. W. G.; *A Stereocomparator Technique for Aerial Triangulation*, (Ordnance Survey Professional paper, New Series No. 20, London: 1955).

Brown, Duane; "A Solution to the General Problem of Multiple Station Analytical Stereotriangulation", *RCA Data Reduction Technical Report No. 43*: (1958).

Case, James B.; "The Utilization of Constraints in Analytical Photogrammetry", *PERS* 27, No. 5 (1961).

Case, James B.; "The Analytical Reduction of Panoramic and Strip Photography", *Photogrammetria* 22, No. 4 (1967).

Church, Earl; *The Geometry of Aerial Photograph* (Syracuse University, N.Y.: 1934).

Church, Earl; *Theory of Photogrammetry* (Syracuse University, New York: 1948).

Doyle, Frederic J.; "The Historical Development of Analytical Photogrammetry", *PERS* 30, No. 2 (1964).

Keller, M and G. C. Tewinkel; *Block Analytical Aerotriangulation*, Tech. Bull. No. 35, US Dept of Commerce, ESSA, C&GC, Washington, DC (1967).

Lambert, J. H.; *Freie Perspektive* (Zurich: 1759).

Laussedat, Aimé; *Recherches sur les instruments, les méthodes et les dessins topographiques* (Gauthier-Villars, Paris: Vol.I, 1898; Vol.II, 1901-03).

Merrit, Everett; *Analytical Photogrammetry* (Pitman, New York: 1958).

Schmid, Hellmut; *A General Analytical Solution to the Problem of Photogrammetry* (Ballistic Research Laboratories Report No. 1065; Aberdeen, Maryland; 1959).

Schut, G. H.; "An Analysis of Methods and Results in Analytical Aerial Triangulation", *Photogrammetria* 16, Nos 2 and 3 (1959-60).

Shewell, H. A. L.; "The Use of the Cambridge Stereocomparator for Aerial Triangulation", *PR* 1, No. 2 (1953).

von Gruber, Otto; *Photogrammetry, Collected Lectures and Essays* (American Photographic, Boston: 1942).

2

INSTRUMENTATION

In analytical photogrammetry the primary requirement of data acquisition instrumentation is to obtain the input data (coordinates x, y) of photographic image points. There are two approaches in such data-acquisition, viz., monocular and stereoscopic measurements. With regard to the data-processing, the approach is mathematical with the help of a computer. This can be done either *"off-line"* (where the devices in the computer system are not in direct communication with the data-acquisition outfit), or *"on-line"* (where the operations of terminals, files and other auxiliary equipment are in direct communication with the data-acqui-sition outfit to eliminate or minimise the need for human intervention at any stage between initial input and computer output). In view of the various possibilities, therefore, one can use one of the following types of instruments:

1. *Comparators* (for off-line applications)
   a) Monocomparators, designed for the measurement of image coordinates on a single photograph.
   b) Stereocomparators, designed for obtaining image coordinates simultaneously on two overlapping photographs.
2. *Stereoplotters* (analog instruments)
   a) Used as comparators (mono or stereo) for off-line applications.
   b) Converted into hybrid analytical plotters for on-line applications.
3. *Analytical plotters*, specially designed for on-line utilisation with computers and plotting tables (coordinatographs).

The other type of instrument, the Radial Triangulator (discussed later in Section 2.5) does not fall into these groups. They are much less in use now-a-days, however.

2.1 BASIC COMPONENTS

The basic components of an instrument are: (i) the viewing system, (ii) the measuring system; and (iii) the readout and recording system.

2.1.1 Viewing Systems

The role of the viewing system is to bring the measuring (or, floating) mark into coincidence with the image (photo) and to present the combination to the eyes of the observer at an appropriate magnification.   There are various kinds used in instruments, as follows:

a. *Single eyepiece.* This, the simplest viewing system, uses one objective (for focussing the illuminated photograph) and one eyepiece to examine the combined image.   There are several elaborations and variations of such systems, e. g., with zooming eyepieces, interchangeable eyepieces of different magnifications, and prisms added to incline the eyepiece for comfortable viewing.

b. *Binocular eyepiece.* In single-image instruments, both eyes see the same image, making such an instrument very comfortable to the observer.   In a double image instrument, however, each eye sees one image such that a 'fused' stereo-image is viewed only after appropriate settings are made.

c. *Projection viewing.* In some instruments, both the measuring mark as well as the photo image are projected on a screen, where the observer's viewing can be made without the aid of additional optical elements.

d. *Photo-electric setting.* Such systems, of recent development, can be attached to the instruments.   This is to assure that the reticle is exactly centered on a symmetrical image.   For example, a beam-splitter is used in the Mann Comparator so that visual observations on a viewing screen at 22x magnification may be coupled with photoelectric settings.   Such systems are excellent for symmetrical images like marked points or star images.   Some viewing systems (e.g., the Autometric-Gilliland instrument) have image detecting devices which automatically locate the center of the image.   The detector determines the center of gravity of image-density within the area being scanned.   These are, therefore, ideal for symmetrical images.

2.1.2 Measuring Systems

The function of a measuring system is to obtain the relevant data on the photograph.   The various available devices are listed below.

a. *Leadscrews.* The most common measuring device is the leadscrew or spindle (in combination with a nut). A large drum attached to the end of the screw, graduated in decimal divisions would give the distances (and coordinates, accordingly) to the smallest unit possible in such a system. For example, if the pitch of the screw is 1mm (which is very common) and the graduations on the drum are 1000 divisions, this would give each division to represent $1\mu m$ translation. A supplementary revolution counter or scale would give the full revolutions (corresponding to pitches of the screw), while partial revolutions can be read with an index on the graduated drum.

Some comparators have the viewing microscopes moving over fixed photographs while others have fixed viewing systems with the possibility of translating the photographs. The movements can be made faster with added motor drives.

Some comparators (e.g., Mann, Type 841) have single leadscrews with which only one coordinate can be read at a time. After all points are read in one coordinate (say, x), the plate is rotated through 90° and the other coordinate (y) for all the points are read next. This requires double pointing, and consequently, more time and some complications in data refinement result. Accordingly, double leadscrew comparators are generally preferred. The plate carriers in these are usually rotatable for making the photograph fiducial lines approximately parallel to the measuring axes.

The leadscrew comparators can have errors in the observed coordinates caused by lack of straightness and orthogonality of the screws, variations in the pitch of the screws, instrumental back-lash and effects of temperature variations.

b. *Scales and Micrometers.* The movements of the plate under the viewing system are referenced to scales (glass or metal) parallel to the measuring axes. When a point is observed, the measuring mark may fall between two full divisions of such a scale. A micrometer or vernier measures the translation necessary to bring the index to the closest full division. The sum of the full divisions of the scale and the micrometer reading will then give the complete coordinate value. Such a system, in general, uses the *Abbé Comparator Principle.*
Note: Abbé Comparator Principle, first presented in Ernst Abbé, *Gesammelte Abhandlungen*, vol. 2 (Zeiss Jena, 1906), p. 207, states: The object to be measured and the measuring standard or agent must be in contact or lie in the same plane. To quote Abbé, "The design be based on the following requirements: (i) To exclusively base the measurement in all cases on a longitudinal graduation with

which the distance to be measured is directly compared; (ii) To always design the measuring apparatus in such a way that the distance to be measured will be recti-lineal extension of the graduation used as a scale." It has the following advantages: (i) Mechanical errors in straightness or orthogonality of axes have only secondary effects on the measuremets. (ii) If scales and diapositives (and negatives) are both made of glass, their temperature variations are nearly ident-ical. This reduces the need for temperature control in the laboratory. (iii) The micrometer (or, vernier) needs to be only of the length of the increment between two scales divisions. This make the instrument very convenient in manufacturing and in precision measurements.

The spiral micrometer (like one used by Zeiss, Jena) is one of the simplest devices of this kind, which permits easy reading to 0.1 μm.

c. *Grid (réseau) plate and Micrometers.* The basis of measurement is a glass grid plate with a series of points which is superimposed on the photograph to be measured. The grid can be precalibrated. The increment from the nearest grid point (or, line) to the image point is measured with micrometers. Such grid plates are usually represented by crosses (e.g., in Zeiss PSK stereocomparator) or black dots (e.g., in Canadian NRC monocomparator).

Minor variations in this system are in the movements of the grid plate or of the optics. A typical example is the Zeiss PSK stereocomparator where the grid plates are translated in the x-direction (along with the superimposed photographs) while the viewing optics are translated in the y-direction. The leadscrews for x and y translations need to be precise enough to count the full divisions (in cm) on the grid plate. When the image to be measured has been brought into coincidence with the reticle, an optical switch brings the reticle and the micrometer plate simultaneously into focus. Rotations of the x and y handwheels translate this micrometer plate to measure the increments to the nearest grid lines.

The greatest advantage of this system is that once calibrated, the grid is not subject to variations from wear. Its temperature expansion coefficient is the same as that of the photo (diapositive or negative) and all accuracy requirements are met by the glass grid.

d. *Ferranti Fringes.* In this system, a length of an optical diffraction grating having a precisely known number of lines per unit length (e.g., 2160 lines per mm) is used. A grating as long as the axis to be measured is attached to the movable carriage and a short piece is placed over the photocells which do the counting. With two sections of such a grating superimposed with the line structure at a slight angle to each other, a moiré fringe pattern with an approximately sinusoidal distribution of density is produced at right angles to the grating lines.

When one grating moves along the other, the fringe pattern moves across the grating at the rate of one fringe cycle per grating pitch. A set of Ferranti silicon photocells are used, either directly for coarse gratings or by means of a special lens and slit assembly for finer gratings (e.g., 40 lines to a mm). A high speed bidirectional electronic counter is essential for successful applications of moiré fringe measurements.

Such a measuring system is entirely free from friction and wear. Minor sources of errors like dust or scratches have no appreciable effect on the measurements. The signal on each photocell is derived from a strip of grating (about 1 cm x 0.25 cm). Metric gratings with structures of upto 250 lines per mm corresponding to the least count of 1 μm are readily available.

e. *Interferometer Measurements.* Such a system is based upon the interference phenomemon produced by superimposing beams of monochromatic light. This has been used in ballistic photogrammetry where occasional operational problems have been reported (Chitayat, 1960).

f. *DIG Linear Measurements.* This is a non-incremental system capable of determining absolute positions over an unlimited range (developed by Bausch & Lomb, Inc. and General Measurement Research, Inc.) with a least count of 1 μm. The essential elements in this are: a precise glass scale, a reading head and a display panel. It has several interesting features including the possibility of measuring along up to three axes. It has not, however, been used in conventional applications of photogrammetry.

g. *Computer - controlled Measurements.* In a recently developed system (see Roos, 1975), the Automated Réseau Measuring Equipement (ARME), it is possible to accurately center on réseaus, stars and marked points on photographs with homogeneous or heterogeneous background. It is a precise computer-controlled comparator with a TV camera, an operator console, a point locator and a computer system with card, magnetic tape and hard copy output possibilities. The most interesting feature of this equipment is the automatic centering program, in which the largest number of bits that can be stored is 255^2 or 65,025.

2.1.3 Readout Systems

The function of a readout systems is to permanently record all the measured coordinates. The various available systems are given below:

a. *Manual, optical-mechanical.* This is the simplest approach, which involves an optical readout by the operator and manual recording by the operator from verniers, micrometers, drums or scales of the instrument. Such manual recording can be time consuming and are liable to human faults and errors.

b. *Hard-copy printout.* The output from such a system (e.g., with shaft encoders) can be fed to various kinds of typewriters. Some units also permit typing desired comments associated with particular points in addition to recording point numbers (for identification) and their coordinates.

c. *Automated, complete systems* permit point identification, recording of coordinates on punched cards, punched paper (or, magnetic) tapes in such formats as are directly usable by a digital computer or an automatic plotter. Such an automated recording system, adapted to any photogrammetric instrument, has several advantages. Firstly, the system eliminates human blunders and mistakes. Secondly, this increases the speed of observational work. Thirdly, it presents the data in computer compatible forms. Additional refinements in the form of photographic recording of each image point (with identification) is possible in some instruments.

2.2 COMPARATORS

2.2.1 Standard Monocomparators

Monocomparators make measurements (x,y coordinates) of points on one photo at a time. In such an approach, the point images to be meausred have to be recorded on the photo as natural features on the object or, marked artificially, by a point marking (or, transferring) device in appropriate locations, i.e., these points must be unmistakably identifiable on the photo.

There can be three categories of points: (a) Signalized points, marked on ground (object) before photographing, e.g., paneled control points; (b) Detail points, as are readily identifiable on the photograph, e. g., a street intersection on a photograph taken from air; and (c) Marked (artificial) points, which are directly marked or transferred (by a point marking/transferring instrument) in proper locations.

A representative example is the PK-1 Monocomparator (see Fig. 2.1) introduced in 1976 by Carl Zeiss, Oberkochen, West Germany. In this, a photo-holder carries the photograph on its upper side and the index grating on the under side moves along a plane surface. There is a guide ensuring parallel motions of the photo-holder. Test points are set by first shifting the photo-holder by free hand and tilting a plate (provided for this purpose) to obtain a precise shifting motion. One glass scale is mounted on a U-beam which at the same time serves to guide the carriage with the scanning head. An image of the photograph is formed in a nearby intermediate image plane in which the measuring marks are located. It offers the operator a choice of using one of three types of luminous floating marks or a black floating mark. Binocular viewing is possible with 5x, 12x, 20x, or 30x magnification. The two-dimensional linear measuring system of this monocomparator is illustrated in Fig. 2.2. This uses a photoelectric linear measuring system. The index grating is contained on the photo-holder. This grating, in conjunction with the scale-grating, produces Moiré fringes, which are required for counting. The length of scale lines is equivalent to the test length in the opposite coordinate. The design combines the principles of linear pulse measurements with that of guide-error compensation.

Another example is the Mann comparator type 422-F (of American manufacture), in which three motions are incorporated. Two translatory motions permit the photo-holder (or, stage plate) to be transported along two mutually perpendicular directions (x and y). The other motion allows the stage plate to be rotated. There are slow motion screws for fine adjustments usually provided for each motion. Another popular monocomparator is the Space Optic comparator (see Fig. 2.3). In order to measure the coordinates of a point, the photograph is placed on the photo carrier, which is rotated and adjusted so that one of the fiducial axes to the photo becomes parellel to one of the instrument axes. The movement of rotation is then locked and readings of the x, y coordinates of all points along with all of the fiducial marks are made with regard to the translatory motions only. The fiducial center coordinates are obtained by averaging the observed values of the fiducial marks. The coordinates of the fiducial center are then subtracted from the coordinate readings of all the points to obtain the initial (i.e., unrefined) photo coordinates.

In practice, more than one set of readings should be taken on each point to eliminate the possibility of blunders and improving on the precision of obser-vation. It is better if such repeat observations are taken with care by eliminating the possibilities of errors due to instrumental back-lash, personal

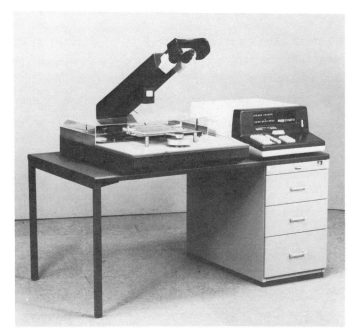

Fig. 2.1 Monocomparator PK-1 with Ecomat 12
(Courtesy, Carl Zeiss, Oberkochen, FR Germany)

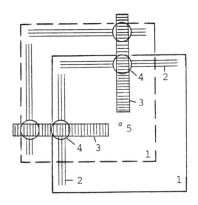

1 Photo-holder plate

2 Index grating

3 Scale

4 Scanning head

5 Measuring mark

Note: Broken line indicates
      center position and
      solid line indicates
      off-center position.

Fig. 2.2 Two-dimensional linear measuring system with index-
          grating and fixed scales of PK-1 comparator

(observer) bias, etc. The actual number of repeat observations may be influenced
by time and cost considerations.

2.2.2 Multilaterative Monocomparator

During recent years, the general availability of digital computers has made feasible an altogether new approach in designing (by DBA, Inc.) this large format (245 x 245 mm) plate measuring comparator (with Least Count 1 μm). The instrument is (see Fig. 2.4) a single-image, portable (weight, 10 kg) comparator, available both with and without automatic digital readout. It operates on the principle of trilateration. The essential measuring element is a glass scale arm with precision graduation. The measuring arm is free to rotate about the pivot at its base. Length measurements are made by rotating this measuring arm about the pivot and simultaneously moving the eyepiece (microscope) such that the point to be measured comes within a circular reticle. The glass scale along with a micrometer reads the distance. Four distances between the pivot and the particular point (with rotations of 90° of the photo on the stage plate) are measured. The x, y coordinates of the fiducial marks and all image points are obtained by computation in an arbitrary x, y system.

Figure 2.5 (after Brown, 1969) illustrates the theoretical basis of this comparator. Four measurements (distances), r_{1j}, r_{2j}, r_{3j} and r_{4j} of a point are made. The actual measurements, r_{ij}, are from the zero mark of the scale to the point, rather than from the pivot. To convert the measurements to radial distances from pivots, one must consider the tangential offsets (α and β). If x_i^C, y_i^C are coordinates of the pivot corresponding to the i th position (i = 1, 2, 3, 4) of the photograph, one can write the following set of observation equations, where x_j, y_j are the desired photo coordinates:

$$
\left.
\begin{aligned}
(r_{1j} + \alpha)^2 + \beta^2 &= (x_j - x_1^C)^2 + (y_j - y_1^C)^2 \\[2mm]
(r_{2j} + \alpha)^2 + \beta^2 &= (x_j - x_2^C)^2 + (y_j - y_2^C)^2 \\[2mm]
(r_{3j} + \alpha)^2 + \beta^2 &= (x_j - x_3^C)^2 + (y_j - y_3^C)^2 \\[2mm]
(r_{4j} + \alpha)^2 + \beta^2 &= (x_j - x_4^C)^2 + (y_j - y_4^C)^2
\end{aligned}
\right\}
\qquad (2.1)
$$

If the ten parameters of the comparator (i.e., α, β and four sets of x_i^C, y_i^C) were exactly known, the process of coordinate determination would be reduced to a four-station, two-dimensional, straightforward Least Squares trilateral solution.

AP-C

Fig. 2.3 Space Optic monocomparator in operation
(Courtesy, Wild Heerbrugg Instruments, Switzerland)

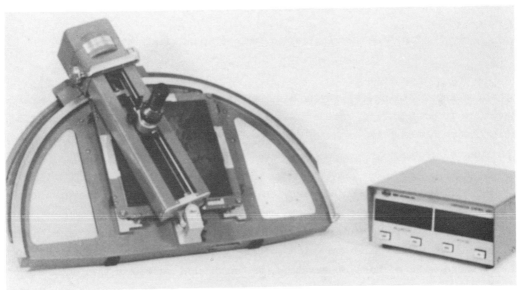

Fig. 2.4 Multilaterative monocomparator
(Courtesy, DBA System, Inc., USA)

In practice, however, the comparator parameters are not known with sufficient
accuracy. Therefore, a self-calibrating solution to recover those parameters
(while simultaneously executing the trilateration) is desirable. This can be done

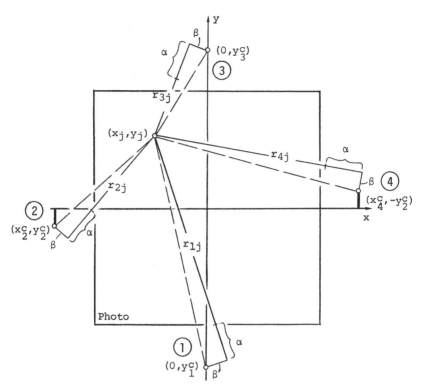

Fig. 2.5 Geometrical equivalent of Multilaterative
monocomparator (After Brown, 1969)

by enforcing certain simplifying conditions such that the eight unknown coordinates are reduced to five. These are: $x_1^C = x_3^C = 0$ and $y_4^C = -y_2^C$ (see Fig. 2.5).
This choice has also the merit of placing the origin of the photo coordinates near
the fiducial center.

By virtue of this arrangement, only seven independent parameters of the
comparator (viz., α, β, y_1^C, y_3^C, x_2^C, x_4^C and y_2^C) need be recovered. This means, if n
number of points are measured on the plate, the number of unknowns is 2n + 7. For
each point one writes four equations of the type of Eq. 2.1. Accordingly, if
$n \gtrsim 4$ there will be more observation (or, condition) equations than unknowns. A
Least Squares adjustment solution leading to 2n+7 by 2n+7 system of *Normal
equations* can then be performed. The size of the normal equations would increase
linearly with the number of measured points. However, they possess a patterned
coefficient matrix that can be exploited to collapse the system to one of order
7 x 7, which would involve only the comparator parameters. Hence, their solution
presents no difficulty.

The manufacturer (DBA System, Inc.) has developed a FORTRAN program, fully documented, for the data processing in order to obtain adjusted photo coordinates (i.e. x_j, y_j) of all measured points. This is available to the customer.

2.2.3 Stereocomparators

A stereocomparator is used for measuring simultaneously the coordinates of corresponding points on a stereopair of photographs, particularly when such readings are made without resorting to some form of point transfer. Usually, the measuring, viewing and readout systems are of the same type as those employed in the monocomparators. Alternately, each stage of a stereocomparator can be used as a monocomparator.

It is advantageous for the computational photogrammetric techniques to have completely separate measuring systems for the two photographs of a stereo pair. It is, however, necessary to translate both stage plates simultaneously under the viewing optics in order to continuously scan the stereo pair (without losing the stereo impression). In the classical construction of a stereocomparator (see Fig. 2.6), two stages are utilized: (i) the x-carriage (upper-stage) with its own measuring system, carries the photographs. The right side photograph can be moved in x relative to the left photo. It records the coordinate (x_1) of a point on the

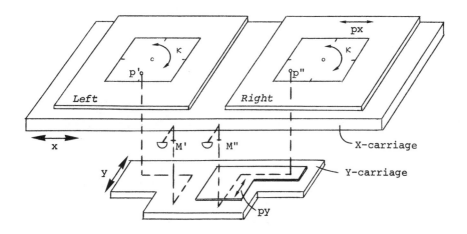

Fig. 2.6 Schematic of a stereocomparator, 1818 of Jenoptik Jena
(M' and M" are the measuring marks; optical paths are shown in broken lines)

left photo and the differential x movement (px) corresponding to the right photo; and (ii) the y carriage (lower stage) containing the rest of the necessary measuring devices, can be translated by the amounts necessary to remove and record the y_1 coordinate for the point on the left photo and the differential y movement (py) corresponding to the right photo. The values px and py are the x and y parallaxes, respectively. Thus, the observed values are: x_1, y_1, px and py. Coordinates x_2, y_2 for the right photo are:

$$x_2 = x_1 + px \text{ and } y_2 = y_1 + py$$

Brief characteristic features of some of the numerous stereocomparators are discussed below:

Zeiss-Jena Stecometer. In this instrument (see Fig. 2.7), the common x motion is given to the lower stage and common y motion is given to the optics (microscope). The px motion is given to the right photograph on one upper stage and the py motion to the left photograph on a second upper stage. It can use photographs up to 23 x 23 cm size. The photographs are illuminated through a condenser from above and are observed from below with a magnification, 6x, 12x or 18x. It is possible to choose one of six luminous measuring marks, each differing in size and shape. Three different colours of measuring marks can be selected also. One can optically transform px into py with built-in Dove prisms.

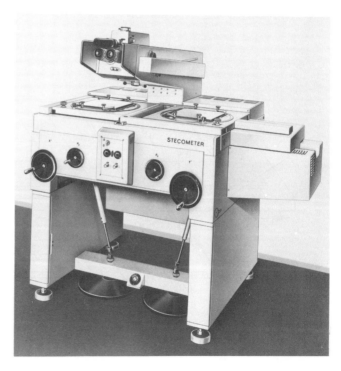

Fig. 2.7

Stecometer, Zeiss-Jena
(Courtesy, ZENA Optical
Works, East Germany)

Hilger-Watts Recording Stereocomparator. In this instrument, the measuring system
is based on the use of a 1 cm grid, which is defined by fine crosses. It can be
printed on the negative at the time of exposure or a grid plate can be placed on
the nagative in the stereocomparator.

The grid permits the elimination of the influence of film distortion and
permits simple corrections for distortions due to lens and the errors of the grid
marks as known from calibration. Scanning in the x direction is by moving the
stage plates and in the y direction by moving the optics. The instrument is
provided with a device for plate rotations up to ±22.5 degrees. Magnification is
possible between 6x and 12x. A single control can give a differential magnification up to ±1.2 times between the left and right photographs. The built-in Dove
prisms permit rotations of the images as may be necessary for convenient stereoscopic viewing. Additional coupled Dove prisms can be used to rotate images
jointly through 90° for transforming px into py.

In view of the grid (réseau), an observation method developed by J. G. F.
Lawrence (Ordnance Survey, UK publications, 1949) is used in this stereocomparator.
In this, the réseau crosses serve the following purposes: (a) Control the distortion of the negative and print material, (b) provide a convenient source of 'minor
control' as may be necessary in photo-triangulation, and (c) define a coordinate
system on the photograph. The binocular observing system has floating (measuring)
mark graticule half crosses in the left and right sides, which are fused
stereoscopically to form a cross with arms parallel and at right angles to the eye-
base (Fig. 2.8).

The operation can be visualized through Fig. 2.9. Photograph No. 1 is aligned
so that its lines of réseau crosses are parallel to the instrument axes.
Photograph No. 2 is adjusted to give comfortable stereo vision over the area around
the point to be observed. The stereoscopic pointing is completed with the finer
adjustments so that the two halves of the floating mark appear as a single cross
resting on the ground model, bisecting the observed point. The x, y readings for
the aligned photo No. 1 are recorded. The half mark associated with photo No. 1 is
then brought over the réseau cross nearest to the observed point and the readings
for photo No. 1 are again recorded. The differences of the second readings from
the first ones give $\Delta x'$ and $\Delta y'$, the x- and y-steps from the réseau cross to the
observed point, with respect to photo No. 1. These are then added to the
calibrated réseau coordinates of the cross to obtain those of the point. For
points on the ground (trigonometric stations, pass points, etc.), the procedure has

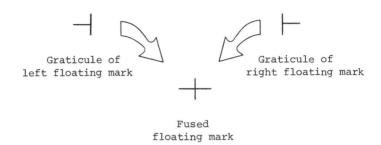

Graticule of   Graticule of
left floating mark   right floating mark

Fused
floating mark

Fig. 2.8   Floating marks in Hilger-Watts stereocomparator

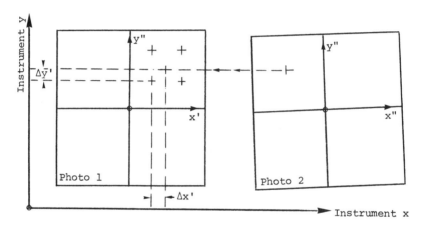

Fig. 2.9   Lawrence method of observation

to be repeated by aligning photo No.2 with its line of réseau crosses parallel to the instrumental axes, adjusting photo No. 1 to give comfortable stereo vision over the area around the same observed point.   Thus, one obtains new $\Delta x''$ and $\Delta y''$ values, i.e., new x- and y-steps from the réseau cross to the observed point with respect to photo No. 2.   These are then added to the calibrated réseau coordinates of the cross to obtain those of the point.

In this system, *minor controls* are generally réseau crosses.   If so, these have to be coordinated on the photo on which they are not marked.   The coordinates on the photo on which they are recorded are already known from the calibration data for the réseau.   Thus, left-hand points have to be observed on the right-hand photo and the right-hand points, likewise, on the left-hand photo.

Zeiss PSK-2 Stereocomparator. This instrument (see Fig. 2.10) is worthy of notice because of its design and portability. Plates with measuring réseau grids are used. Photographs are placed with emulsion surface directly in contact with these grid plates, one on either side of instrument. Prisms permit inversion of images and change of viewing sequence as may be necessary in bridging (left side photo to be viewed by right eye and vice versa). Built-in *amici* (or, roof-angle) prisms can optically adjust any rotation required for stereo viewing.

During the observation procedure, the photo holders are moved in the x-direction while the optical element containing the measuring mark moves in the y-direction. After the measuring mark is stereoscopically focussed on the point to be measured, the photo coordinates of this point are read by means of a measuring grid and a mm reticle (G and R, respectively, in Fig. 2.11) placed in the field of view of the eyepiece. The coarse readings of the x and y coordinates are obtained with reference to the réseau and the fine readings by coincidence between the reticle and the réseau.

The six digit coordinate and parallax values, x_1, y_1, px and py are read (with the least count of 1 μm) at the illuminated instrument counters or computer cards are directly punched at the connectable card punching outfit. A recording unit, e.g., Ecomat 21, can be obtained from the manufacturer.

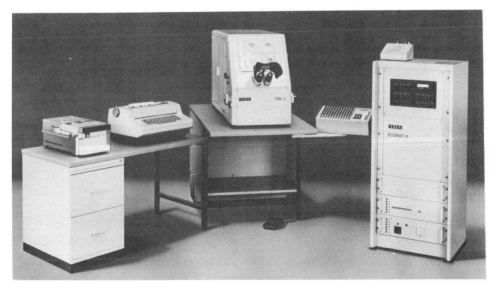

Fig. 2.10 Stereocomparator PSK-2 with Ecomat 21
(Courtesy, Carl Zeiss, Oberkochen, West Germany)

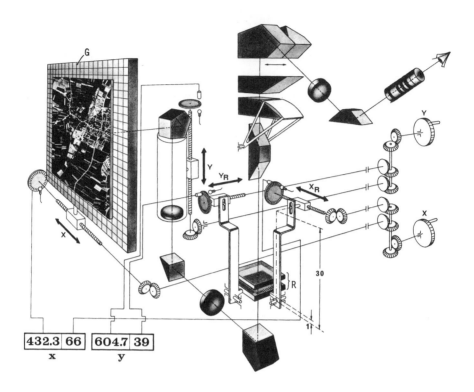

Fig. 2.11   Functional diagram of stereocomparator PSK-2
(Courtesy, Carl Zeiss, Oberkochen, West Germany)

2.3 STEREOPLOTTERS

In the absence of a comparator, if a precision stereoplotter is available, one can use such an instrument conveniently as a comparator. The operations are simple and straightforward. The procedures explained in the following are applicable in any precision stereoplotter like Wild A10 (Fig. 2.12), Zeiss C8, Thomson-Watts plotter or Galileo Santoni Stereosimplex.

2.3.1 Monocular Measurements

Monocular comparator measurements can be made by using either the left or the right side camera (projector). All elements must be set to their zero positions (i.e., $\omega = \varphi = \kappa = bx = by = bz = 0$). The principal distance (camera constant) should be set to an arbitrary value ($\bar{s}$ in Fig. 2.13; e.g., 150.00 mm), regardless of the focal length of the taking camera. The carriage should be brought to a Z-column setting of a round multiple of the principal distance setting (e.g., $Z = 2\bar{s}$

Fig. 2.12

Autograph Wild A10
(Courtesy, Wild Heerbrugg
Instruments, Switzerland)

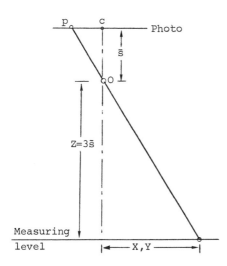

Fig. 2.13

Monocular measurement
at a stereoplotter

or $3\bar{s}$) such that the entire photograph can be observed within the instrument's limitations. The fiducial center of the photograph being c, the photo coordinates of a point (p) can be obtained from simple relations (considering X, Y as instrument coordinates in terms of the counters or scales connected to the carriages):

$$x = -\frac{\bar{s}}{Z} X \quad \text{and} \quad y = -\frac{\bar{s}}{Z} Y \qquad (2.2)$$

where $\qquad X = X_{observed} - X_c \quad \text{and } Y = Y_{observed} - Y_c$

Note: X_c and Y_c are the instrument coordinates of the fiducial center of the photo, i.e., average of the observed X, Y coordinates of the fiducial marks.

2.3.2 Stereoscopic Measurements

A stereoplotter can be used as a stereocomparator by using both the cameras (projectors) of the instrument with observations in stereo. The stereo overlap can be accomplished in either base-in or base-out mode. The base-in mode is illustrated in Fig. 2.14.

Note: *Base-in* and *Base-out* are permissible settings in some instrument systems. With alternate base-in and base-out settings, it is possible to perform instrumental strip triangulation with only two cameras in such instruments (see Ghosh, 1975).

In a Base-in model (assuming an air-photo strip flown left to right, Photo No. 1 in the left camera of the instrument and Photo No. 2 in the right camera), all the elements excepting bx must be set to their zero positions, i.e., $\omega' = \omega'' = \varphi' = \varphi'' = \kappa' = \kappa'' = by' = by'' = bz' = bz'' = 0$. The settings of bx, $\bar{s}$ and Z must be realistic round figures, in keeping with the intersection geometry of the stereo pair. For example, with *Standard* (i.e., Wide angle camera and 60 per cent forward overlap) photography, the possible settings are: bx = 200.00 mm, $\bar{s}$ = 150.00 mm and Z = 300.00 mm (see Fig. 2.14, drawn with these values in mind).

Other instrumental settings are: (i) Instrument gears and levers are set such that all readings (X, Y and H) are in the same units (e.g., mm); (ii) The H counter must read positive values at all points in the stereo overlap. This can be done by initially setting the H index to read a large value (e.g., $\bar{H}$ = 200.00 mm) at the instrument Z level (in Fig. 2.14, it is 300.00 mm).

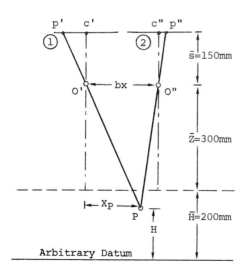

Fig. 2.14

Stereoscopic measurement
at a stereoplotter

The X and Y hand wheels and the Z disc (or pedal) are to be used for scanning the stereo model and reaching the specific points. Y-parallaxes are to be removed with the by" element, whose readings are to be recorded along with the readings of the X, Y and H scales (or counters). The photo coordinates of a point in the left side photo are obtained by using the following expressions:

$$x' = - (X - X_{c'}) \frac{\bar{s}}{(500.00 - H)} \left.\begin{array}{c} \\ \\ \\ \\ \end{array}\right\} \qquad (2.3)$$
$$y' = - (y - Y_{c'}) \frac{\bar{s}}{(500.00 - H)}$$

The photo coordinates of the same point in the right side photo are given by:

$$x'' = x' + px \left.\begin{array}{c} \\ \\ \\ \end{array}\right\} \qquad (2.4)$$
$$y'' = y' + py$$

where $px = \bar{s} \dfrac{bx}{(500.00 - H)}$ and $py = \bar{s} \dfrac{(by'' - by')}{(500.00 - H)}$ (2.5)

This procedure can be followed for both negatives and diapositives. Note that the number 500.00 appearing in the denominators of Eqs 2.3 and 2.5 is due to the sum of 300.00 (value in mm of the Z column setting) and 200.00 (value also in mm of the H index setting).

In a Base-out model, the data can be obtained in a similar manner, with Photo No. 1 in the right side camera and Photo No.2 in the left side camera and by using the by' element for parallax elimination. Many recent studies (see Salmenpera, 1970) indicate that by using such stereoplotters one can obtain accuracies comparable with stereocomparators.

2.4 ANALYTICAL PLOTTERS

An analytical plotter consists of: (a) a Viewing Unit (precision stereocomparator with control) and (b) a Coordinatograph, interfaced with (c) an electronic Digital Computer (see Fig. 2.15). These instruments are capable of solving a wide variety of photogrammetric problems, conventional and unconventional. The early models required a certain amount of manual operations. More recent ones, however, incorporate electronic image correlators and other components, which make them operate almost completely automatically. Their capabilities are limited by the

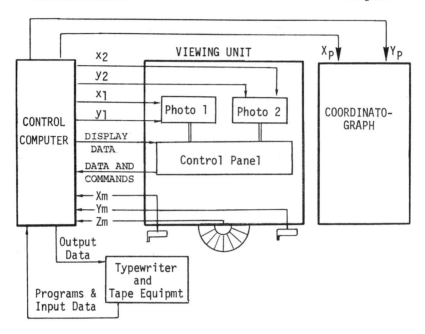

Fig. 2.15 System diagram for an analytical plotter

dimensions of the photo-carriers in the comparator and the limitations of the computer. Many analogical solutions like Relative Orientation, Scaling, Absolute Orientation, Orthophoto printing, etc. are possible in such an instrument apart from it being used as a stereocomparator only. Several commercially available analytical plotters are shown in Figs 2.16 through 2.19. Some of the numerous such plotters available on the market are: Aviolyt BC-1 of Wild, AP-C/4 of OMI Corporation, Planicomp C-100 of Carl Zeiss, US-2 Of Helava Associates, Traster SST77 of Matra Optique, DSR11 of Kern and Digital Stereocartograph of Galileo. Certain simpler versions with limited capabilities like Stereocord G2 fo Carl Zeiss, MPS - 2 of Adam Technology and APPS-IV of Autometric are also available. These indicate the world wide trend towards on-line analytical solutions with computer capabilities.

Such an instrument operates by solving equations based on the observation data (point locations on photo), stored data and the mathematical model relating the problem. Output from the comparator-computer combination activates servo motors to drive the coordinatograph plotting device (pencil or scriber), which presents the graphical, plotted information. Some of them can even provide computer support for analog plotters in parallel.

It should be recognized that there are always necessary communications (dialog)

Fig. 2.16 Aviolyt BC-2 of Wild
(Courtesy, Wild Heerbrugg Instruments, Switzerland)

between the computer and other revelant components of the analytical plotter. This
is essential for on-line solutions of various problems. The standard procedures
involved in topographic mapping with a stereopair of aerial (or satellite)
photographs are illustrated in Fig. 2.20.

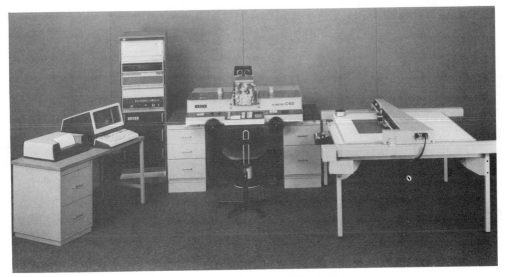

Fig. 2.17 Planicomp C-100 of Zeiss
(Courtesy, Carl Zeiss, Oberkochen, West Germany)

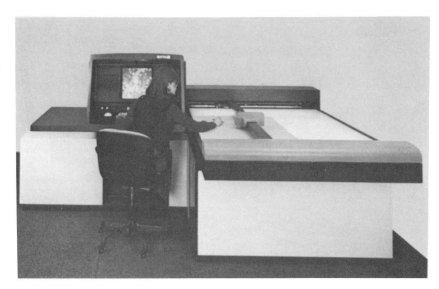

Fig. 2.18   Traster SST-77 of Matra
(Courtesy,   Matra Optique, France)

Fig. 2.19   Digital Stereocartograph of Galileo
(Courtesy,   Officine Galileo, Florence, Italy)

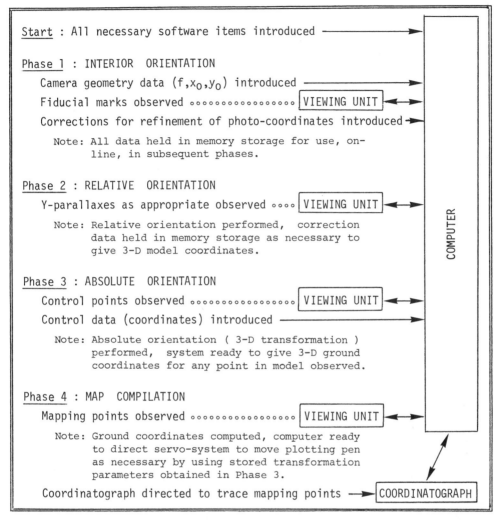

Fig. 2.20 Typical communication diagram for mapping of a
stereo-model at an analytical plotter

The adaptability of the analytical plotter to various systems and problems is
its prime asset. For example, any portion of a photograph with the NASA Large
Format Camera (Fig. 10.8) can be used inspite of the fact that the perspective
center could be set off-center. The problems of orienting strip and panoramic
photographs (Chap. 10) are solved easily and adequately at such a plotter.
Likewise, radiographs or electron micrographs can be handled successfully. For
their use with conventional (frame) photography, the operations follow a pattern
similar to, yet more than, those at a conventional optical-mechanical stereoplotter. For example, the following steps would be pertinent with regard to
panoramic phogography:

1. *Interior Orientation* of each photo. The inputs at this stage are,

    a) Diapositives (or negatives) placed on the plate carriers of comparator.

    b) Constants (for the computer):

        F —   Camera focal length corrected for uniform film shrinkage;

        C_f —   Differential film-shrinkage constant, which is used to calculate such correction as is applicable to one set of photo coordinates (say, y) compared to the other (say, x);

        R —   Radius of the Earth Sphere in the model scale;

        $\bar{X}, \bar{Y}$ —   The coordinates of the points in the model at which the Earth Sphere is assumed to be tangent to the X-Y plane of the model;

        C_e, C_h —   Correction constants which are determined by fitting correction equations to appropriate distortions due to lens and atmospheric distortions;

        X_n, Y_n —   Coordinates of the camera Nadir point in the model system;

        K_{im} —   The image motion constant which corrects for the Image Motion Compensation (IMC) of the camera;

        K_{xr}, K_{yr} —   These two apply to panoramic photography only, being the relative vehicle motion constants (relative to the Earth) during exposure.

    c) Photo centers (x_0, y_0), established from the observed fiducial marks constitute the only observation data for Interior Orientation.

2. *Relative Orientation* of the stereo pair.

    a) Y-parallaxes observed at <u>five</u> or more locations (in the stereo model);

    b) The elements of relative orientation, generally 'Dependent' case (i.e., bz, by, ω, φ, and κ) are computed and stored.

Note: With appropriate software, the relative orientation can be performed by also applying the Collinearity or the Coplanarity condition.

3. *Absolute Orientation* of the stereo model.

    a) <u>Three</u> control points (at least) are identified and used for absolute orientation (scaling and leveling). The elements of transformation between model coordinates and ground (survey) coordinates are computed and stored.

4. *Map Compilation* of necessary details and contour lines in the model.

    a) δX and δY are computed from model coordinates and applied to the photo-carriages on a real-time basis.

    b) Map coordinates are computed from model coordinates using the stored parameters of transformation from Step 3 above.

c) The compilation proceeds on a real-time basis. Alternately, model coordinates (X_m, Y_m, Z_m) or the corresponding map or ground coordinates (X_p, Y_p, Z_p) for discrete points can be recorded or displayed.

Simple versions of analytical plotters, some of them indegenous (see for example, Ladouceur et al., 1982), are becoming popular for applications where accuracy demand and scopes are limited. One recent example is the Stereocord G2 of Zeiss developed after the Analytical Photogrammetric Positioning System (APPS). The APPS, developed at the US Army Engineer Topographical Laboratories, is a modified Zeiss Stereotope, the analog mechanical computers having been replaced by an electronic desk calculator (Hewlett-Packard Model 9810). The measurement values are digitized with the aid of a commercial pulse generator in conjunction with a counter (e.g., DIREC-1 in Steroecord G2) and an interface system. All numerical data for each stereo pair (i.e., camera position, elevation, attitude, camera calibration data, refraction corrections, etc.) are stored on a magnetic tape cassette together with the calculator program required for data reduction. The Stereotope part is used as a stereo viewer. A shaft-angle encoder, mounted on the Stereotope x-parallax micrometer, provides X measurements which can be used to determine the elevation of any point being viewed in stereo. All data reduction is performed automatically by the calculator and three-dimensional coordinates are displayed. When a plotter (e.g., Hewlett-Packard Model 9872A) is connected to the Stereocord G2, it becomes a complete analytical plotter (albeit, for limited applications).

Another simple analytical plotter is the APPS-IV of Autometric, Inc. This instrument has linear encoders on x, y, Δx and Δy motions (i.e., the two photo coordinates at a point and two parallaxes, Δx and Δy, at the same point). These motions are driven by servo motors and are also displayed for manual uses. Other features include an electronic subsystem for internal data handling and facilities for communications with a remote computer. There is a modern trend towards fully integrated relational database systems wherein an analytical plotter remains the workstation. The S9-AP of Wild is a good example in this regard.

2.5 RADIAL TRIANGULATORS

These instruments are designed for computational radial triangulation, which may be performed somewhat conveniently now-a-days because of the use of aircraft of improved stability. Such stability would restrict the tilt of the photograph to

AP-E

within very narrow limits, which would permit generally successful principal point triangulation. The precision is, however, extremely limited. Their use is, accordingly, much restricted. This brief description is presented here for the sake of completeness.

One oft-used example of such an instrument is Wild RT1. In this instrument, the photographs remain fixed on the photo carriers during the measuring process while two rotatable glass scales, one on each photo of the stereo pair, are shifted. Each glass scale is provided with a series of measuring marks (engraved on the scale). To measure a point, the scale is rotated into the same polar direction of the point and the nearest measuring mark of the series on the glass scale is set on the point by a small shift and rotation of the scale. The values of the rotations of the two glass scales are read on two corresponding 'theodolite' horizontal circles (reading least count being 1^C, estimated to $\approx 0^C.1$). Similarly, the length of the radius vector (estimated to ≈ 0.01 mm) for the points may be determined. These two measurement capabilities make it possible to use the instrument also as a stereocomparator for polar coordinates. Depending on the tilt, circumstances and job requirements, either the principal point, or the nadir point, or the isocenter (or any other reference point) of the photograph can be used as the radial center. Good stereo observation is possible by means of Dove prisms in the viewing system.

2.6 POINT MARKING AND TRANSFERRING DEVICES

With a view to avoiding possible ambiguity in the identification, selection and description of photo points obtained from natural details, it is often desirable to mark unmistakable points in the emulsion of the photograph. Depending on whether or not stereo- or mono- observations are desired, such points may or may not be transferred onto the adjacent photographs. In some areas (e.g., forest or desert) it may be impossible to locate natural points and the cost of providing presignalized points on ground may be prohibitive. Such artificial points are desirable in these cases. Several point marking and transfering devices are commercially available. Each device has, of course, its limitations in the type of point it can mark and the accuracy with which such points are marked and transferred. Brief descriptions of some of these are given below:

a. *MK MARKING device by Carl Zeiss* (Fig. 2.21). It has a rectangular metal frame within which is a glass plate with a spotting device (punctiform setting mark) and a marking device, both of which can be mutually adjusted so that the observed point

Fig. 2.21 MK marking device
(Courtesy, Carl Zeiss,
Oberkochen, West Germany)

appears in the center of the annular mark, engraved on the lower plane (in touch
with photograph). A steroescopically selected point is marked in the emulsion of
photo by a circle of 1 mm diameter around the point. Artificial transfer points
can be marked by a minute needle prick. A 10-power magnifying lens is povided to
facilitate the observation of the point. Two such units are necessary for
stereoscopic marking and transfering under a stereoscope.

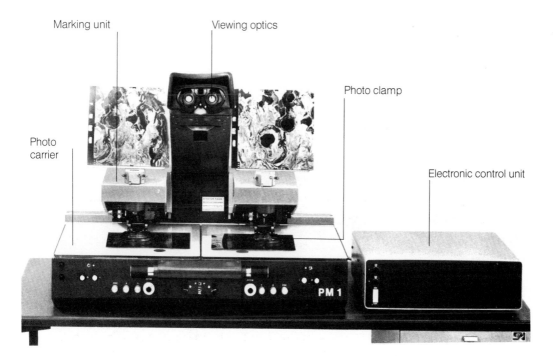

Fig. 2.22 PM-1 marking device
(Courtesy, Carl Zeiss, Oberkochen, West Germany)

b.   *PM-1 Marking device by Carl Zeiss* (Fig. 2.22) is much more sophisticated and precise than the MK cited above. It uses heated needles for marking the points. This creates annular bulges around the points and provides high contrast against bright or dark image detail. It permits a viewing zoom magnification of between 6x and 26x.   Point mark diameters vary from 40 μm to 200 μm for optimum matching to the floating mark size of the instrument to be used later for measurement.   Photo carriers permit formats upto 42.5 cm x 48.0 cm.   There is a choice of point- or ring- mark or both.   Individual or common image rotations through 90° and 180° are permissible for point transfers between strips and for ortho-pseudo switching.

c.   *PUG-5 of Wild Heerbrugg* (Fig. 2.23).   This instrument is meant for marking and transferring of points on glass or film by stereoscopically viewing the photo-graphs and drilling holes in the emulsion.   A metal box frame supports two glass plates which act as picture carriers, with a range of ± 10 mm, in x and y directions.   Independent differential movements in both x and y directions are also provided.

 Two *drilling heads*, each consisting of a drive mechanism, a drill holder, a drill and a marker are provided.   When the drilling lever is depressed, a rotation

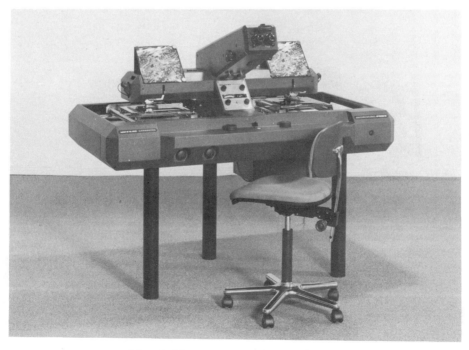

Fig. 2.23 PUG-5 marking device
(Courtesy, Wild Heerbrugg Instruments, Switzerland)

and simultaneous lowering of the drill holder is caused. PUG drills of 60, 100, 120 and 180 μm diameters are available. Black measuring marks of 30 μm apparent diameter are used for accurate setting under stereo viewing. Each optical system includes a zoom lens of range 1:4, whereby the magnification in each system can be varied continuously from 6x to 24x. The drills are motorized. The constant drill speed and constant pressure ensure clean and sharp round holes. The viewing system is equipped with Dove prisms which permit necessary rotations of the observed pictures. The pictures are actually viewed from below through the carrier plates.

d. *Multiscale marker by Bausch & Lomb.* This was designed to handle photographs with large variations in scale and format. It can work with relative ease for scale ratios up to 1:16, can take film or glass plates up to thickness of 0.5 inch and 9 x 18 inch format. The mark is made with a thermal marking die, for which there is a choice of six different types ranging from a 40 μm dot to 200 μm and 2000 μm circles. The die molds a mark in the emulsion as it is lowered onto the emulsion and heated for a fraction of a second.

The optical system contains two identical trains, one for each eye, with continuous magnification ranging from 2.8x to 48x (in two steps), 360° image rotators and the binocular eyepiece having 5x magnification.

The instrument has two tables, one located above the other and each with a carriage which can travel in any direction at speeds from 0.5 mm to 25 mm (in coarse mode) or from 2 μm to 100 μm (in fine mode) per second. Each photo holder has a reference mark to position the photo, vacuum and acetate masks to hold it in three leveling screws to rectify the scanning and marking plane as may be necessary.

Interesting ideas on the working of such point marking and transferring devices, in themselves, and in combination with photogrammetric measuring instruments have been presented by Okang (1971, 1972). Okang's studies indicate that the performance of a point marking device depends primarily on three factors: (i) photo image quality; (ii) stereoscopic ability of observer and (iii) instrumental errors which include also the incompatibility between the produced mark and the measuring mark of the measuring instrument. The statistical analyses of the results of computational relative orientation using the marked points give standard errors (at picture scale) of the relative orientation adjustment between 14 and 23 μm. Okang also observed that certain point marker and measuring instrument combinations work better than other such combinations. He suggested the method of Regression Analysis for calibration of point marking devices. Such a calibration would provide corrections to observed image coordinates for analytical-computional uses. Okang's studies also indicate that there is no significant difference between natural and artificial points so far as the final mensural accuracy is concerned at individual points. The transferred point may, however, be not always in the correct locations.

2.7 CALIBRATION

Calibration should be considered as (see also Eisenhart, 1963) a refined form of measurement for the purpose of assigning numbers to specific properties (elements, or parameters) with statistically sound expressions for their systematic errors and precisions. Error predication, intended to characterize the process, is obtained after the measurement procedure has achieved a state of statistical control in view of properly established specifications indicating allowable ranges or variations. The process seems simple enough, but there are some difficulties one must consider and try to eliminate:

1. The instrument's sensitivity to factors other than the desired input (in our case, the photograph);

2. The difficulty in obtaining the "Standard" against which all measurements can be made; and

3. The failure of the instrument to have the same output (say, photo coordinates) for repeated applications of any particular value of input.

2.7.1 Difficulties to Consider

a. *Sensitivity to Other Factors*

Unfortunately, an instrument may present an output for the factors in which we are not interested. For example, a coordinate value may contain error input due to temperature variation in the room or fluctuation of power supply to the instrument. To avoid errors in calibration, it is necessary to control these unwanted inputs so that any change in output of the instrument is due only to the corresponding change of the input being measured. Usually, this can be achieved by carefully controlling the environment in which the calibration is performed. In some cases it may be necessary to know the 'static' characteristics of the instrument, i.e., when the unwanted factors (inputs) are varied singly and the primary input is maintained at a constant value. It may, therefore, be necessary to perform several such static calibrations, one for each possible factor. For the rest of our discussions on the topic, we will assume that we need to be concerned

only with the principal input and that no unwanted factors are present. The
primary requirement for this concept is that the calibration procedure be conducted
under circumstances which are reasonably representative of those "working
conditions" under which the calibration would be applied.

b. *Standards*

A standard is defined to be a quantity item that can be used as a reference in
determining values of unknown quantities of the same item. Through the spirit of
international cooperation and agreement, such a reference system has been established, known as the *International Prototype Standard*. From the International
Prototype Standard are derived the *National Prototype Standards* as maintained by
the various countries. In the USA the National Bureau of Standards (NBS) has been
charged with maintaining the various standards. In order to protect the National
Prototype Standard from deteriorations (e.g., due to wear and tear, oxidation, or
other effects), it is not used routinely. A third level of standard, therefore, is
derived from the National Prototype, known as the *National Reference Standard*. A
fourth group, the *Working Standards* are next developed by comparison with the
Reference Standards.

On the other hand, all these standards are carefully maintained and used under
controlled and guarded conditions. They are not really intended to be used under
the normal working conditions of the offices and laboratories. The standard normally used in such cases is the *Interlaboratory Standard*. This standard should
have a calibration that can be traced to the appropriate standard at the National
Bureau of Standards.

Since all the above mentioned derived standards are obtained by comparison, it
is possible that the values will be somewhat in error. This error may be extremely small but one must remember that, no measured quantity can be known
exactly. Also, one should be aware that such standards are not known exactly, but
should be (and generally are) guaranteed to be within some specific range
(confidence limit or tolerance).

The use of such standards is imperative when 'absolute' values or data are
required. However, for 'relative' information, an *Ad hoc Standard* (sometimes with
assumed accuracy) may be used in practice. Yet, at other times, one may have to
work with *Generated Standards* (e.g., generating a standard for the third dimension by using a two-dimensional standard grid, see Electron Micrography, Chap. 10).

In such a case, however, the dependability of the generated standard would rest on various factors (including the application set-up). In all cases, nevertheless, it is desirable that one uses a reference standard of proven stability with the concept of 'repetition' being well established in the working system (see Eisenhart, 1969).

In this connection, it will be desirable to discuss the numerical values, *Units* (see Wildi, 1973) – that are assigned to the various standards. We are familiar with the customary system of units that is used in our country. Similarly, other countries use their systems, each in a workable manner. In using them universally and internationally, there are two disadvantages: (i) The variety of units assigned to a particular quantity may require some conversion factors (e.g., to inches, feet or fathoms); and (ii) There are some differences among units known by the same name in various national systems. Such differences and inconsistencies should better be eliminated. In an effort to do just that, the *International System of Units* (SI) has been proposed. This system (a form of the 'metric' system) is not yet completely developed but it is expected that it will be adopted by all the nations of the world.

c. *Repeatability*

The enigma can be illustrated in the following problem of testing a scale of standard length (say, 100 mm). As we know that several trials are better than one, we repeat the measurement several times and obtain the following results:

TRIAL	READING	MEAN VALUE	DEVIATION FROM MEAN	STANDARD DEVIATION
1	101.3 mm		0.8 mm	
2	99.3		−1.2	
3	100.9	100.51 mm	0.4	± 0.77 mm
4	99.9		−0.6	
5	101.1		0.6	
6	100.6		0.1	

None of the readings is correct. The average of the readings (100.51 mm) is not the value of the input. The average result, inspite of a variety of individual indications, is useful. But the question remains as to how one should deal with the individual readings. Supposing that it is possible to make only one reading, is there any way to indicate where this reading might be with respect to the mean? We must consider that for each possible input (scale value) there are infinite number of possible outputs and that the outputs are distributed in some fashion. The next question is, what is the nature of this distribution? Knowing full well that the instrument has its limitations, we can not expect the output to deviate from the true value of the input by an amount as large as infinity. We know that the chances of obtaining, such extreme outputs are nil. Experience indicates that most of such outputs would be grouped near the mean value. A very strong assumption can now be made that the factors that cause the outputs to be in error are randomly active and are independent of one another. Now, the differences of the individual values from the mean would help us calculate the *Standard deviation* of the observations. The standard deviation is a measure of the way the outputs are scattered about the mean value. It is often adequate to simply report these two values, mean and standard deviation. But it may sometimes be more convenient to state the information in a different form such as to include the probability consideration at a certain per cent confidence limit. This is expressed by

$$\underline{x} = m \pm z \cdot \sigma \qquad (2.6)$$

where $\underline{x}$ is the expected output

   m is the mean value

   z is the degree of probability; it is obtainable from the Probability table (see any book on Statistics)

and σ is the standard deviation.

   In the present case of example, m = 100.51 mm; σ = 0.77 mm and z = 1.65 at 90 per cent confidence limit. These give, $\underline{x}$ = 100.51 ± 1.27 (mm). This can be interpreted as follows: For an input of 100 mm, we can expect the output to be between 101.78 mm and 99.24 mm, at 90 per cent confidence.

   It will be also helpful at this point to consider two terms: The first term is *Bias*. It is the difference between the input and the mean value of the output, i.e., Bias = Mean value - Input. The second term, *Precision*, indicates the scattering of the output values. It is defined as the measure of the ability of the instrument to give the same output for repeated applications of a given input. An instrument of high precision gives outputs which are very narrowly scattered. The standard deviation would indicate the precision. However, the outputs can be related to the input by *Accuracy* also in the entirety of the system. To specify Accuracy completely, we must specify both a range of values within which we expect the output to lie and the probability that this will occur. Therefore the following definitions are pertinent:

Precision: Degree of mutual agreement among individual measurements (made under prescribed like conditions).

Accuracy: Degree of agreement of individual measurements with an accepted reference value.

The concept of *System Calibration* in contrast to Components' calibration can also be emphasized. This is, however, out of the scope of this book.

2.7.2 Calibration of a Comparator

Apart from the possibility of having accidental (random) errors, the following errors of systemetic nature may occur in a precision comparator:

a) Errors of the Instrument System

  - Scaling and periodic errors (of the x, y measuring systems involving scales, spindles, coordinate counters, etc.;
  - Affinity errors (being the scale difference between x and y directions);
  - Errors of rectilinearity (bending) of the guide rails;
  - Lack of orthogonality between x and y axes (also known as 'rectangularity error').

b) Backlash and tracking errors.

c) Dynamic errors (e.g., microscope velocity does not drop to zero at points to be approached during the operation).

d) Errors of automation in the system:

  - Digital resolution (smallest incremental interval);
  - Errors due to deviation of the direction. This is because the control system may not provide for the continuously variable scanning directions.

Each of the above mentioned errors can be mathematically modelled with respect to each comparator (even each carriage). However, in a systems approach, from the practical standpoint, the task can be performed by the transformation of the measured coordinates of a precalibrated array of points to the given (known) coordinates of points in the array. The array of points would consist of a precision grid (réseau) plate. Considering all possible errors, the transformation equations (error model) of the form given below would be very appropriate (see Kern publications, undated, on calibration):

$$x_C = a_1 + a_2x + a_3y + a_4xy + a_5x^2 + a_6y^2 + a_7x^2y + a_8xy^2 + a_9x^3 + a_{10}y^3$$
$$y_C = b_1 + b_2x + b_3y + b_4xy + b_5x^2 + b_6y^2 + b_7x^2y + b_8xy^2 + b_9x^3 + b_{10}y^3$$

(2.7)

where x_C, y_C are the known coordinates of measured points;

$\quad\quad\quad\quad$ x, y   are the instrument (observed) coordinates of measured points;

and $a_1, a_2...a_{10}$
$\quad\quad\quad b_1, b_2...b_{10}$ are the coefficients of the error model (to be determined).

In this, each measured point generates one x equation and one y equation. If more than ten points are measured, the system of equations is solvable by applying the method of Least Squares to yield the desired error model coefficient (or, calibration constants). In case points fewer than ten are used, the terms containing higher orders in x and y can be discarded (ignored) to obtain working solutions. Such a solution of limited scope may not portray the situation adequately, though. In such calibration jobs, it is recommended to use at least twentyfive evenly distributed points.

Any such calibration procedure which accounts for nonlinear errors requires that an invariant coordinate system be adopted, i.e., the origin and the coordinate system as used at the time of calibration must be used for all subsequent work in which the calibration is to be utilized. Furthermore, the unit of instrument measurement must also be held invariant. Any such calibratiion should also be considered to be valid only for that area of the comparator surface (corresponding to the run of the screws or scales) over which the calibration is performed.

The parameters in Eqs 2.7 may be considered as uncorrelated. The right hand sides are identical and the 'normal' equations would consist of a single coefficient matrix with two constant vectors (one for the x equation and one for the y equation). The inverse of the coefficient matrix multiplied by both constant vectors would yield the solution vectors for x and y. After the calibration constants are known, the equations may be evaluated for all checked points so as to determine the residuals (deviations) between the given (known) and the measured coordinates. The standard deviations for each axis (x or y) can next be computed from such residuals.

In some cases, it is possible that all ten terms in each of Eqs 2.7 are not really needed. It may actually be of interest to know as to which terms are superfluous. The polynomials are based on theoretically sound error propagation laws. Unfortunately, unless the handling process is controlled statistically, the nature of the required polynomial will vary for each application. On the other hand, in view of a fixed set of conditions, the perfomance of the instrument should result in a standard polynomial for each coordinate. These standard polynomials could be found empirically by using the analysis of variance (ANOVA) technique over a test grid plate. Any standard text book of Statistics may be referred to for the ANOVA technique. This way, many combinations of variables can be tested until the combination which gives the best reductions (in sum of squares of the residuals) is obtained. The final form of the best polynomial should then be used.

Alternately, from the practitioner's point of view, the equations can be solved several times, each time constraining certain terms to zero.   Table 2.1 illustrates this suggested principle. Whether any of the higher order terms are necessary or not can be assessed by examining the residuals from each solution.

Table 2.1

Check of effective terms in calibration

(Note: e = term is effective)

Solution Number	Terms									
	Const	x	y	xy	x^2	y^2	x^2y	xy^2	x^3	y^3
1	e	e	e	e	e	e	e	e	e	e
2	e	e	e	e	e	e	e	e		
3	e	e	e	e	e	e				
4	e	e	e	e						
5	e	e	e							
6	e									

Such a procedure of calibration would be applicable also to the analytical plotters.   It is suggested that this be done separately for each photo carrier, such that the *model deformation* caused by the local deviations can be directly applicable to the generated three-dimensional coordinates, if necessary.   See Ghosh (1972) for ideas on model-deformation.

Ideally, a complete calibration of a comparator should provide statistics to indicate the following:

1)   Pointing precision (man-machine cooperation);
2)   Quality (status) of instrument before calibration;
3)   Quality (status) of instrument after removal of linear systematic errors;
4)   Quality (status) of instrument after removal of non-linear systematic errors;
5)   Quality of the given grid coordinates (against an accepted standard); and
6)   An assessment of the time and cost involved in the calibration.

2.7.3 Calibration of a Projection Instrument

As in the case of a comparator, an improvement in the accuracy and efficiency of a stereoplotter (projection instrument) can be obtained by using redundant observations and a computer to handle the mathematical model describing the specific functions for which the instrument is used. Calibration procedures for such instruments can be divided into three broad groups according to their fucntions

1. Those designed to determine the instrument parameters and zero-settings, viz.,

   (a) Elements of exterior orientation, X_0, Y_0, Z_0, ω_0, φ_0, κ_0, bx, by and bz;

   (b) Elements of interior orientation, f, x_0 and y_0.

2. Those designed to test the instrument and provide the information necessary for the operator/technician.

3. Those designed to speedily test the performance of the instrument in terms of one or more of the three coordinates (X, Y and Z).

   Most frequently needed information and their sample uses are listed in Table 2.2.

Table 2.2

Frequently needed parameters at a projection instrument

Parameters	Notations	Sample Uses
Principal distance	f	All uses of instrument
Principal point location	x_0, y_0	All uses of instrument
Perspective center	X_0, Y_0, Z_0	Photo-triangulation by Independent models method
Zero settings of rotation elements	$\omega_0, \phi_0, \kappa_0$	Terrestrial photogrammetry
Zero settings of base components (and their values)	$\begin{cases} bx, by, bz\ \& \\ by', by'' \\ bz', bz'' \end{cases}$	Instrument calibration Use of auxiliary data Instrument use as comparator
Elevation values (in model)	Z	Compilation of contours
Planimetric model coordinates	X, Y	Compilation of planimetric details, use as comparator

   Spatial resection for each camera (projector) of the instrument can be performed in order to obtain information on the aforementioned parameters. This can be done with a precision grid plate and having observations made at one Z = constant plane (in model space). The resection can be formulated in two ways (see Dowman, 1973):

FORMULA I

$$\frac{X - X_0}{Z - Z_0} = \frac{a_{11}x + a_{12}y + a_{13}f}{a_{31}x + a_{32}y + a_{33}f}$$

$$\left. \right\}$$ (2.8)

$$\frac{Y - Y_0}{Z - Z_0} = \frac{a_{21}x + a_{22}y + a_{23}f}{a_{31}x + a_{32}y + a_{33}f}$$

where x, y are the photo coordinates (of grid intersections);

X, Y, Z are the model coordinates (observed at the instrument counters);

X_0, Y_0, Z_0 are coordinates of the perspective center in model system;

and $a_{11}...a_{33}$ are nine elements of the rotation matrix.

The elements of the rotation matrix (explanations in Chap. 3) consist of sine and cosine functions of three independent unknowns (ω, φ and κ). There are, thus, six unknowns (X_0, Y_0, Z_0, $d\omega$, $d\varphi$ and $d\kappa$), which can be determined from observations to at least three points in one Z=constant plane in the instrument. Equations 2.8, however, are not linear and the computations are more than what some desk calculators can handle. There is another disadvantage in using Eqs 2.8, that they make no allowance for errors in the interior orientation elements which may affect the results. On the other hand, because very small rotation angles are involved, one can express the space resection problem by yet other equations (see Ghosh, 1972 for the derivations of the equations):

FORMULA II

$$dx = -\frac{xy}{f} d\omega + f\left(1 + \frac{x^2}{f^2}\right) d\varphi - y.d\kappa + dx_0 - \frac{x}{f} df + \frac{f}{Z} dX_0 + \frac{x}{Z} dZ_0$$

$$\left. \right\}$$ (2.9)

$$dy = -f\left(1 + \frac{y^2}{f^2}\right) d\omega + \frac{xy}{f} d\varphi + x.d\kappa + dy_0 - \frac{y}{f} df + \frac{f}{Z} dy_0 + \frac{y}{Z} dZ_0$$

where dx, dy are differences, at photo scale, between model coordinates and known grid coordinates;

$d\omega, d\varphi, d\kappa$ are the six unknown parameters, corresponding to Eq. 2.8 and
dX_0, dY_0, dZ_0 Table 2.2 (with observations made at one Z = constant plane);

dx_0, dy_0 are the differences at the principal point;

and   df   is the error in the principal distance (corresponds to focal length).

In such a situation, f and Z being highly correlated to each other, if the observations are made only one Z = constant plane, the solutions may not be conclusive in view of possible "critical geometry". However, if the observations are made in two Z = constant planes (rather than just one), the elements of interior orientation for each point (dx_0, dy_0, and df) are also obtainable. In this connection, interesting ideas are given by Ghosh (1975).

In view of Eqs 2.9, a step by step procedure for this solution can be suggested such as can be performed at a desk calculator:

Step 1: Set all elements to zero values (as previously obtained). These are good approximate values to start with.

Step 2: Rotate κ element to obtain κ_0 setting. This being a tertiary rotation element, has no effect on any other element and thus, does not propagate any error.

Step 3: At this stage, if a programmable computer is available, a calibration can be undertaken by using Eqs 2.9, with respect to one camera (monocular grid observations) at a time. If not, one may continue as follows:

Step 1: The principal distance (f) and the perspective center coordinates (X_0, Y_0, Z_0) can be obtained by observing at least two points in two Z = constant planes (see the procedure described in Chap. 8, Ghosh, 1975).

Step 2: Set the measuring mark to X_0, Y_0 position of the instrument carriage and bring the principal point (cross) onto the mark by using ω and φ elements. This will give the ω_0 and φ_0 positions.

Step 3: The inclination of the stage plate (interior orientation) can be determined from grid observations in one plane. The pattern of distortion can be seen in a plot of the residuals and the magnitude of rotations can be calculated by using the following equations:

$$
\left.
\begin{aligned}
dx &= \frac{x^2}{f}\, d\varphi - \frac{xy}{f}\, d\omega \\[2ex]
dy &= \frac{xy}{f}\, d\varphi - \frac{y^2}{f}\, d\omega
\end{aligned}
\right\}
\tag{2.10}
$$

These are reduced from Eq. 2.9 after assuming all other parameters to be zero. The coodinates x, y are reduced to the principal point as origin and scaled to photo-scale (e.g., by using a symmetrical pair of grid lines, in the model) which are not affected by a rotation of the grid plate.

Step 4: Rotations $d\omega$ and $d\varphi$, when found, can be applied to the instrument (being rotations around the respective axes passing through the perspective center) with additional adjustments of the principal point (dx_0 and dy_0).

Step 5:   Repetition of Step 3 along with iterative observations can be continued until satisfactory results are finally obtained.

Note: The parameters, bx by and bz, as also their necessary components (by' by", bz' and bz") may be derived from basic considerations of the particular instrument.

BIBLIOGRAPHY

Brown, Duane; "Computational Trade-offs in the Design of a Comparator", *PE* 35, No. 2 (1969).

Chitayat, A.; "Interference Comparators for Coordinate Measurement of Ballistic Plates". *Photographic Science and Engineering* 4, No. 5 (1960).

Dowman, I. J.; "A Working Method for the Calibration of Plotting Instruments Using Computers", *PR* 7, No. 42 (1973).

Eisenhart, Churchill; "Realistic Evaluation of the Precision and Accuracy of Instrument Calibration Systems", *Journal of Research*, National Bureau of Standards-C-Engineering and Instrumentation, Vol. 67c, No. 2 (1963).

Eisenhart, Churchill; *Precision Measurement and Calibration* (NBS Special Publication 300, Vol. 1: 1969).

Ghosh, Sanjib K.; *Theory of Stereophotogrammetry* (2nd Ed) (The Ohio State Univ. Bookstores, Columbus, Ohio: 1972).

Ghosh, Sanjib K.; *Phototriangulation* (Lexington books, Lexington, Massachussetts: 1975).

Ghosh, Sanjib K.; "Some Thoughts on Instrument Calibration"; *Proceeding of the ASP,* Fall Convention; Seattle, Washington (1976).

Ghosh, Sanjib K.; "Standard for three-dimensional mensuration with electron micrographs"; Optical Testing and Metrology, *SPIE Proceedings,* Vol. 661 (1986).

Gugel, R. A.; "Comparator Calibration"; *PE* 31, No. 5 (1965).

Hallert, Bertil P.; "Test measurement in Comparators and Tolerances for Such Instruments"; *PE* 29, No. 2 (1963).

Helava, U. V. and R. H. Seymour; "US-1 Universal Stereoplotter"; *ISP Archives* (XIII Congress; Helsinki, Finland; 1976).

Hempenius, S. A.; "Physical Investigations on Pricked Points Used in Aerial Triangulation"; *Photogrammetria* 19, No. 7 (1962-64).

Herda, Klaus; "The Performance Capability of the TRANSMARK Laser Point Transfer Machine"; *ISP Archives* (XIII Congress; Helsinki, Finland: 1976).

Hobbie, D.; "C100 Planicomp – The analytical Stereoplotting System"; *ISP Archives* (XIII Congress; Helsinki, Finland: 1976).

Jeyapalan, K.; "Calibration of a Comparator" *PE* 38, No. 5 (1972).

Karara, H. M. and G. W. Marks; *Mono Versus Stereo Analytical Photogrammetry* – (Part II Civil Engineering Studies, Photogrammetry Series No. 14; University of Illinois, Urbana, Illinois: 1986).

Kern Instruments, Inc.; *Generalized Program for the Calibration of Monocomparators and Coordinatographs* (Aarau, Switzerland, Undated).

Konecny, G.; "Software Aspects of Analytical Plotters"; *ISP Archives* (XIII Congress; Helsinki, Finland: 1976).

Kratky, V.; "Image Transformation; *PE* 38, No. 5 (1972).

Ladouceur, G.; P. Trotier and R. Allard; "Zeiss Stereotope Modified into an Analytical Stereoplotter"; *PERS* 48, No. 10 (1982).

Marckwardt, W.; "Geometrical Checking and Testing Methods for Precision Coordinatographs"; *Vermessungs Informationen*, No. 26; Jena, DDR: (1973).

Okang, Joseph P.; "Errors in Point Marking"; *PE* 37, No. 10 (1971).

Okang, Joseph P.; *Comparative Study of Point Marking Devices and Their Suitability for Photogrammetric Problems.* (Ph.D. Dissertation, The Ohio State University, Columbus, Ohio: 1972).

Roelofs, R.; "The Future of Radial Triangulation"; *Photogrammetria* 12, No.4 (1956).

Roos, Maurits; "The Automatic Réseau Measuring Equipement (ARME)"; *PERS* 41, No. 9 (1975).

Salmenperä, Hannu; "Use of the Wild A7 in Measuring Coordinates for Analytical Aerotriangulation"; *Photogrammetric Journal of Finland* 4, No. 1 (1970).

Schut, G. H.; Methods and Fortran Programs for Self-calibration of Position Measuring Devices; *NRC of Canada division of Physics* (Pub. No. P–PR 45; Ottawa, Canada: 1974).

Wildi, Theodore; *Understanding Units:* (The Book Society of Canada, Ltd.: 1973).

3

COORDINATE SYSTEMS

A coordinate system is one of reference for defining points, lines or geometric objects in space by means of distances or angles or both. This reference can be made with respect to designed axes, planes or surfaces. In Surveying and Mapping, two general types of references are distinguished:

1. *Rectangular.* This can be two or three dimensional, where points are defined by linear distances from two mutually perpendicular axes (in two dimensions) or from three mutually perpendicular planes (in three dimensions).

2. *Spherical.* In this, points in space or on a spherical or spheroidal surface are defined in terms of angles subtended at specific points with respect to specified directions or planes.

There are, however, instances where features of one are combined with the features of another to develop a special system of coordinates, for example:

A. *Plane-polar system,* which is much used in land surveying. In this, points in a plane (two-dimensional) are defined by distances from a point of reference (pole) along direction angles (with regard to a reference direction).
B. *Geographical system,* in which two direction angles (latitude and longitude) are combined with one distance (height above a reference surface (whose dimensions and form are fixed)
C. *Cylindrical system,* in which two distances (radial distance from an axis of reference and height above a reference plane) are combined with one direction angle (with regard to a reference direction). Ghosh (1966) used this system in calibrating solar collectors.

A spherical system by itself alone (i.e., by considering direction angles only) suffers from the lack of dimensional information. A well known example is its use in astronomy with regard to Altitude and Azimuth or Declination and Hour Angle. A rectangular system by itself does not suffer from any such drawback because directions are always derivable from dimensional data.

Directly associated with a coordinate system is often the necessity of defining the direction to a point or of a line (camera axis, etc.). For this, one usually finds it convenient to use a *Roll-Pitch-Yaw* (or *Tilt - Tip - Swing*) sequence. In this, roll (Ω or ω) is the rotation around the X-axis, pitch (Φ or φ) is around the Y-axis and yaw (K or κ) is around the Z-axis (see Section 3.3). In earth-related aerial photography, one may also use a variation, such as the *Tilt-Swing-Azimuth* sequence, where tilt is the angle from the nadir direction, swing is the rotation around the camera axis and azimuth is the angle from the north direction.

The use of a coordinate system in analytical photogrammetry can be with regard to a photograph, a stereo-model or the corresponding object. Accordingly, one may refer to photographic, model or object space coordinate systems. We shall study these in detail and in terms of their variations.

3.1 PHOTOGRAPHIC COORDINATE SYSTEM

It is a three-dimensional, orthogonal and right-handed system. Ideally, the origin of the system lies at the perspective center (Fig. 3.1) and the plane of the photograph is the x, y plane, z being a constant. The optical axis of the camera lens is considered to be normal to the plane of the photograph at the 'principal point' (see Chap. 5 for the definition). In the physical reality, there being no reference direction or plane of reference at the perspective center, one has to relate to the obtainable references on the photograph. The set of fiducial or collimation marks provide the x, y reference in which the x-axis is customarily considered along the direction of flight or the camera-base. The principal point (0') in the fiducial system has coordinates,

$$x_0, \ y_0, \ 0$$

The perspective center (0) of the objective lens lies on the optical axis. Its distance from the plane of the photograph is the focal length (f). Therefore, the perspective center has coordinates,

$$x_0, \ y_0, \ f$$

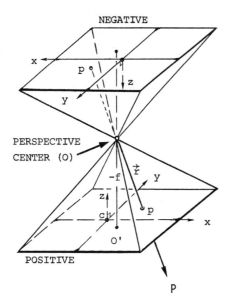

Fig. 3.1

Photographic coordinate system

Any image point (p) on the photo, in this fiducial reference system, is definable by its coordinates,

$$x_p, \ y_p, \ 0$$

Therefore, the vector ($\vec{r}$) defining the location of point p with respect to the perspective center is

$$\vec{r} = \begin{bmatrix} x_p - x_0 \\ y_p - y_0 \\ 0 - f \end{bmatrix}$$

In a well built and properly adjusted camere, the x, y fiducial coordinates of the principal point are practically zero. Then the image location vector $\vec{r}$ can be written as

$$\vec{r} = \begin{bmatrix} x_p \\ y_p \\ -f \end{bmatrix}$$

In some cameras, the fiducials marks are located in the corners of the image format. This corresponds to either a rotation or translation or both in the x, y

coordinates of the image point as will be obvious. Another variation is present
when the photograph negatives (instead of positives) are utilized. Associated with
this coordinate system are the rotations, ω, φ, and κ, around x-, y- and z- axes,
respectively. Variations are provided by the sequence in which they are considered
in operation -- giving 'primary', 'secondary' and 'tertiary' rotations, being
different in different cases.

3.2 MODEL COORDINATE SYSTEM

It refers to the spatial coordinates of points imaged in a stereoscopic model
(established mathematically or analogically at a stereo-plotting instrument), which
usually relates its position with reference to the camera base or to the instrument
axes. Coordinates are defined in terms of X, Y, Z; X, Y, H (Height); Easting,
Northing, Elevation; or any other set of 3-D reference.

The most used (and preferred) system is the one agreed upon at the Intenational
Congresses of Photogrammetry in 1956 and 1960 (see ISP Archives, 1957 and 1961).
It is right-handed and orthogonal (Fig. 3.2). The origin is at the projection
center of the left side photograph. The X direction coincides with the camera base
(or, general flight direction in the aerial case), and the Z direction coincides

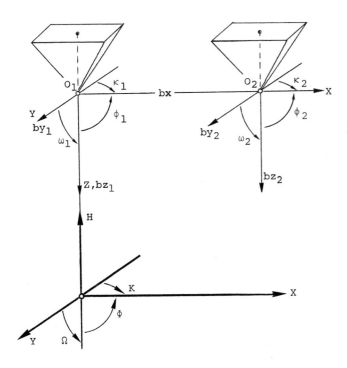

Fig. 3.2

Model coordinate system

(International)

with the camera axes in the zero position, The base components, bx, by, and bz, coincide with the X, Y and Z directions respectively. The model rotations, Ω (around X-axis), Φ (around Y-axis) and K (around Z-axis) are analogous to ω, φ and κ rotations, respectively, for single photographs. The positive directions are indicated by arrowheads on the respective lines (for the coordinates or linear dimensions) or on the respective planes (for realisation of rotations). See Ghosh (1972) for a more detailed description of this system and several other systems used by many organizations.

In phototriangulation, for convinience, sometimes one works with *Strip coordinates,* which are nothing but extensions of the coordinates of the first model in the strip, i.e., any point in the strip is referred to the origin and axes of the coordinate system of the first stereo-model. Similarly, strip coordinates may be extended into *Block coordinates,* the origin of which would refer to an arbitrary model in the block.

3.3 OBJECT SPACE COORDINATE SYSTEMS

These refer to coordinate systems used to define the positions of points in the object space, as distinguished from the image or the model. In the context of the earth as the object, broadly speaking, we may consider one of three coordinate systems: (a) The Geodetic coordinates of Latitude, Longitude and Height above the particular ellipsoid (Φ, λ, h); (b) The Geocentric Universal (Space Rectangular) system ($\overline{X}$, $\overline{Y}$, $\overline{Z}$), explained later in detail; and (c) The Local Space Rectangular system (X, Y, Z), also explained later. Of these, the Geodetic system is not used in analytical photogrammetry directly due to the inherent inconvenience of having to express the values in non-linear units (of degrees, grades, etc.). These are generally converted into one of the rectangular systems. For many applications, however, where the earth's curvature is of very minor importance, one may use a plane coordinate system, e.g., one of the 'state' coordinate systems, one of the standard map projections, or any 'local' surveyors' system.

3.3.1 Geocentric Universal System

This system is extensively utilized for phototriangulation, particularly when a large portion of the earth's surface is involved. The system is shown in Fig. 3.3. This is an orthogonal system whose origin is at the center of the earth. The $\overline{XY}$-

plane contains the Equator, the $\bar{X}$-axis passes through the zero (greenwich) meridian and the $\bar{Z}$-axis passes through the North Pole. The $\bar{Y}$-axis coincides with the 90° east longitude in a right-handed system.

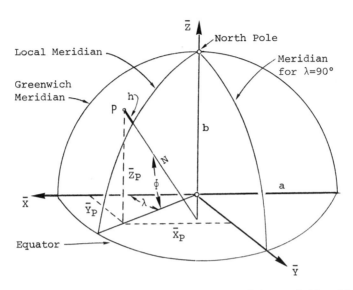

Fig. 3.3 Geocentric Universal system and its relationship
with the Geodetic system

The earth can be considered to be represented by a pre-determined rotational ellipsoid, which is established by two quantities (a and b, Fig. 3.3), where a is the semi-major axis and b is the semi-minor axis.
Further, the first eccentricity, e $= \sqrt{\{(a^2 - b^2)/a^2\}}$

and the second eccentricity, $e' = \sqrt{\{(a^2 - b^2)/b^2\}}$
Any point p (e.g., an object point on ground or a camera station in space) has the following geodetic coordinates: Latitude (Φ), Longitude (λ) and Elevation or Height above the ellipsoid (h).

Additional, derived, parameters are given here for their possible uses in practice. For details of such geodetic systems and derivations of the equations, one may refer to any standard book on Geodesy, e.g., Bomford (1971), Jordan-Eggert (1962), Zakatov (1962), etc.

The Fundamental quantities:

$$W = \sqrt{(1 - e^2 \sin^2\Phi)} \left.\begin{array}{c} \\ \\ \end{array}\right\}$$

$$V = \sqrt{(1 - e'^2 \cos^2\Phi)}$$

(3.1)

The radius of curvature at a point along the meridian:

$$M = \frac{a(1 - e^2)}{W}$$

(3.2)

The radius of curvature at a point along the prime vertical:

$$N = a/W$$

(3.3)

The Universal Geocentric coordinates may be expressed as functions of the geodetic coordinates and may be computed by using the following formulas (known as the *Direct Formulas*);

$$\bar{X} = (N + h) \cos\Phi \cos\lambda$$

$$\bar{Y} = (N + h) \cos\Phi \sin\lambda$$

(3.4)

$$\bar{Z} = \{ N (1 - e^2) + h \} \sin\Phi$$

The *Inverse Formulas*, to obtain geodetic coordinates from the universal geocentric coordinates, are given below:

$$\lambda = \text{arc tan } \frac{\bar{Y}}{\bar{X}}$$

(3.5)

Note: for λ near 90° where the tangent function discontinues,

$$\lambda = \text{arc cos } \frac{\bar{X}}{R} = \text{arc sin } \frac{\bar{Y}}{R}$$

(3.6)

where

$$R = \sqrt{(\bar{X}^2 + \bar{Y}^2)}$$

The values of Φ and h cannot be determined explicitly in the same way as the λ because of strong correlation between them. The initial value of Φ is given by

$$\Phi = \text{arc tan } \frac{\bar{Z} (N + h)}{R \{(1 - e^2)N + h\}} = \frac{\bar{Z}\{a^2 + ah \sqrt{(1 - e^2\sin^2\Phi)}\}}{R\{b^2 + ah \sqrt{(1 - e^2\sin^2\Phi)}\}}$$

(3.7)

A value of h has to be estimated in order to use Eq. 3.7, which is effective when Φ is less than 45° . In case Φ is larger than 45°, the cotangent fucntion is more effective. After Φ has been calculated, h can be obtained by using Eq. 3.8:

$$h = \frac{\bar{Z}}{\sin\Phi} - \frac{a (1 - e^2)}{\sqrt{(1 - e^2 \sin^2\Phi)}} \qquad (3.8)$$

Note that near the Equator, both $\bar{Z}$ and Φ have values close to zero. Therefore, in practice, Eq. 3.8 should not be used for points where 3° > Φ > -3°. In such cases an alternate formula can be used:

$$h = \frac{R}{\cos\Phi} - \frac{a}{\sqrt{(1 - e^2 \sin^2\Phi)}} \qquad (3.9)$$

A variation geocentric system is important for satellite triangulation where, of necessity, a reference to the astronomic system of coordinates is imperative. This is similar to the one discussed above (illustrated in Fig. 3.3), with the $\bar{X}$-axis passing through the Vernal Equinox, λ is replaces by Right Ascension (R. A.) and Φ is replaced by Declination (δ). The two systems are mutually related through local Sedereal Time.

3.3.2 Local Coordinate System

This one is another much favored object space coordinate system often used in phototriangulation. This system, illustrated in Fig. 3.4, is also right-handed and orthogonal. It has the Z-axis normal to the selected ellipsoid at an origin (0) in the area. The Y-axis coincides with the north direction and the elevation (h_0) of the origin is usually considered negative for the sake of convenience, such that all points on the ground and camera stations will automatically have positive values. Note, the origin (0) may be below one camera station, one of the control points, the origin of a superimposed grid system of local mapping or any other convenient point.

This system, while retaining all features of the Geocentric system, contains two advantages. Firstly, because it is local, one need not carry too many digits. This would often permit the computations to be performed in "single precision" with considerable saving in computer utilization. Secondly, the Z-axis parallels the local vertical, which further simplifies the work permitting a separation of planimetry from elevation values.

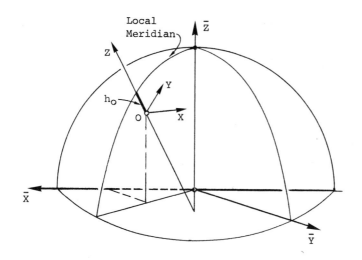

Fig. 3.4

Local coordinate system

in relation to

the Geocentric

Universal system

The local coordinates are easily obtainable from the geocentric coordinates by three-dimensional transformation, which contains a translation, a rotation and, possibly, a scale change (explained later in Section 3.4). Further simplifications or variations of such a local system can be made when coordinates need not relate to the earth. Such systems may be arbitrary and may be job related, e.g., a system referred to the object for non-topographic mapping or a local survey system for engineering projects.

3.4 TRANSFORMATION OF COORDINATES

It is often necessary to establish the relationship between two coordinate systems in order to transfer a number of points from one to the other. There are numerous methods of transformation for use in three-dimensional problems, simplified versions of which are applicable to two-dimensional space. The effect of transformation of a body can be a simple change in location and attitude (i.e., without any change in shape and in size) or a complex one (i.e., change in both shape and size) or something in between, e.g., variation in size (scale) with no change in shape or location or attitude.

3.4.1 General Three-dimensional Transformation

Known as *Similarity Transformation,* it involves translations, rotations and a scale change. Referable to the same object, consider two systems of coordiantes, X, Y, Z and $\bar{X}$, $\bar{Y}$, $\bar{Z}$, both being rectangular. The three-dimensional tansformation involving no change in shape is symbolized by:

$$X = kM^T\bar{X} + X_O \tag{3.10}$$

where $X = [X\ Y\ Z]^T$ coordinates after transformation

$\bar{X} = [\bar{X}\ \bar{Y}\ \bar{Z}]^T$ coordinates before transformation

$X_O = [X_0\ Y_0\ Z_0]^T$ vector of three shifts indicating the X, Y, Z
coordinates of the origin of the $\bar{X}$, $\bar{Y}$, $\bar{Z}$ system.

M = an orthogonal three-angle rotation matrix (of three sequential
rotations)

and,   k = scale factor.

In order to study these in detail, consider first only the rotations,
sequentially, Ω around $\bar{X}$, Φ around $\bar{Y}$ and K around $\bar{Z}$ axes.

The *Primary Rotation*, (Ω) transforms the axes $\bar{Y}$ and $\bar{Z}$ into the positions Y_Ω and
Z_Ω, respectively (see Fig. 3.5). This is expressed by the rotation matrix

$$M_\Omega = \begin{bmatrix} 1 & 0 & 0 \\ 0 & \cos\Omega & \sin\Omega \\ 0 & -\sin\Omega & \cos\Omega \end{bmatrix} \tag{3.11}$$

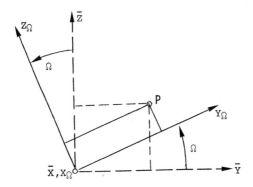

Fig. 3.5

Primary rotation, Ω

The coordinates of any point P in this, primary rotated, X_Ω, Y_Ω, Z_Ω system are:

$$X_\Omega = \overline{X}$$

$$Y_\Omega = \overline{Y}\cos\Omega + \overline{Z}\sin\Omega \qquad\qquad (3.12)$$

$$Z_\Omega = -\overline{Y}\sin\Omega + \overline{Z}\cos\Omega$$

The Secondary Rotation (Φ) transforms the axes X_Ω and Z_Ω into the positions $X_{\Omega\Phi}$ and $Z_{\Omega\Phi}$, respectively (see Fig. 3.6). This is expressed by the rotation matrix

$$M_\Phi = \begin{bmatrix} \cos\Phi & 0 & -\sin\Phi \\ 0 & 1 & 0 \\ \sin\Phi & 0 & \cos\Phi \end{bmatrix} \qquad\qquad (3.13)$$

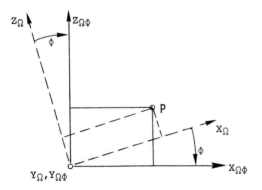

Fig. 3.6

Secondary rotation, Φ

The coordinates of the same point P in the twice rotated $X_{\Omega\Phi}$, $Y_{\Omega\Phi}$, $Z_{\Omega\Phi}$ system are:

$$X_{\Omega\Phi} = X_\Omega \cos\Phi - Z_\Omega \sin\Phi$$

$$Y_{\Omega\Phi} = Y_\Omega \qquad\qquad (3.14)$$

$$Z_{\Omega\Phi} = X_\Omega \sin\Phi + Z_\Omega \cos\Phi$$

The *Tertiary Rotation* (K) next transforms the axes $X_{\Omega\Phi}$ and $Y_{\Omega\Phi}$ into the positions $X_{\Omega\Phi K}$, and $Y_{\Omega\Phi K}$, respectively (see Fig. 3.7). This is expressed by the rotation matrix

$$M_K = \begin{bmatrix} \cos K & \sin K & 0 \\ -\sin K & \cos K & 0 \\ 0 & 0 & 1 \end{bmatrix} \qquad (3.15)$$

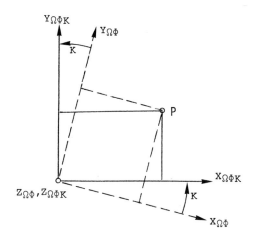

Fig. 3.7

Tertiary rotation, K

The coordinates of the same point P now in the final, thrice rotated, $X_{\Omega\Phi K}$, $Y_{\Omega\Phi K}$, $Z_{\Omega\Phi K}$ system are:

$$\left.\begin{array}{l} X_{\Omega\Phi K} = X_{\Omega\Phi} \cos K + Y_{\Omega\Phi} \sin K \\[2mm] Y_{\Omega\Phi K} = -X_{\Omega\Phi} \sin K + Y_{\Omega\Phi} \cos K \\[2mm] Z_{\Omega\Phi K} = Z_{\Omega\Phi} \end{array}\right\} \qquad (3.16)$$

It may be noted that $\bar{X}$ remained unchanged in the primary rotation because the $\bar{X}$ and X_{Ω} axes remained coincident in this rotation. Similarly, the Y and Z axes remained unchanged in the secondary and tertiary rotations, respectively.

The final effect of all the three rotations is then expressed by the *rotation matrix* (M) as used in Eq. 3.10, M^T being its transpose.

$$M = M_{\Omega} \cdot M_{\Phi} \cdot M_K \qquad (3.17)$$

In view of mathematical procedures, i.e., the order of matrix multiplications, it is better written as follows:

$$M = M_K \cdot M_\Phi \cdot M_\Omega \tag{3.18}$$

The elements of this rotation matrix can be expressed in various ways:

$$M^T = \begin{bmatrix} m_{11} & m_{21} & m_{31} \\ m_{12} & m_{22} & m_{32} \\ m_{13} & m_{23} & m_{33} \end{bmatrix} \tag{3.19a}$$

or,

$$M^T = \begin{bmatrix} \cos\Phi\,\cos K & -\cos\Phi\,\sin K & \sin\Phi \\ \cos\Omega\,\sin K & \cos\Omega\,\cos K & -\sin\Omega\,\cos\Phi \\ +\sin\Omega\,\sin\Phi\,\cos K & -\sin\Omega\,\sin\Phi\,\sin K & \\ \sin\Omega\,\sin K & \sin\Omega\,\cos K & \cos\Omega\,\cos\Omega \\ -\cos\Omega\,\sin\Phi\,\cos K & +\cos\Omega\,\sin\Phi\,\sin K & \end{bmatrix} \tag{3.19b}$$

The rotation matrix M can also be considered as composed of the direction-cosines, which relate to the angles between the corresponding axes in the two systems, X, Y, Z and $\overline{X}$, $\overline{Y}$, $\overline{Z}$. These (nine) matrix elements, expressed in terms of the direction cosines, are:

$$M^T = \begin{bmatrix} \cos X\overline{X} & \cos Y\overline{X} & \cos Z\overline{X} \\ \cos X\overline{Y} & \cos Y\overline{Y} & \cos Z\overline{Y} \\ \cos X\overline{Z} & \cos Y\overline{Z} & \cos Z\overline{Z} \end{bmatrix} \tag{3.19c}$$

The rotation matrix being orthogonal, the normal rules for such matrices apply here also, i.e., $M^{-1} = M^T$ or, $MM^T = MM^{-1} = I$, the Identity matrix. In this respect, for easy solution of the rotation-translation-scaling problem, it has been suggested (see, Sanso, 1973, for example) to use the quaternion algebra. That approach holds some potential.

3.4.2 Affine Transformation in Three Dimensions

The general transformation as described in the previous section assumes that the scale in the three dimensional space is the same in any direction. If one can assume that there exist three different scales along the three directions, X, Y and Z, an affine relationship is thereby assumed. Often, due to various reasons, such a situation may persist (e.g., in a stereo model due to the introduction of a focal length which is different from the correct one, oft-quoted in literature discussing the use of 'super-wide-angle' photography). In such cases, Eq. 3.10 of the general case may be modified by using k = 1 and

$$\bar{X} = \begin{bmatrix} k_{\bar{X}} \, \bar{X} & k_{\bar{Y}} \, \bar{Y} & k_{\bar{Z}} \, \bar{Z} \end{bmatrix}^T \tag{3.20}$$

where $k_{\bar{X}}$, $k_{\bar{Y}}$ and $k_{\bar{Z}}$ are the respective scales along $\bar{X}$, $\bar{Y}$ and $\bar{Z}$ axes. See also Ghosh (1972, 1975) for further discussions related to this aspect.

3.4.3 Polynomial Transformation in Three Dimensions

In view of the propagated error or orderly and systematic deformation in a stereo model or the final output (as done in a map projection, for example), often a polynomial transformation is found to be convenient. Polynomials of various types are used, depending on the most appropriate "mathematical model" the photogrammetrist may find adequate. Two typical sets of polynomials used in three-dimensional transformation are presented in Eqs 3.21 and 3.22. Here also, as before, X, Y, Z are considered coordinates after transformation, and $\bar{X}$, $\bar{Y}$, $\bar{Z}$ are those before transformation.

A. General polynomials in three-dimensions (see Ghosh, 1975):

$$X = a_0 + a_1\bar{X} + a_2\bar{Y} + a_3\bar{Z} + a_4\bar{X}^2 + a_5\bar{Y}^2 + a_6\bar{Z}^2 + a_7\overline{XY} + a_8\overline{YZ}$$

$$+ a_9\overline{ZX} + a_{10}\overline{XY}^2 + a_{11}\overline{X^2Y} + a_{12}\overline{XZ}^2 + \dots$$

$$Y = b_0 + b_1\bar{X} + b_2\bar{Y} + b_3\bar{Z} + b_4\bar{X}^2 + b_5\bar{Y}^2 + b_6\bar{Z}^2 + b_7\overline{XY} + b_8\overline{YZ}$$

$$+ b_9\overline{ZX} + b_{10}\overline{XY}^2 + b_{11}\overline{X^2Y} + b_{12}\overline{XZ}^2 + \dots$$

$$Z = c_0 + c_1\bar{X} + c_2\bar{Y} + c_3\bar{Z} + c_4\bar{X}^2 + c_5\bar{Y}^2 + c_6\bar{Z}^2 + c_7\overline{XY} + c_8\overline{YZ}$$

$$+ c_9\overline{ZX} + c_{10}\overline{XY}^2 + c_{11}\overline{X^2Y} + c_{12}\overline{XZ}^2 + \dots \tag{3.21}$$

B.   Three-dimensional polynomials which are conformal in the three planes (see Mikhail, 1964):

$$X = A_0 + A_1\overline{X} + A_2\overline{Y} - A_2\overline{Z} + A_5(\overline{X}^2 - \overline{Y}^2 - \overline{Z}^2) + 0 + 2A_7\overline{ZX} + 2A_6\overline{XY} + \ldots$$

$$Y = B_0 - A_2\overline{X} + A_1\overline{Y} + A_4\overline{Z} + A_6(-\overline{X}^2 + \overline{Y}^2 - \overline{Z}^2) + 2A_7\overline{YZ} + 0 + 2A_5\overline{XY} + \ldots$$

$$Z = C_0 + A_3\overline{X} - A_4\overline{Y} + A_1\overline{Z} + A_7(-\overline{X}^2 - \overline{Y}^2 + \overline{Z}^2) + 2A_6\overline{YZ} + 2A_5\overline{ZX} + 0 + \ldots \quad (3.22)$$

Note: In Eqs 3.21 and 3.22, the a's, b's, c's, A's, B_0 and C_0 are certain constant terms.   The O's in Eqs 3.22 are put there with the purpose of indicating zeros as the coefficients for terms, $\overline{YZ}$ in X, $\overline{ZX}$ in Y and $\overline{XY}$ in Z.   These polynomials, however, do not give conformal transformations and should, therefore, be used only when rotation angles are sufficiently small.

3.4.4 Projective Transformation in Three Dimensions

Any two coordinates systems are in *projective relation* and are said (in mathematical language) to form a projectivity if a one-to-one correspondence exists between the elements of the two such that each four harmonic elements of one correspond to four harmonic elements of the other.

One can correctly assume in practice that there exists a one-to-one correspondence between the space to be transformed from and the space to be transformed into.   This concept is fundmental to the problems of mensuration.   If that is not so, one may have, for example, a line in one space (say, ground) corresponding to only one point in the other space (say, stereo-model).   That is, mathemetically speaking, two different functions (F and f) in two different spaces are related to each other (considering that X, Y, Z and $\overline{X}$, $\overline{Y}$, $\overline{Z}$ convey the same sense as in the previous section):

$$F\ (X,Y,Z)\ =\ f\ (\overline{X},\overline{Y},\overline{Z}) \qquad (3.23)$$

In this relationship, no variable would stay in second or higher degree by itself or even in conjunction with other variables.   In that case, one can express the relation as:

$$\frac{A_1X + A_2Y + A_3Z + A_4}{D_1X + D_2Y + D_3Z + D_4} = \frac{a_1\overline{X} + a_2\overline{Y} + a_3\overline{Z} + a_4}{d_1\overline{X} + d_2\overline{Y} + d_3\overline{Z} + d_4} \qquad (3.24)$$

Note: in Eqs 3.24 through 3.30, the A's...D's and the a's...g's indicate certain coefficients having unique values in each case.

Equation 3.24 has 16 unknown terms (coefficients and constants), not all of which are independent. The expression with only independent unknowns (eleven) has the form of Eq. 3.25a (see Ghosh and Das, 1966 for derivation):

$$\frac{Y + A_3 Z + A_4}{A_1 X + A_2 Z + 1} = \frac{a_1 \bar{X} + a_2 \bar{Y} + a_3 \bar{Z} + a_4}{d_1 \bar{X} + d_2 \bar{Y} + d_3 \bar{Z} + 1} \qquad (3.25a)$$

The one-to-one correspondence could be established if only eleven points are known and identified in both systems (e.g., stereo-model and ground). One requires three independent equations to solve for all unknowns in order to transform values of X, Y and Z into $\bar{X}$, $\bar{Y}$ and $\bar{Z}$ or vice-versa, i.e., in addition to Eq. 3.25a, one needs the following two also:

$$\frac{Z + B_3 X + B_4}{B_1 Y + B_2 X + 1} = \frac{b_1 \bar{X} + b_2 \bar{Y} + b_3 \bar{Z} + b_4}{e_1 \bar{X} + e_2 \bar{Y} + e_3 \bar{Z} + 1} \qquad (3.25b)$$

$$\frac{X + C_3 Y + C_4}{C_1 Z + C_2 Y + 1} = \frac{c_1 \bar{X} + c_2 \bar{Y} + c_3 \bar{Z} + c_4}{f_1 \bar{X} \quad f_2 \bar{Y} \quad f_3 \bar{Z} + 1} \qquad (3.25c)$$

A special case of the degenerated form of the obove transformation is obtained by assuming $A_1 = A_2 = B_1 = B_2 = C_1 = C_2 = 0$ in Eqs 3.25. This gives:

$$Y + A_3 Z + A_4 = \frac{a_1 \bar{X} + a_2 \bar{Y} + a_3 \bar{Z} + a_4}{d_1 \bar{X} \quad d_2 \bar{Y} \quad d_3 \bar{Z} + 1}$$

$$Z + B_3 X + B_4 = \frac{b_1 \bar{X} + b_2 \bar{Y} + b_3 \bar{Z} + b_4}{e_1 \bar{X} + e_2 \bar{Y} + e_3 \bar{Z} + 1} \qquad (3.26)$$

$$X + C_3 Y + C_4 = \frac{c_1 \bar{X} + c_2 \bar{Y} + c_3 \bar{Z} + c_4}{f_1 \bar{X} + f_2 \bar{Y} + f_3 \bar{Z} + 1}$$

AP-G

From these, if one solves for X, Y and Z separately, one gets:

$$X = \lambda_1 \left\{ \frac{a_1\overline{X} + \ldots}{d_1\overline{X} + \ldots} \right\} + \lambda_2 \left\{ \frac{b_1\overline{X} + \ldots}{e_1\overline{X} + \ldots} \right\} + \lambda_3 \left\{ \frac{c_1\overline{X} + \ldots}{f_1\overline{X} + \ldots} \right\}$$

$$Y = \mu_1 \left\{ \frac{a_1\overline{X} + \ldots}{d_1\overline{X} + \ldots} \right\} + \mu_2 \left\{ \frac{b_1\overline{X} + \ldots}{e_1\overline{X} + \ldots} \right\} + \mu_3 \left\{ \frac{c_1\overline{X} + \ldots}{f_1\overline{X} + \ldots} \right\} \qquad (3.27)$$

$$Z = \nu_1 \left\{ \frac{a_1\overline{X} + \ldots}{d_1\overline{X} + \ldots} \right\} + \nu_2 \left\{ \frac{b_1\overline{X} + \ldots}{e_1\overline{X} + \ldots} \right\} + \nu_3 \left\{ \frac{c_1\overline{X} + \ldots}{f_1\overline{X} + \ldots} \right\}$$

where λ's, μ's, and ν's are certain constants.

A careful inspection of Eqs 3.27 would reveal that the situation is complex, for example,

$$Z = \frac{\text{one cubic expression in } \overline{X}, \overline{Y}, \overline{Z}}{\text{another cubic expression in } \overline{X}, \overline{Y}, \overline{Z}}$$

This, however, is simplified if one considers all the coefficients, except the constant term, in the denominator to be zero. Then one obtains, as a particular case, for example, Z = one cubic polynomial expression in $\overline{X}$, $\overline{Y}$, $\overline{Z}$. Here, if for example, one consider Z = constant, (i.e., say, a horizontal plane in the ground space), one obtains a curved surface in the corresponding space (say, the one in the instrument model space). In a strict linear or projective transformation, the degree of the surface should remain the same, i.e., a plane should transform into a plane , or a quadratic surface into a quadratic surface, and so on.

In view of the above, with regard to "error surfaces" to represent 3-D error propagations (for example, in phototriangulation), one may consider a compromise solution, as follows: In the polynomial expression, Z = two constants, k_1, and k_2, would give the same error surface but with a parallel shift, i.e., the surfaces obtained due to this parallel shift (corresponding to the different values of Z) are identical in nature but the change is continual. Such a concept may be desirable in treating the surface deformations when one is working, for example, on phototriangulation in an extremely mountainous terrain.

In such a transformation, one would need nine points. This means that, although cubic in nature, the expression may be degenerated into a general quadratic form (since there are nine unknown coefficients also in a general quadratic polynomial), e.g.,

$$g_1X^2 + g_2Y^2 + g_3Z^2 + g_4XY + g_5ZX + g_6YZ + g_7X + g_8Y + g_9Z = \text{a constant.}$$

This could, further, be simplified for use in practice. For example, peculiar to the uses of stereoplotters where axial planes (viz., X = a constant, Y = another constant and Z = a third constant) would remain planes. With this consideration, Eqs 3.26 would become (see Okamoto, 1981):

$$X = \frac{c_1\bar{X} + c_2\bar{Y} + c_3\bar{Z} + c_4}{f_1\bar{X} + f_2\bar{Y} + f_3\bar{Z} + 1}$$

$$Y = \frac{a_1\bar{X} + a_2\bar{Y} + a_3\bar{Z} + a_4}{d_1\bar{X} + d_2\bar{Y} + d_3\bar{Z} + 1} \quad (3.28)$$

$$Z = \frac{b_1\bar{X} + b_2\bar{Y} + b_3\bar{Z} + b_4}{e_1\bar{X} + e_2\bar{Y} + e_3\bar{Z} + 1}$$

It may be noted here that even this expression is neither linear nor projective. They are "bi-projective" (see Das, 1952b). An arbitrary plane in one (say, ground) space, $1X + mY + nZ = p$, where p is a constant, would become (considering Eqs 3.28):

$$1\left\{\frac{c_1\bar{X} + \ldots}{f_1\bar{X} + \ldots}\right\} + m\left\{\frac{a_1\bar{X} + \ldots}{d_1\bar{X} + \ldots}\right\} + n\left\{\frac{b_1\bar{X} + \ldots}{e_1\bar{X} + \ldots}\right\} = p \quad (3.29)$$

which is another cubic expression in $\bar{X}, \bar{Y}, \bar{Z}$. It is interesting to note further that although $Z = k_1$ is a plane, $Z = k_1, k_2, k_3 \ldots$ etc. family of axial planes get transformed (in the other space) into another family of planes (non-parallel) and the degree of freedom of this envelope is seven. Thus, a seven-point transformation would serve the purpose practically in small units. This means that in hilly areas where a polynomial expression may fail, we may safely use 7, 9 or 11 points and obtain satisfactory results by using the continually varying family of surfaces. This transformation, further degenerated, would give the following expressions (see also Okamato, 1981):

$$X = \frac{a_1'\bar{X} + a_2'\bar{Y} + a_3'\bar{Z} + a_4'}{d_1'\bar{X} + d_2'\bar{Y} + d_3'\bar{Z} + 1}$$

$$Y = \frac{b_1'\bar{X} + b_2'\bar{Y} + b_3'\bar{Z} + b_4'}{d_1'\bar{X} + d_2'\bar{Y} + d_3'\bar{Y} + 1} \qquad (3.30)$$

$$Z = \frac{c_1'\bar{X} + c_2'\bar{Y} + c_3'\bar{Z} + c_4'}{d_1'\bar{X} + d_2'\bar{Y} + d_3'\bar{Z} + 1}$$

where

$$\begin{vmatrix} a_1' & a_2' & a_3' & a_4' \\ b_1' & b_2' & b_3' & b_4' \\ c_1' & c_2' & c_3' & c_4' \\ d_1' & d_2' & d_3' & d_4' \end{vmatrix} \neq 0$$

The denominators here are the same in each of the expressions for X, Y and Z. This is the 'projective' transformation used so frequently by photogrammetrists. For interesting ideas in this, see Novakovskiy (1974) and Okamoto (1981).

It was first observed by G. B. Das of Survey of India while working on a strip of aerial photographs over a highly mountainous terrain (with ruggedness of more than 3,000 m in alomst each model) that the height differences play a very important role in correctly adjusting a triangulated strip. In such a case, different sets of error profile curves drawn for varying ground elevations give a better adjustment than a single set of profiles (corresponding to a single error surface) as are expressed in one set of polynomials (see Ghosh, 1975), which are customarily used. Furthermore, Eqs 3.28 can be used in other applications. The first two (X, Y) can establish a relationship between 2-D photocoordinates and 3-D ground coordinates ($\bar{X}$, $\bar{Y}$, $\bar{Z}$). In case the two photos in a stereo-overlap are coplanar, the equations become projective (by having the denominators as constant for a particular point). In such a case they can be used to derive the ground height of a fifth point if the heights of four points in the overlap are known. See Das (1952a) for further interesting ideas on this.

3.4.5 Two-dimensional Transformations

Two-dimensional cases may be viewed as the simplified versions of the three-dimensional ones in which the third coordinate (dimension) is constant and may not appear at all in practice. The ones mostly used are listed below:

A: From *Plane-Polar to a Rectangular* (Cartesian) system:

$$X = r \cdot \cos\theta$$
$$Y = r \cdot \sin\theta$$
(3.31)

where r is the distance of the point from the origin (pole) and θ is the angle subtended by its direction with the X-axis.

Note: For example, certain instruments like Kern PG2 use this form of transformation in principle to obtain planimetric coordinates in a model.

B: From *one Rectangular system to another* (Regular, Similarity transformation):
Consider Eq. 3.10 with all elaborations subsequently discussed in Section 3.4.1. Also consider Z = a constant and $\Omega = \Phi = 0$. This gives:

$$\begin{bmatrix} X \\ Y \end{bmatrix} = k \begin{bmatrix} \cos K & + \sin K \\ -\sin K & \cos K \end{bmatrix} \begin{bmatrix} \overline{X} \\ \overline{Y} \end{bmatrix} + \begin{bmatrix} X_0 \\ Y_0 \end{bmatrix}$$
(3.32)

or,

$$X = k \cdot \cos K \cdot \overline{X} + k \cdot \sin K \overline{Y} + X_0$$
$$Y = -k \cdot \sin K \cdot \overline{X} + k \cdot \cos K \overline{Y} + Y_0$$
(3.33)

or,

$$X = a_1 \overline{X} + a_2 \overline{Y} + a_0$$
$$Y = -a_2 \overline{X} + a_1 \overline{Y} + b_0$$
(3.34)

This has four unknown parameters, viz., a_1, a_2, a_0 and b_0.

Note: For example, one would use this type of transformation to obtain observed
       (at a comparator) photo coordinates referred to the fiducial marks.

C. *Affine Transformation in Two-Dimensions:*

Considering Eq. 3.32 and the affinity (note, Eq. 3.20) in two-dimensions, i.e.
$k = [k_{\bar{x}}\ k_{\bar{y}}]^T$

$$\begin{bmatrix} X \\ Y \end{bmatrix} = \begin{bmatrix} \cos K & \sin K \\ -\sin K & \cos K \end{bmatrix} \begin{bmatrix} k_{\bar{x}}\bar{X} \\ k_{\bar{y}}\bar{Y} \end{bmatrix} + \begin{bmatrix} X_0 \\ Y_0 \end{bmatrix} \tag{3.35}$$

This gives:

$$X = k_{\bar{x}} \cdot \cos K \cdot \bar{X} + k_{\bar{y}} \cdot \sin K \cdot \bar{Y} + X_0 \left.\right\} \tag{3.36}$$

$$Y = -k_{\bar{x}} \cdot \sin K \cdot \bar{X} + k_{\bar{y}} \cdot \cos K \cdot \bar{Y} + Y_0$$

or,

$$X = a_1 \bar{X} + a_2 \bar{Y} + a_0 \left.\right\} \tag{3.37}$$

$$Y = b_1 \bar{X} + b_2 \bar{Y} + b_0$$

This has six unknown parameters, the a's and the b's, although the real unknows
are only five, viz., $k_{\bar{x}}$, $k_{\bar{y}}$, K, X_0 and Y_0.

Note: For example, this type of transformation would be effective in two
       typical cases, (1) Non-orthogonality of axes in a comparator inspite of
       their having the same scale factor, or (2) Linear stretching of film causing
       scale affinity on the photo.

D. *Polynomial Transformation in Two-Dimensions:*

Considering Z = a constant, one obtains from Eqs 3.21, the following general,
two-dimensional polynomials:

$$X = a_0 + a_1 \bar{X} + a_2 \bar{Y} + a_3 \bar{X}^2 + a_4 \bar{Y}^2 + a_5 \bar{X}\bar{Y} + \ldots \left.\right\} \tag{3.38}$$

$$Y = a_0 + b_1 \bar{X} + b_2 \bar{Y} + b_3 \bar{X}^2 + b_4 \bar{Y}^2 + b_5 \bar{X}\bar{Y} + \ldots$$

The conformal version in two-dimensions will be obtained by considering $\bar{Z} = a$ constant in Eq. 3.22:

$$X = A_0 + A_1\bar{X} + A_2\bar{Y} + A_3(\bar{X}^2 - \bar{Y}^2) + A_4(2\overline{XY}) + \dots$$

$$Y = B_0 + A_2\bar{X} + A_1\bar{Y} + A_4(\bar{X}^2 - \bar{Y}^2) + A_3(2\overline{XY}) + \dots \Bigg\} \quad (3.39)$$

Note: For example, this type of transformation would be effective in say, (1) establishing the effect of non-linear distortion due to the objective lens on a photograph, or (2) Calibrating a comparator (note Eq. 2.7).

E. *Projective Transformation in Two-Dimensions:*

For single image photogrammetric works, the projectivity between planes may be of special interest sometimes. It is a case of two dimensions in each space, and the number of coordinates per point is two. For such cases, Eqs 3.30 lead into the following:

$$X = \frac{a_1'\bar{X} + a_2'\bar{Y} + a_3'}{d_1'\bar{X} + d_2'\bar{Y} + d_3'} = \frac{a_1\bar{X} + a_2\bar{Y} + a_3}{d_1\bar{X} + d_2\bar{Y} + 1}$$

$$Y = \frac{b_1'\bar{X} + b_2'\bar{Y} + b_3'}{d_1'\bar{X} + d_2'\bar{Y} + d_3'} = \frac{b_1\bar{X} + b_2\bar{Y} + b_3}{d_1\bar{X} + d_2\bar{Y} + 1} \Bigg\} \quad (3.40)$$

This indicates that the projectivity between two planes is uniquely determined if a total of eight coefficients are known. This requires at least four points whose both X and Y coordinates in both the spaces are known. After computing the coefficients, they may be used for calculating all X, Y values of the other points in one plane whose coordinates in the other plane are known. The only condition to validate these expressions is that three of the points used in the transformation in either plane be not collinear, i.e.,

$$\begin{vmatrix} a_1' & a_2' & a_3' \\ b_1' & b_2' & b_3' \\ d_1' & d_2' & d_3' \end{vmatrix} \neq 0$$

Note: These equations are of use in the problem of rectification of single photos.

F. *Cross (or Anharmonic) Ratio:*

The general concept of projectivity, the theory of cross ratio, is illustrated
in Fig. 3.8. Consider a bundle of rays originating from the photo image
points, a, b, c and d passing through the perspective center (0), are located
on plane 1 at A_1, B_1, C_1 and D_1 and on plane 2 at A_2, B_2, C_2 and D_2,
respectively. By considering the inherent linearity of the rays, the following
relationships of cross ratio can be established:

$$\frac{A_1C_1}{B_1C_1} : \frac{A_1D_1}{B_1D_1} = \frac{\sin A_1OC_1}{\sin B_1OC_1} : \frac{\sin A_1OD_1}{\sin B_1OD_1} = \text{a constant}$$

In the same way, one can prove that the same constant value is true for the
corresponding points A_2, B_2, C_2 and D_2 and also for every other corresponding
point sequences. In this context, one can state that two figures are
projective when their elements correspond to each other and when the cross
ratio between any four elements in one figure equals the corresponding cross
ratio in the other figure. Therefore, projective elemental figures can be
arranged in a prespective configuration. One can now say (see Fig. 3.8) that

$$\frac{A_1C_1}{B_1C_1} : \frac{A_1D_1}{B_1D_1} = \frac{A_2C_2}{B_2C_2} : \frac{A_2D_2}{B_2D_2} \qquad (3.41)$$

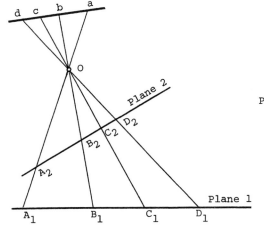

Fig. 3.8

Projectivity and cross-ratio

If the coordinates of points A_1, B_1, C_1 and D_1 in plane 1 are x_1, x_2, x_3 and x_4 and of points A_2, B_2, C_2 and D_2 in plane are x_1', x_2', x_3' and x_4', respectively, from Eq. 3.41,

$$\frac{x_3 - x_1}{x_3 - x_2} : \frac{x_4 - x_1}{x_4 - x_2} = \frac{x_3' - x_1'}{x_3' - x_2'} : \frac{x_4' - x_1'}{x_4' - x_2'} \qquad (3.42)$$

By using this equation, if one coordinate, e.g., x_4 is unknown, it can be determined from the rest of the known coordinates. The genaral expression can be derived from the above:

$$X = \frac{a_1' \bar{X} + a_2'}{d_1' \bar{X} + d_2'} = \frac{a_1 \bar{X} + a_2}{d_1 \bar{X} + 1} \qquad (3.43)$$

The number of coefficients here is three. The coefficients are functions of the reciprocal positions of the point sequences and the perspective center (see also Hallert, 1960). To make the operation possible, there should be one condition that the determinant

$$\begin{vmatrix} a_1' & a_2' \\ d_1' & d_2' \end{vmatrix} \neq 0$$

3.5 DIFFERENTIAL FORMS

In computer programming such transformations, the partial derivatives of the orientation (or, rotation) matrix M are required frequently. Consider the sequential rotations $M = M_\Omega \cdot M_\Phi \cdot M_K$ (Eq. 3.17). The partial derivatives of M with respect to Ω, Φ and K, respectively can be shown to be:

$$\frac{\partial M}{\partial \Omega} = M_K \cdot M_\Phi \frac{\partial M_\Omega}{\partial \Omega} = M \begin{bmatrix} 0 & 0 & 0 \\ 0 & 0 & +1 \\ 0 & -1 & 0 \end{bmatrix}$$

By using Eq. 3.19b, one now obtains the detailed differential form with regard to the element Ω :

$$\frac{\partial M}{\partial \Omega} = \begin{bmatrix} 0 & \begin{matrix} -\sin\Omega \ \sin K \\ +\cos\Omega \ \sin\Phi \ \cos K \end{matrix} & \begin{matrix} \cos\Omega \ \sin K \\ +\sin\Omega \ \sin\Phi \ \cos K \end{matrix} \\[1em] 0 & \begin{matrix} -\sin\Omega \ \cos K \\ -\cos\Omega \ \sin\Phi \ \sin K \end{matrix} & \begin{matrix} \cos\Omega \ \cos K \\ -\sin\Omega \ \sin\Phi \ \sin K \end{matrix} \\[1em] 0 & -\cos\Omega \ \cos\Phi & \sin\Omega \ \cos\Phi \end{bmatrix} \qquad (3.44)$$

By comparing the terms in this with the terms in the M^T matrix of Eq. 3.19b, one obtains:

$$\frac{\partial M}{\partial \Omega} = \begin{bmatrix} 0 & -m_{13} & m_{12} \\ 0 & -m_{23} & m_{22} \\ 0 & -m_{33} & m_{32} \end{bmatrix} = \begin{bmatrix} M_{\Omega_1} \\ M_{\Omega_2} \\ M_{\Omega_3} \end{bmatrix} \qquad (3.45)$$

Similarly,

$$\frac{\partial M}{\partial \Phi} = M_K \frac{\partial M_\Phi}{\partial \Phi} M_\Omega = M \begin{bmatrix} 0 & \sin\Omega & \cos\Omega \\ -\sin\Omega & 0 & 0 \\ \cos\Omega & 0 & 0 \end{bmatrix}$$

$$= \begin{bmatrix} 0 & 0 & -\cos K \\ 0 & 0 & \sin K \\ \cos K & -\sin K & 0 \end{bmatrix} M$$

$$= \begin{bmatrix} -\sin\Phi \ \cos K & \sin\Omega \ \cos\Phi \ \cos K & -\cos\Omega \ \cos\Phi \ \cos K \\[1em] \sin\Phi \ \sin K & -\sin\Omega \ \cos\Phi \ \sin K & \cos\Omega \ \cos\Phi \ \sin K \\[1em] \cos\Phi & \sin\Omega \ \sin\Phi & -\cos\Omega \ \sin\Phi \end{bmatrix} = \begin{bmatrix} M_{\Phi_1} \\ M_{\Phi_2} \\ M_{\Phi_3} \end{bmatrix} \qquad (3.46)$$

Further,

$$\frac{\partial M}{\partial K} = \frac{\partial M_K}{\partial K} M_\Phi \cdot M_\Omega = \begin{bmatrix} 0 & +1 & 0 \\ -1 & 0 & 0 \\ 0 & 0 & 0 \end{bmatrix} M$$

$$= \begin{bmatrix} -\cos\Omega \ \sin K & \begin{matrix} \cos\Omega \ \cos K \\ -\sin\Omega \ \sin\Phi \ \sin K \end{matrix} & \begin{matrix} \sin\Omega \ \cos K \\ +\cos\Omega \ \sin\Phi \ \sin K \end{matrix} \\[1em] -\cos\Phi \ \cos K & \begin{matrix} -\cos\Omega \ \sin K \\ -\sin\Omega \ \sin\Phi \ \cos K \end{matrix} & \begin{matrix} -\sin\Omega \ \sin K \\ +\cos\Omega \ \sin\Phi \ \cos K \end{matrix} \\[1em] 0 & 0 & 0 \end{bmatrix}$$

$$
= \begin{bmatrix} m_{21} & m_{22} & m_{23} \\ -m_{11} & -m_{12} & -m_{13} \\ 0 & 0 & 0 \end{bmatrix} = \begin{bmatrix} M_{K_1} \\ M_{K_2} \\ M_{K_3} \end{bmatrix} \qquad (3.47)
$$

Note: The rotations Ω, Φ and K in a stereo-medel are analogous to rotations ω, φ and κ in a single photograph. Therefore, such differential forms can be used with respect to an orientation matrix whose rotations are ω, φ and κ in that same order. In case a change in the sequence is necessary, the matrix can be appropriately formed for use in practice.

3.6   OTHER CAPABILITIES WITH 3-D COORDINATES

The use of 3-D coordinates data for mensuration has been the unique strength of analytical photogrammetric procedures. Although the following topics are beyond the general scope of this book, they are briefly mentioned here as certain examples in view of their growing importance in the fields where photogrammetry may be applied:

A. *Digital Terrain Modelling* (DTM)

A Digital Terrain Model (DTM) is regarded as a numerical description of the surface of an object based on measured or derived coordinates of numerous scattered points on this surface. The concept of DTM has been widely used in many engineering applications since its inception in 1955 at the Massachusetts Institute of Technology. Such applications have been exemplified by solutions related to highway planning, automatic profile construction, etc. In recent years, DTM has been used in contourning algorithms to find efficient two-dimensional graphical displays of three-dimensional topographical surfaces. The importance of three-dimensional rectangular systems of coordinates in such applications is unsurpassed (see, for example, ISPRS Archives, 1976, 1980, 1984).

B. *Differential Mapping*

By Differential Mapping is meant the mapping of an object-surface relative to itself, in view of changes in time and space or relative to another object with which it may bear some physical, dimensional relationship. Qualitative and quantitative studies of dynamic objects are best made with photogrammetric (space or aerial, terrestrial, microscopic, etc.) procedures. Selected studies like those on shoreline erosion problems, changes in glacial patterns, growth patterns in urban areas, etc. can be made better in terms of the time the photographs are taken and the occuring changes observed through the use of repetitive photographic coverage. This is comparative photogrammetry. Techniques of handling numerical data involving conversion of three-dimensional stereo-photogrammetric models into digital information for subsequent treatments at a high speed computer have been developed in numerous agencies.

The DTM and differential mapping procedures have two essential components, viz., a set of scattered points measured in three-dimensions and interpolation algorithms for finding new (unobserved or derived) points also in three-dimensions. Three-dimensional transformation of one type or the other is essentially involved in all such works. Various interpolation techniques (surface fitting and prediction) are inherent in such works also. The interested reader would benefit from the work of numerous authors and from the proceedings of numerous recent conferences in this general area, in particular the Auto Carto Symposia organized under the auspices of the ASPRS.

C. *Polylateration*

A simple method of deriving 3-D coordinates of unknown points in terms of their direct distances to five or more known points has been developped by Das (1973). This brings not only in geodetic measurements the full pontentialities of Electronic Distance Measurements (EDM) but also in photogrammetry the tremendous possibilities in view fo the use of modern electronic calculators.

The entire theory is based on the simple analytical expression of the distance between two points: P (p_1, p_2, p_3) and A (a_1, a_2, a_3). The subscripts 1, 2 and 3 here refer to the X, Y and Z coordinates, respectively. The distance can be expressed by

$$(PA)^2 = (p_1 - a_1)^2 + (p_2 - a_2)^2 + (p_3 - a_3)^2 \qquad (3.48)$$

Similarly, for a second point, B

$$(PB)^2 = (p_1 - b_1)^2 + (p_2 - b_2)^2 + (p_3 - b_3)^2 \qquad (3.49)$$

Hence, $(PA)^2 - (PB)^2 = -2 (a_1 - b_1)p_1 - 2 (a_2 - b_2)p_2$

$$- 2 (a_3 - b_3)p_3 + [(a_1^2 + a_2^2 + a_3^2) - (b_1^2 + b_2^2 + b_3^2)] \qquad (3.50)$$

Eq. 3.50 is a linear expression in p_1, p_2, p_3 of the form

$$S_{AB} = \underline{1}_1 p_1 + \underline{1}_2 p_2 + \underline{1}_3 p_3 + \underline{1}_4 \qquad (3.51)$$

where $S_{AB} = (PA)^2 - (PB)^2$

From the above, it would be seen that if the origin is shifted to A i.e., if $a_1 = a_2 = a_3 = 0$ then the parameters $\underline{1}_1 = 2b_1$; $\underline{1}_2 = 2b_2$ and $\underline{1}_3 = 2b_3$ are really twice the coordinates of B.

If, therefore, five points are known then the four independent quantities S_{AB} can be related to four of the points in terms of the fifth point considered as the ad hoc origin, and the four parameters $\underline{1}_1$, $\underline{1}_2$, $\underline{1}_3$, $\underline{1}_4$ can be derived from the four linear equations. In case more than five points are known, then the method of least squares can be utilised for an acceptable solution.

With regard to the expected error propagation, to quote Das (1973), "If the unknown points fall inside the space covered by the known points, the deduced coordinates will be more reliable than for points falling outside the space. The error will vary directly as the distance of the unknown point from this space and inversely as the separation between the extreme points in a particular direction."

The concept can be obviously simplified in 2-D space also, for example, with regard to obtaining photo coordinates being derived from observed distances; such as could be possible with the calibrated data on four fiducial marks and the principal point.

BIBLIOGRAPHY

American Society of Photogrammetry; *Manual of Photogrammetry (4th Ed.)* (ASPRS, Falls Church, Virginia: 1980).

Bomford, G.; *Geodesy* (The Clarendon Press, Oxford, U.K.: 1971).

Buchholtz, A. by Rüger, W. et al; *Photogrammetrie* (VEB Verlag für Bauwesen, Berlin, Germany: 1973).

Das, G. B.; "Deformation of a Stereogram"; *PE* 18, No. 1 (1952a).

Das, G. B.; "Supplementary Height Control;" *PE* 18, No. 1 (1952b).

Das, G. B.; *Polylateration* (Academia Scientiarum Bulgarica; Vol. Vladimiro K. Hristov - Septuagenario: 1973).

Ghosh, Sanjib K.; "Solar Collector Calibration"; *PE* Vol. 32, No.2 (1966).

Ghosh, Sanjib K.; and Gouri B. Das: "Some New Ideas in Aerotriangulation"; *Proceedings of ISP Symposium in Commission III* (Urbana, Illinois: 1966).

Ghosh, Sanjib K.; *Theory of Stereophotogrammetry (2nd Ed.)* (The Ohio State Univ. Bookstores, Columbus, Ohio: 1972).

Ghosh, Sanjib K.; *Phototriangulaiton* (Lexington Books, Lexington, Massachusettts: 1975).

Hallert, Bertil; *Photogrammetry* (McGraw-Hill: 1960).

International Society for Photogrammetry; Archives, Vol. 13, 1957; Vol. 14,1961; Vol. 15, 1965; Vol. 16, 1969; Vol. 17, 1974; Vol. 21, 1976; Vol. 22, 1978; Vol. 23, 1980; Vol. 24, 1982; Vol. 25, 1984.

Jordan-Eggert; *Jordans's Handbook of Geodesy;* Translation of 8th Edition,1941 by Martha W. Carta (US Army Map Service, Washigton, DC: 1962).

Kratky, V.; "Image Transformation"; *PE* 28, No. 5 (1972).

Light, D. L.; "The Orientation Matrix"; *PE* 32, No. 3 (1966).

Mikhail, E. M.; "Simultaneous Three-dimensional Transformation of Higher Degrees"; *PE* 30, No. 4 (1964).

Moffitt, F. H. and Mikhail, E. M.; *Photogrammetry (3rd Ed.);* (International Text-Book Co.: 1980).

Novakovskiy, B. A.; "Stereophotogrammetric Processing of Photographs of Nontopographical Types of Surveys with Unknown Orientation Elements"; *Geodesy, Mapping and Photogrammetry 16,* No. 1 (1974).

Okamoto, Atsushi; "Orientation and Construction of Models". Parts I, II, III, Respectively; *PERS* 47, Nos 10, 11 and 12 (1981).

Sanso, Fernando; "An Exact Solution of the Roto-translation Problem"; *Photogrammetria* 29, No. 6 (1973).

Schut, G. H.; "Construction of Orthogonal Matrices and Their Application in Analytical Photogrammetry"; *Photogrammetria* 15 (1958/59).

Schut, G. H.; "Similarity Transformation and Least Squares"; *PE* 39, No. 6 (1973).

Zakatov, P. S.; *A Course in Higher Geodesy* (Translated from Russian by Israel Program for Scientific Translation for National Science Foundation; No. OTS-6 1-31212: 1962).

4

GEOMETRY OF PHOTOGRAPHS

Photographs taken with a camera permit reconstruction of the bundles of rays with which the object is projected on the negative. They, in turn, permit reconstruction of the object-model, which is used for the measurements. The various phases of such reconstructions are denoted with the general term "Orientation". Specific definitions of various orientations are given below. The orientation of a bundle of rays can be divided into interior and exterior orientations. The latter, in analogical approaches, is further subdivided into relative and absolute orientations. The following definitions would be pertinent.

Definitions:

ORIENTATION: The determination of the position and attitude of a camera, photograph, model, triplet or such a unit in space relative to a system of coordinate reference.

ORIENTATION, INTERIOR: The recovering of the projected cone of rays geometrically identical with the cone of rays that entered the camera lens to make the original exposure. The parameters that define the actual relative relationships are called the *elements of interior orientation,* which normally include: (a) the *camera constant* (also called focal length or principal distance); (b) *location of the principal point* with respect to the fiducial marks; and (c) all the *distorsion parameters* (in the interior of the photographic system, referenced to the principal point and the fiducial marks). Interior orientation, at the plotting instrument, is an attempt to duplicate the cone of rays by setting the elements.

ORIENTATION, EXTERIOR: The recovering of the interior oriented ray bundles (also models, triplets or such units generated from such bundles) in the system of reference coordinates. The exterior orientation consists of two sets of parameters (elements), viz., (a) the location of the perspective center (three-dimensional) and (b) the angular orientation of the camera axis or the photo-plane defining the attitude of the camera at an instant of exposure.

ORIENTATION, RELATIVE: The reconstruction of the same perspective conditions between a pair of photographs which existed when the photographs were taken. In a stereo-pair this is achieved when all pairs of conjugate rays are coplanar with the base i.e., all y-parallaxes are eliminated.

ORIENTATION, ABSOLUTE: Following relative orientation, the establishment of the model or models by way of fixing the scale, positions, tilts and azimuths (i.e., the rotations) with reference to the object (ground) system of coordinates.

Analytical photogrammetry consists of mathematical modeling of the relationship between different systems (e.g., photo and ground, photo and model, model and ground). Such relationships are virtually independent of the applications, i.e., the same formulation may be valid for aerial, spatial, terrestrial or microscopic cases. To arrive at a solution, one may have to use a set of *condition equations* to establish first the relationship between the observed values and the unknown parameters. The condition equations most commonly used are: (i) Collinearity Condition, (ii) Coplanarity Condition, and (iii) Scale Restraint Condition. Each condition equation has specific functions, scopes and limitations. The choice of condition equations may, therefore, lead to different approaches to the solution of any specific problem. Representative characteristics of the various condition equations are given in Table 4.1. Depending on the circumstances, any condition equation may have to be modified in order to make it adaptable to the working system in view of the desired results.

4.1 COLLINEARITY CONDITION

The basic transformation (projective) equations describing the relationship between two mutually associated three-dimensional systems of coordinates is (see Fig. 4.1 and cf. Eq. 3.10):

Table 4.1

Various conditions and their characteristics

(Representative examples)

	Applications	Observation Data	Parameters Knowns	Parameters Unknowns
COLLINEARITY CONDITION	Camera Calibration	x' y'	$X_o\ Y_o\ Z_o\ \omega_p\ \phi_p\ \kappa_p$	$x_o\ y_o\ f\ \omega_o\ \phi_o\ \kappa_o$
	Space Resection	x' y'	$x_o\ y_o\ f\ X_P\ Y_P\ Z_P$	$X_o\ Y_o\ Z_o\ \omega\ \phi\ \kappa$
	Space Intersection	x' y' x" y"	$x_o\ y_o\ f$ $X'_o\ Y'_o\ Z'_o\ X''_o\ Y''_o\ Z''_o$ $\omega'\ \phi'\ \kappa'\ \ \omega''\ \phi''\ \kappa''$	$X_P\ Y_P\ Z_P$
	Strip Photography (Stereo)	x' y' x" y"	$X'_o\ Y'_o\ Z'_o\ f$ $X''_o\ Y''_o\ Z''_o\ v_F$	$X_P\ Y_P\ Z_P$
	Panoramic Photography (Stereo)	x' y' x" y"	$X'_o\ Y'_o\ Z'_o\ f$ $X''_o\ Y''_o\ Z''_o\ \theta$	$X_P\ Y_P\ Z_P$
COPLANARITY CONDITION	Relative Orientation (Dependent)	x' y' x" y"	$x_o\ y_o\ f\ by'\ bz'$ $\omega'\ \phi'\ \kappa'\ bx$	$by''\ bz''$ $\omega''\ \phi''\ \kappa''$
	Relative Orientation (Independent)	x' y' x" y"	$x_o\ y_o\ f\ bx$ $by\ bz\ \omega'$	$\kappa'\ \phi'$ $\kappa''\ \phi''\ \omega''$
SCALE RESTRAINT CONDITION	Scale Transfer	– – – –	$k_{i-1}\ \ k_i$ $X_{o_{i-1}}\ Y_{o_{i-1}}\ Z_{o_{i-1}}$ $X_{o_i}\ Y_{o_i}\ Z_{o_i}$	$X_{o_{i+1}}\ Y_{o_{i+1}}\ Z_{o_{i+1}}$ $bx_i\ by_i\ bz_i$ k_{i+1}
ANGULAR (Church) CONDITION	Space Resection	x' y'	$x_o\ y_o\ f\ X_P\ Y_P\ Z_P$	$X_o\ Y_o\ Z_o$

Note: See the List of Symbols for their explanations. Single prime refers to one photo or the one on the left side and double prime refers to the photo on the right side (of photo-pair). Subscripts o, i, p and P refer to the center of perspectivity, the photo, the point on photo and the point on ground, respectively.

AP-H

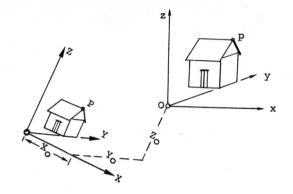

Fig. 4.1

Transformation of coordinates
in three dimensions

$$
\begin{bmatrix} x \\ y \\ z \end{bmatrix} = k\,M \begin{bmatrix} X - X_o \\ Y'- Y_o \\ Z - Z_o \end{bmatrix}
\tag{4.1}
$$

where x, y, z are the coordinates in the system to be transformed into

k   is the scale factor

M   is the rotation matrix

X_o, Y_o, Z_o are the coordinates of the origin (O) in the X, Y,Z
                system which is to be tranformed from.

As described in Chapter 3, the rotation matrix M is a 3×3 orthonormal matrix
and is made up of three independent rotations around the three axes. It is usually
expressed in one of the following forms:

$$
M = \begin{bmatrix} m_{11} & m_{12} & m_{13} \\ m_{21} & m_{22} & m_{23} \\ m_{31} & m_{32} & m_{33} \end{bmatrix} = \begin{bmatrix} \cos Xx & \cos Yx & \cos Zx \\ \cos Xy & \cos Yy & \cos Zy \\ \cos Xz & \cos Yz & \cos Zz \end{bmatrix}
\tag{4.2}
$$

Here, cosXx, cosYx, etc. are the cosines of the space angles between the
respective, x, y, z axes of the system to be transformed into and the X, Y, Z axes
of the system to be transformed. Various authors have selected different
directions and sequences for these rotations. Nonetheless, the numerical values of
the nine elements of M are identical, regardless of the choice of the angles
involved therein. Because of the peculiar nature of rotation matrix M, its inverse
and its transpose are identical.

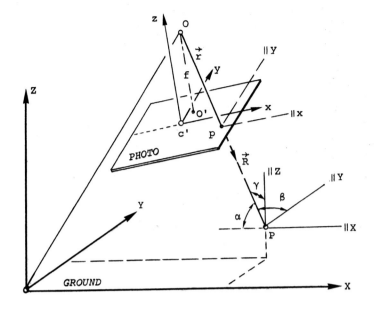

Fig. 4.2

Collinearity condition
and exterior orientation

Considering a diapositive, any image point p (see Fig. 4.2) may be located in the photograph by its coordinates: x_p, y_p (the third dimension being zero). The optical (camera) axis intersects the diapositive plane at O' whose coordinates are: x_o, y_o (the third dimension is also zero). The optical axis being normal to the plane of the diapositive and parallel to the z axis (of the photograph system), one gets the coordinates of the perspective center: x_o, y_o, f.

In the photographic system of coordinates, the vector defining the location of the point p is

$$\vec{r} = \begin{bmatrix} x_p - x_o \\ y_p - y_o \\ 0 - f \end{bmatrix} \tag{4.3}$$

In the ground system of coordinates, the perspective center (O) is located at X_o, Y_o, Z_o, and the corresponding ground point (P) is located at X_p, Y_p, Z_p. Thus, the vector defining the location of the ground point P is

$$\vec{R} = \begin{bmatrix} X_p - X_o \\ Y_p - Y_o \\ Z_p - Z_o \end{bmatrix} \tag{4.4}$$

When the exterior orientation of the photograph is correctly established, the two location vectors $\vec{r}$ and $\vec{R}$ are collinear. The two vectors differ only in length, one being a scalar multiple of the other. This gives the scale factor:

$$k = \frac{|r|}{|R|} \qquad (4.5)$$

In keeping with the fundamental relationship expressed in Eq. 4.1, the collinearity condition may be written as:

$$\vec{r} = \begin{bmatrix} X_p - X_o \\ Y_p - Y_o \\ -f \end{bmatrix} = k\,M \begin{bmatrix} X_p - X_o \\ Y_p - Y_o \\ Z_p - Z_o \end{bmatrix} = k \cdot M \cdot \vec{R} \qquad (4.6)$$

or,

$$\vec{R} = \frac{1}{k} \cdot M^T \cdot \vec{r} \qquad (4.7)$$

4.1.1 Standard Form

The matrix multiplication indicated in Eq. 4.6 may be carried out by the components along rows and columns. If the first and second rows are divided by the third row and the resulting expressions are multiplied by $-f$, one obtains the collinearity condition equations with respect to the two photo coordinates:

$$x = (x_p - x_o) = -f\,\frac{(X_p - X_o)m_{11} + (Y_p - Y_o)m_{12} + (Z_p - Z_o)m_{13}}{(X_p - X_o)m_{31} + (Y_p - Y_o)m_{32} + (Z_p - Z_o)m_{33}}$$

$$\qquad (4.8)$$

$$y = (y_p - y_o) = -f\,\frac{(X_p - X_o)m_{21} + (Y_p - Y_o)m_{22} + (Z_p - Z_o)m_{23}}{(X_p - X_o)m_{31} + (Y_p - Y_o)m_{32} + (Z_p - Z_o)m_{33}}$$

These two equations imply that the two vectors, $\vec{r}$ and $\vec{R}$ are collinear, i.e., the object point (P), the perspective center (or, the exposure station, O), and the image point (p) lie on the same straight line.

This assumed condition, however, does not hold true always in the physical reality. A variety of disturbances, (e.g., lens distortion, atmospheric refraction, and others) may cause the actual ray to deviate from the collinearity situation. However, if these disturbances are known and can be determined in advance, one can apply appropriate corrections and use refined data before imposing the collinearity condition. In certain cases, one can compensate for such disturbances by way of augmenting the collinearity equations also. Chapter 5 deals with such refinement considerations.

Each measured point on the photograph leads to two condition equations, one for each of the x and y coordinates. These equations contain practically all the elements of the problem (viz., of interior orientation and exterior orientation). They contain the image coordinates as well as the object space coordinates and are sufficient in themselves for the solution of any problem in conventional photogrammetry. They can be used in various other forms also as discussed below.

4.1.2 Matrix Form

Eqs. 4.8, in matrix form are

$$x = -f \frac{M_1 \bar{X}}{M_3 \bar{X}} \quad \text{and} \quad y = -f \frac{M_2 \bar{X}}{M_3 \bar{X}} \tag{4.9}$$

where f is calibrated focal length of the camera, as before.

$$M = \begin{bmatrix} M_1 \\ M_2 \\ M_3 \end{bmatrix} \quad \text{and} \quad \bar{X} = \begin{bmatrix} X_p - X_o \\ Y_p - Y_o \\ Z_p - Z_o \end{bmatrix}$$

The elements M_1, M_2 and M_3 are the corresponding row matrices which, in general notations, are

$$M_i = [m_{i1}, m_{i2}, m_{i3}]$$

Collinearity condition equations in such forms are conveniently used for various expressions.

4.1.3 Direction Cosine Form

Consider that the location vector $\vec{R}$ (OP in Fig. 4.2) subtends angles α, β and γ with the X, Y, and Z axes, respectively. These define the direction cosines of this vector in the X-Y-Z system. In Eq. 4.8, the quantities $(X_p - X_o)$, $(Y_p - Y_o)$ and $(Z_p - Z_o)$ are proportional to the direction cosines of the vector from 0 to P ($\vec{R}$). Therefore, with proper substitutions, one gets the collinearity condition equations in the form:

$$\left.\begin{aligned}(x_p - x_o) &= -f\ \frac{m_{11}\cos\alpha\ +\ m_{12}\cos\beta\ +\ m_{13}\cos\gamma}{m_{31}\cos\alpha\ +\ m_{32}\cos\beta\ +\ m_{33}\cos\gamma}\\[2ex](y_p - y_o) &= -f\ \frac{m_{21}\cos\alpha\ +\ m_{22}\cos\beta\ +\ m_{23}\cos\gamma}{m_{31}\cos\alpha\ +\ m_{32}\cos\beta\ +\ m_{33}\cos\gamma}\end{aligned}\right\} \qquad (4.10)$$

The condition equations in this form are useful in certain special problems when scale of the object is no consideration, e.g., for camera calibration using photographs of collimator-banks or stars. When the directions to some points used as control are known, equations in such forms permit numerical evaluations of their corresponding direction cosines, which help in determining the angular orientation of the photograph and the interior orientation of the camera.

Most of the agencies using the computational methods with the conventional frame cameras have programs involving the collinearity equations, which are almost routinely applied in aerial mapping jobs. However, in non-conventional applications, where the concept of a simple central projection is no longer adequate to describe the geometry of the physical characteristics, it becomes a problem. Cases in point are, for example, Continous Strip Photography, Panoramic Photography, etc. Simple modifications of the equations whereby the same computer programs can be used will be advantageous in such cases. Representative examples of such unconventional systems are discussed in Chap. 10.

4.1.4 Linearization of Collinearity Equations

In theory, the solution of any problem (wherein this condition is applicable) is obtained by inserting the known quantities in the equations and enough image points must be observed to permit a solution for the remaining (unknown) parameters. There are, however, two problems in this. Firstly, the condition equations are non-linear. Secondly, in usual cases, more image points are observed than are necessary for explicit and closed solutions. To obtain a practical and statistically acceptable solution, therefore, linearized forms of the condition equations are developed first and, next, the mothod of Least Squares is applied to account for the extra (redundant) data. Generally, the equations are linearized by using a 'Taylor' expansion and (in view of an iterative solution) only the first order terms are retained.

The condition equation may be written as a function (F) of observations and parameters equated to zero:

$$F(O,X) \; = \; 0 \tag{4.11}$$

where   O   symbolizes the observations (or, directly related quantities)

and   X   symbolizes the variable parameters.

If the observations and a set of approximate values of the parameters are substituted, the equations cannot be satisfied exactly. They can, however, be satisfied by adding (to this function) terms involving the residual errors in the observations and the corrections to the approximate values of the parameters. This gives:

$$(F_O) \; + \; [A] \; (V) \; + \; [B] \; (\Delta) \; = \; 0 \tag{4.12}$$

where F_O is the function, F, evaluated with the observations and the approximate values (initial values in an iterative procedure) of the parameters

A   is a row matrix composed of the partial derivatives of F with respect to each of the observed quantities, i.e., $\partial F/\partial$ (observations)

V   is a column vector composed of the residuals to the observations

B   is a row matrix composed of the partial derivatives of F with respect to each of the parameters, i.e., $\partial F/\partial$ (parameters)

Δ   is a column vector composed of the corrections (or, alterations) to the approximate values of the parameters.

The partial derivatives (see the Appendix) in A and B are with respect to the approximate values of the paremeters and hence become the coefficients in a linear equation in which F_O is the constant term. The partial derivatives of the collinearity condition equations with respect to thier application in aerial triangulation (interior orientation elements considered as known) cases are given in the Appendix.

By way of substituting the quantities containing the rotation angles, transposing and clearing fractions, one obtains from Eq. 4.8 (for the m elements, one may refer to Eqs. 3.17 and 3.18),

$$
\left.
\begin{aligned}
&x[(X-X_o)\sin\varphi + (Y-Y_o)(-\sin\omega\,\cos\varphi) + (Z-Z_o)\cos\omega\,\cos\varphi] + f[(X-X_o)\cos\varphi\,\cos\kappa \\
&+(Y-Y_o)(\cos\omega\,\sin\kappa + \sin\omega\,\sin\varphi\,\cos\kappa) + (Z-Z_o)(\sin\omega\,\sin\kappa - \cos\omega\,\sin\varphi\,\cos\kappa)] \\
&\qquad = 0 \\
\\
\\
&y[(X-X_o)\sin\varphi + (Y-Y_o)(-\sin\omega\,\cos\varphi) + (Z-Z_o)\cos\omega\,\cos\varphi] + f[(X-X_o)(-\cos\varphi\,\sin\kappa) \\
&+(Y-Y_o)(\cos\omega\,\cos\kappa - \sin\omega\,\sin\varphi\,\sin\kappa) + (Z-Z_o)(\sin\omega\,\cos\kappa + \cos\omega\,\sin\varphi\,\sin\kappa)] \\
&\qquad = 0
\end{aligned}
\right\}
\quad (4.13)
$$

Eqs 4.13 are 'transcendental' and in most general cases all of the twelve terms within the square brackets are considered unknowns. They simply represent another form of the same collinearity condition. If per chance the condition does not exist, it is desirable to allow incremental corrections (differentials) to the observed coordinates x, y such that they fulfill the principles of Least Squares. Harris et al (1963) used a form of Newton's method (see Eshbach, 1957) to solve them. This considers an iterative method based on initial approximations, which are easily obtainable in any problem for all unknowns. After partial differentiations and rearranging the terms, one may consider $dx = v_x$ and $dy = v_y$.

Note: dx and dy are corrections or deviations to measured photo coordinates x and
    y. They may be interpreted as residual errors in the measurements.

One obtains now the following simplified forms of the linearized observation equations for the case where all of the interior orientation elements are known:

$$
v_{x_{ij}} = (p_{11_{ij}} + p_{12_{ij}}d\omega_i + p_{13_{ij}}d\varphi_i + p_{14_{ij}}d\kappa_i - p_{15_{ij}}dX_{o_i} - p_{16_{ij}}dY_{o_i}
$$

$$
-\,p_{17_{ij}}dZ_{oi} + p_{15_{ij}}dX_j + p_{16_{ij}}dY_j + p_{17_{ij}}dZ_j)\Big/ A_{ij} \qquad (4.14a)
$$

$$
v_{y_{ij}} = (p_{21_{ij}} + p_{22_{ij}}d\omega_i + p_{23_{ij}}d\varphi_i + p_{24_{ij}}d\kappa_i - p_{25_{ij}}dX_{o_i} - p_{26_{ij}}dY_{o_i}
$$

$$
-\,p_{27_{ij}}dZ_{oi} + p_{25_{ij}}dX_j + p_{26_{ij}}dY_j + p_{27_{ij}}dZ_j)\Big/ A_{ij} \qquad (4.14b)
$$

where subscripts i and j refer to the photograph and to the point, respectively;

also, p_{11} and p_{12} are the residual errors (misclosures) in x and y, respectively (i.e., the observed value minus the value computed by using the approximate values of the unknowns);

p_{12} ... p_{17} are the partial derivatives of Eqs 4.8 or 4.13,

p_{22} ... p_{27} evaluated by using the approximate values of the unknowns;

$d\omega$, $d\varphi$, $d\kappa$ are the small corrections to be applied to the approximate (initial) values of the unknowns ω, φ and κ;

dX_o, dY_o, dZ_o are the small corrections to be applied to the approximate (initial) values of X_o, Y_o and Z_o;

dX, dY, dZ are the small corrections to be applied to the approximate (initial) values of X, Y and Z;

and A_{ij} is a constant for the point observed and the photo containing it.

Harris et al (1963) have given convenient equations for computing the p coefficients. These equations are in a sense 'universal'. They can be used to solve different problems, e.g., Relative Orientation, Resection, Block Triangulation, etc. However, they have to be adapted to the requirements of specific problems. In the case of *Block Triangulation*, the presence of all nine terms ($d\omega$ ... dZ) is necessary. In *Space Resection* computations, where X, Y, and Z ground coordinates of all points are known, one would use the first six terms ($d\omega$ ... dZ_o) because the terms dX, dY and dZ would be zero in this case. The equations can be further simplified in the case of a *Relative Orientation* problem because one of the two photos (say, the left side one) can be considered 'fixed' as in a 'dependent' method, that perspective center can be selected as the origin of the system of coordinates) and the distance to the second perspective center can be selected as unity (whereby dX_o has then no significance). The terms, dX, dY and dZ can be eliminated by substitution and expressed in terms of other unknowns ($d\omega$, $d\varphi$, dκ and dZ_0). This will give the special observation equations for a 'dependent' case of Relative Orientation:

$$v_x = a_1 d\omega + a_2 d\varphi + a_3 d\kappa + a_4 dY_0 + a_5 dZ_0$$

$$v_y = d_1 d\omega + d_2 d\varphi + d_3 d\kappa + d_4 dY_0 + d_5 dZ_0$$

(4.15)

The pair of Eqs. 4.15 occurs for each image point on each photograph. See also Harris et al (1963) for the full meanings of the coefficients, a's and d's. Corresponding to the use of Y-parallaxes, only the y-equation is significant. Nevertheless, some organizations utilize both x- and y- equations for programming uniformity, even in the realtive orientation cases. The x-equations by themselves can be used profitably only in some special cases where the use of Y-parallaxes may be prohibitive or impossible, e.g., problem models with 'critical surface' in which the element ω may be unsolvable, or models with difficulty in stereo-vision at one or more of standard locations. See Ghosh (1972) for further ideas on this.

Such iterative solutions are best made with a clear indication as to when to terminate the iterations. A sound and realistic logic is to terminate when the incremantal corrections to the parameters (linear or angular) are smaller than their observational precisions. The NOS, for example, terminates such iterations when each of the elements, dω, dφ and dκ is less than 10^{-5} radian. In an interesting study, Pope (1972) suggested that quantities related to both the parameters and the observations should be updated for each such iteration.

The collinearity condition being applicable in various cases of diverse nature, the solution of the corresponding equations are also of different types. These are discussed in detail in the respective chapters 6, 8, 9 and 10.

4.2 COPLANARITY CONDITION

The Coplanarity condition (see Fig. 4.3) implies that the two perspective centers, any object point and the corresponding image points on the two photographs of the stereo-pair, must all lie in a common plane. This condition is fundamental to *Relative Orientation* or *Space Intersection*. When relative orientation is achieved, the vector $\vec{R}_{1i}$ (from O_1 to P_i) will have an intersection with the vector $\vec{R}_{2i}$ (from O_2 to P_i), and these two vectors together with the air-base vector $\vec{b}$ will be coplanar. This means that their scalar triple product is zero. The function

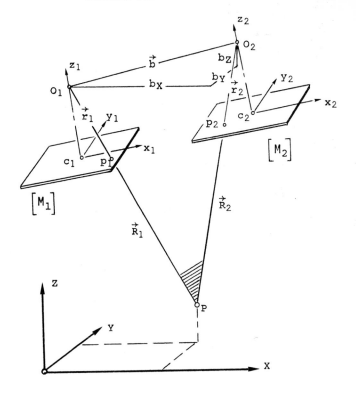

Fig. 4.3

Coplanarity condition

and

intersection for

relative orientation

(mathematical model) F_i is:

$$F_i \;=\; \vec{b} \cdot \vec{R}_{1i} \times \vec{R}_{2i} \;=\; 0 \qquad (4.16)$$

This, written in a determinant form is

$$F_i \;=\; \begin{vmatrix} b_X & b_Y & b_Z \\ X_{1i} & Y_{1i} & Z_{1i} \\ X_{2i} & Y_{2i} & Z_{2i} \end{vmatrix} \;=\; 0 \qquad (4.17)$$

Also, in view of expressions 4.6 and 4.7,

$$\vec{b} \;=\; \begin{bmatrix} b_X \\ b_Y \\ b_Z \end{bmatrix} \;;\quad \vec{R}_{1i} \;=\; k_1 \, M_1^T \, \vec{r}_{1_i} \quad \text{and} \quad \vec{R}_{2i} \;=\; k_2 \, M_2^T \, \vec{r}_{2_i}$$

where k_1 and k_2 are the scale factors of the corresponding location vectors $\vec{r}_1$
                   and $\vec{r}_2$ within the camera spaces; also

        M_1 and M_2 are the orientation matrices for photographs 1 and 2,
                   respectively.

One coplanarity condition equation may be written for each of the object points used in a solution. It has the main advantage that the coordinates of the points in the object space may be avoided in its application. Modifications of Eq. 4.17 are utilized to express the condition in different forms:

a) Y-parallax of a point in the image space (with certain conditions, e.g., alignment of the photo bases in the pair) eqaul to zero;

b) Y-parallax of a point in the model space equal to zero (as is usual in analogical procedures with a stereoplotter); or

c) The minimum distance between corresponding rays equal to zero (discussed later).

The intersection of five pairs of rays $\vec{R}_1$ and $\vec{R}_2$ is the requirement for a relative orientation (see Ghosh, 1972). Since the coordinates of points in object space are not included, the coplanarity condition equations by themselves (without scale and model orientation considerations) are not sufficient for a complete solution of any phototriangulation problem. It has, however, been used for systems involving simultaneous intersection solution of all photographs in the triangulation. Like the Collinearity condition equations, these are also non-linear and need to be linearized. The partial derivatives in this respect are given in the Appendix.

In the simplest procedure of its application, consider a *Dependent* method of *Relative Orientation* and the same scale factor (equated to unity) for all points in the two photos of a stereopair. Also consider the left hand side photo being fixed, i.e.,

$$k_1 = k_2 = 1 \text{ and } \omega_1 = \varphi_1 = \kappa_1 = by_1 = bz_1 = 0$$

also $$b_Y = by_2 - by_1 \quad \text{and} \quad b_Z = bz_2 - bz_1$$

The vectors $\vec{R}_{1i}$ and $\vec{R}_{2i}$ are then reduced to

$$R_{1i} = \begin{bmatrix} X_{1i} \\ Y_{1i} \\ Z_{1i} \end{bmatrix} = \begin{bmatrix} 1 & 0 & 0 \\ 0 & 1 & 0 \\ 0 & 0 & 1 \end{bmatrix} \begin{bmatrix} x_{1i} \\ y_{1i} \\ -f \end{bmatrix} = \begin{bmatrix} x_{1i} \\ y_{1i} \\ -f \end{bmatrix} \tag{4.18}$$

$$R_{2i} = \begin{bmatrix} X_{2i} \\ Y_{2i} \\ Z_{2i} \end{bmatrix} = \begin{bmatrix} x_{2i}\cos\varphi\cos\kappa - y_{2i}\cos\varphi\sin\kappa - f\sin\varphi \\ x_{2i}(\cos\omega\sin\kappa + \sin\omega\sin\varphi\cos\kappa) + y_{2i}(\cos\omega\cos\kappa -\sin\omega\sin\varphi\sin\kappa) + f\sin\omega\cos\varphi \\ x_{2i}(\sin\omega\sin\kappa - \cos\omega\sin\varphi\cos\kappa + y_{2i}(\sin\omega\cos\kappa +\cos\omega\sin\varphi\sin\kappa) - f\cos\omega\cos\varphi \end{bmatrix} \tag{4.19}$$

Here, ω, φ and κ are for the right-hand side camera (i.e., number 2). Now, with substitutions of Eqs 4.18 and 4.19 into Eq. 4.17, and also rearranging, one gets the mathematical model:

$$\begin{aligned}
F_i = & \{b_X\, y_{1i} - by_2\, x_{1i}\}\,\{x_{2i}(\sin\omega\sin\kappa - \cos\omega\sin\varphi\cos\kappa) \\
& + y_{2i}(\sin\omega\cos\kappa + \cos\omega\sin\varphi\sin\kappa) - f\cos\omega\cos\varphi\} \\
& + \{b_X\, f + bz_2\, x_{1i}\}\,\{x_{2i}(\cos\omega\sin\kappa + \sin\omega\sin\varphi\cos\kappa) \\
& + y_{2i}(\cos\omega\cos\kappa - \sin\omega\sin\varphi\sin\kappa) + f\sin\omega\cos\varphi\} \\
& + \{by_2\, f + bz_2\, y_{1i}\}\,\{y_{2i}\cos\varphi\sin\kappa - x_{2i}\cos\varphi\cos\kappa + f\sin\varphi\} \\
= & \;0
\end{aligned} \tag{4.20}$$

4.2.1 Linearization of Coplanarity Equation

The concept as applicable to the linearization of the collinearity condition equations and expressed in Eq. 4.12 is valid in this case also. The observed quantities are the image coordinates, x_{1i}, y_{1i} and x_{2i}, y_{2i}, refined for the systematic errors (distortions) as discussed in Chap. 5. The general form here, therefore, is also

$$(F_o) + [A](V) + [B](\Delta) = 0 \tag{4.21}$$

where, with explanations of the terms similar to Eq. 4.12, one gets:

$$[A_i] = \left[\frac{\partial F_i}{\partial x_{1i}} \quad \frac{\partial F_i}{\partial y_{1i}} \quad \frac{\partial F_i}{\partial x_{2i}} \quad \frac{\partial F_i}{\partial y_{2i}} \right] \tag{4.22}$$

$$[B_i] = \left[\frac{\partial F_i}{\partial by_2} \quad \frac{\partial F_i}{\partial bz_2} \quad \frac{\partial F_i}{\partial \omega_2} \quad \frac{\partial F_i}{\partial \varphi_2} \quad \frac{\partial F_i}{\partial \kappa_2} \right] \tag{4.23}$$

$$(V_i) = \begin{bmatrix} V_{x_1} \\ V_{y_1} \\ V_{x_2} \\ V_{y_2} \end{bmatrix}_i \tag{4.24}$$

$$(\Delta) = \begin{bmatrix} \delta by_2 \\ \delta bz_2 \\ \delta \omega_2 \\ \delta \varphi_2 \\ \delta \kappa_2 \end{bmatrix} \tag{4.25}$$

The partial derivatives are given in Appendix B. For full derivations and ideas of the sizes and forms of these matrices, see Ghosh (1975) Appendix A.

4.2.2 Solution of Coplanarity Equation

For basic ideas on adjustment computations one may refer to several books, e.g., Hirvonen (1971) or Mikhail (1976). With regard to the application of the principle of Least Squares, in this case, one obtains the solution vector (of corrections to the approximate parameters):

$$\Delta = -(B^T M^{-1} B)^{-1} B^T M^{-1} F_o \qquad (4.26)$$

where

$$M = A W^{-1} A^T \qquad \text{Note:} \quad \text{This M is not to be confused with M used for the Rotation matrix used elsewhere in the book.}$$

$$W = \text{Weight matrix associated with the observations.}$$

$$v^T W v = -K_L^T F_o \qquad (4.27)$$

where

$$K_L = -M^{-1}(B\Delta + F_o)$$

The unit variance, m_o^2, is given by

$$m_o^2 = \frac{v^T W v}{r - u} \qquad (4.28)$$

where $(r - u)$ is the *degrees of freedom*; r being the number of condition equations, and u being the number of unknown quantities. The variance-covariance matrix of unknown parameters is

$$\Sigma_\Delta = m_o^2 \, Q_\Delta \qquad (4.29)$$

and the weight coefficient matrix of Δ can be expressed as

$$Q_\Delta = (B^T M^{-1} B)^{-1} \qquad (4.30)$$

The corrections (Δ) are added to the approximate (initial for the particular iteration) values of the parameters used in computing the coefficients of F_i, A_i and B_i. The number of iterations would depend on the initial approximations, the parameters, the geometric strength of the stereo-model and the desired precision. As was discussed in Section 4.1, a good method is to terminate the iterations when the incremental corrections to the parameters are smaller than their observational precision.

4.2.3 Intersected Point and Parallax

The condition for relative orientation of a photo-pair is the intersection of five (evenly distributed) pairs of rays, $\vec{R}_1$ and $\vec{R}_2$. It is quite possible that some rays fail to intersect, giving thereby residual *parallaxes*. One must, therefore, consider an acceptable point which will represent the location of intersection for the purpose of mensurations. Generally, the point midway along the vector $\vec{D}$ representing the parallax (see Fig. 4.4) in the region where the rays come closest, is chosen. The direction (but not the length) of $\vec{D}$, which is perpendicular to both $\vec{R}_1$ and $\vec{R}_2$ is

$$\vec{D} = \vec{R}_1 \times \vec{R}_2 \qquad\qquad (4.31)$$

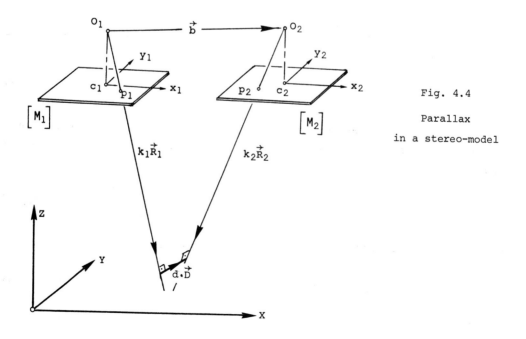

Fig. 4.4

Parallax

in a stereo-model

It will follow directly from Fig. 4.4 that

$$k_1 \cdot \vec{R}_1 - k_2 \cdot \vec{R}_2 + d \cdot \vec{D} = \vec{b} \tag{4.32}$$

where k_1, k_2 and d are three unknown scalar multipliers. Eq. 4.32 can be solved for the three scalars.

Note: From the principles of vector analysis (see for example, Coxeter, 1969), any four vectors, a, b, c, and d in three-dimensional space can be related to each other through

$$(\underline{a} \times \underline{b}) \times (\underline{c} \times \underline{d}) = (\underline{a} \cdot \underline{c} \times \underline{d})\underline{b} - (\underline{b} \cdot \underline{c} \times \underline{d})\underline{a} = (\underline{a} \cdot \underline{b} \times \underline{d})\underline{c} - (\underline{a} \cdot \underline{b} \times \underline{c})\underline{d}$$

This gives,

$$(\underline{a} \cdot \underline{b} \times \underline{c})\underline{d} - (\underline{b} \cdot \underline{c} \times \underline{d})\underline{a} + (\underline{c} \cdot \underline{d} \times \underline{a})\underline{b} - (\underline{d} \cdot \underline{a} \times \underline{b})\underline{c} = 0 \tag{4.33}$$

Consider equating vectors a, b, c and d with $\vec{b}$, $\vec{R}_1$, $\vec{D}$ and $\vec{R}_2$. While Eq. 4.33 is valid for any four vectors, Eq. 4.32 is valid for unique values of k_1, k_2 and d. These considerations give (see Ghosh, 1975 for explanations):

$$k_1 = \frac{\vec{b} \cdot \vec{D} \times \vec{R}_2}{\vec{R}_1 \cdot \vec{D} \times \vec{R}_2} \; ; \qquad k_2 = \frac{\vec{R}_1 \cdot \vec{D} \times \vec{b}}{\vec{R}_1 \cdot \vec{D} \times \vec{R}_2} \qquad \text{and} \qquad d = \frac{\vec{R}_1 \cdot \vec{b} \times \vec{R}_2}{\vec{R}_1 \cdot \vec{D} \times \vec{R}_2} \tag{4.34}$$

The vectors $\vec{R}_1$ and $\vec{R}_2$ are determined by using Eqs 4.18 and 4.19 after orientation matrices M_1 and M_2 are finally evaluated. The base components bx, by and bz are determined after the relative orientation solution. The coordinates of each model point are determined next from

$$\begin{bmatrix} X \\ Y \\ Z \end{bmatrix} = \begin{bmatrix} X_{O_1} \\ Y_{O_1} \\ Z_{O_1} \end{bmatrix} + k_1 \begin{bmatrix} R_{1_X} \\ R_{1_Y} \\ R_{1_Z} \end{bmatrix} + (0.5)d \begin{bmatrix} D_X \\ D_Y \\ D_Z \end{bmatrix} \tag{4.35}$$

The coordinates of the perspective center O_1 in the case of a single model could be assumed to be (0, 0, 0). In the case of a strip formation they are equal to the perspective center O_2 of the preceding model, and by way of adding the components of the base to the previous perspective center coordinates, one can obtain the coordinates of the new perspective center:

$$
\begin{bmatrix} X_{O_2} \\ Y_{O_2} \\ Z_{O_2} \end{bmatrix} = \begin{bmatrix} X_{O_1} \\ Y_{O_1} \\ Z_{O_1} \end{bmatrix} + \begin{bmatrix} bx \\ by \\ bz \end{bmatrix} \tag{4.36}
$$

An expression for the vector $\vec{D}$ (Eq. 4.31) can be written in the form

$$
\vec{D} = \begin{bmatrix} D_X \\ D_Y \\ D_Z \end{bmatrix} = \begin{bmatrix} Y_1 Z_2 - Z_1 Y_2 \\ Z_1 X_2 - X_1 Z_2 \\ X_1 Y_2 - Y_1 X_2 \end{bmatrix} \tag{4.37}
$$

The residual spatial parallax at each model point is computed as follows:

$$
\text{Parallax} = d \cdot (D_X^2 + D_Y^2 + D_Z^2)^{1/2} \tag{4.38}
$$

Because the line of flight is along the X axis, it is possible as a harmless approximation to choose for $\vec{D}$ the unit vector along the Y direction. With such a simplification one obtains the following working expressions (see Fig. 4.5 for simple explanation):

$$
k_1 = \frac{R_{2_Z} \cdot bx - R_{2_X} \cdot bz}{R_{2_Z} \cdot R_{1_X} - R_{2_X} \cdot R_{1_Z}} = \frac{Z_2 \cdot bx - X_2 \cdot bz}{Z_2 \cdot X_1 - X_2 \cdot Z_1} \tag{4.39}
$$

$$
k_2 = \frac{R_{1_X} \cdot bz - R_{1_Z} \cdot bx}{R_{2_Z} \cdot R_{1_X} - R_{2_X} \cdot R_{1_Z}} = \frac{X_1 \cdot bz - Z_1 \cdot bx}{Z_2 \cdot X_1 - X_2 \cdot Z_1} \tag{4.40}
$$

$$
d = (Y_{O_2} + k_2 \cdot R_{2_Y}) - (Y_{O_1} + k_1 \cdot R_{1_Y}) = (Y_{O_2} + k_2 \cdot Y_2) - (Y_{O_1} + k_1 \cdot Y_1) \tag{4.41}
$$

The coordinates of the required point in the model are, in view of the simplifications (cf. Eq. 4.35):

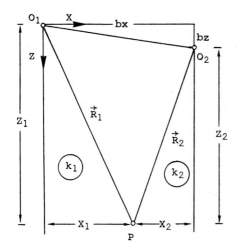

Fig. 4.5

Situation on X-Z plane,

explanation of scale factors

$$X = X_{O_1} + k_1 \cdot X_1$$

$$Y = (0.5)[(Y_{O_2} + k_2 \cdot Y_2) + (Y_{O_1} + k_1 \cdot Y_1)] \qquad (4.42)$$

$$Z = Z_{O_1} + k_1 \cdot Z_1$$

A further practical simplification would be to consider $k_1 = k_2$ in each model. It is now apparent that the Coplanarity Condition involves both interior and exterior orientations of each of the two photographs without considering the object-space coordinates. Such information may be included any time if an identifiable control point appears on two or more photos in the block or strip.

4.3 SCALE RESTRAINT CONDITION

This condition is generally applicable in sequential photo-triangulation procedure. It corresponds to *scale transfer* as performed in the aeropolygon method of phototriangulation (see Ghosh, 1975). In the Independent Models method of photo-triangulation, this is automatically applied through the three-demensional transformation of adjacent models.

The geometry of this condition is illustrated in Fig. 4.6. The three model-(or object-) space vectors $\vec{R}_1$, $\vec{R}_2$ and $\vec{R}_3$ to a point P may fail to intersect at a

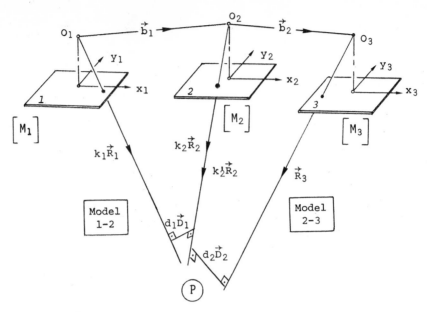

Fig. 4.6   Scale restraint condition geometry

common point due to scale variations even though the two adjacent models have been otherwise properly oriented.   The vectors $\vec{R}_1$ and $\vec{R}_2$ intersect in stereomodel 1-2 while $\vec{R}_2$ and $\vec{R}_3$ intersect in model 2-3.. Therefore, one may consider two scalar multipliers k_2 and k_2' for the same vector $\vec{R}_2$ in the first and second models, respectively.   By applying Eq. 4.34 in stereomodel 1-2,

$$k_2 = \frac{\vec{R}_1 \cdot \vec{D}_1 \times \vec{b}_1}{\vec{R}_1 \cdot \vec{D}_1 \times \vec{R}_2} \qquad\qquad (4.43)$$

Similarly, in stereo-model 2-3, for the same vector $\vec{R}_2$ (which corresponds to k_1 in Eq. 4.34), one gets here,

$$k_2' = \frac{\vec{b}_2 \cdot \vec{D}_2 \times \vec{R}_3}{\vec{R}_2 \cdot \vec{D}_2 \times \vec{R}_3} \qquad\qquad (4.44)$$

In order to obtain the two intersections in the two models at the same point, these two scalar multipliers must match, e.e., they must be equal in magnitude but opposite in sign, i.e.,

$$k_2 + k_2' = 0 \qquad\qquad (4.45)$$

Eq. 4.45, expressing the scale restraint condition, is always used in conjunction with the coplanarity equations. There may arise a question whether a third coplanarity equation assuring an intersection between vectors $\vec{R}_1$ and $\vec{R}_3$ would accomplish the same result. However, in normal strips with straight line flights, it is possible that the three vectors $\vec{R}_1$, $\vec{R}_2$ and $\vec{R}_3$ lie on the same plane. Consequently, the vectors may mutually intersect at three different points, on the same plane. Thus, the coplanarity equation by itself is not enough.

During the strip formation in a sequential phototriangulation process, it is required that the coplanarity and scale restraint conditions (i.e., corresponding to relative orientation and scale transfer, respectively) are applied successively in each model. The practical steps suggested by Ghosh (1975) are as follows:

Step 1: At the $(i-1)$th model (i.e., with photographs $i-1$ and i): $k_{i-1} = k_1$
(i.e., k_1 and k_2 are both known).
Compute X, Y, Z coordinates of all points in this model.
Also known in this model are, X_{01}, Y_{01}, Z_{01} and X_{02}, Y_{02}, Z_{02} i.e., the perspective centers of photographs $i-1$ and i.

Step 2: At the ith model (i.e., with photographs i and $i+1$):
Perform co-orientation (coplanarity equation) considering $k_{1i} = k_{2i-1}$
(i.e., the same scale as of the previous model).
With this k, obtain Z of the points common with the previous model.
Also compute bx, by and bz of this model (i.e., vector $\vec{b}_i$).
If now, $Zp_{i-1} = Zp_i$ within permissible limits, it is alright.

If it is not, obtain corrections to k_{1_i} (i.e., k_1 of this model).

Then correct bx, by and bz proportionately.
Next, obtain the coordinates of the perspective center for the $(i+1)$th photograph, i.e.,

$$X_{0_{i+1}} = X_{0_i} + bx_i ; \quad Y_{0_{i+1}} = Y_{0_i} + by_i \quad \text{and} \quad Z_{0_{i+1}} = Z_{0_i} + bz_i$$

Now, by using Eqs 4.39 and 4.40, check if $k_{1_i} = k_{2_{i-1}}$.

If not, repeat Step 2.
If yes, compute finally X, Y, Z coordinates of all points in this model.

Step 3: At the $(i+1)$th model (i.e., with photographs $i+1$ and $i+2$):
Repeat the operations of Step 2.

4.4 ANGULAR RELATIONSHIP CONDITION

It was first observed by Church (see Church and Quinn, 1944) that in order to maintain correct perspectivity, the angles subtended at the perspective center between points in the object space must equal the corresponding angles in the camera space. By imposing this condition of angular relationship (also known by the name of Church, as the *Church Condition*), one can solve the space resection and other problems (also see, Chap. 6).

By obtaining the photo coordinates (x', y') from observation data and considering the focal length (f) along with the photo coordinates of the principal point (x_o, y_o), one can establish the location vector ($\vec{r}$) of any point observed on the photo (Eq. 4.3). Subsequently, the angles (V) between the vectors subtended at the perspective center are easily obtained.

In Fig. 4.7, a b and c are images of object points A, B, and C, respectively, giving the corresponding camera-space location vectors $\vec{r}_a$, $\vec{r}_b$ and $\vec{r}_c$. Angles V_{ab}, V_{bc} and V_{ca} are subtended at the perspective center, O, between the points as indicated in the subscripts. In view of three components (x, y and f) of these vectors, by using the principles of '*dot product*', one can compute the space-angles between two vectors from the following, for example,

$$\cos V_{ab} = \frac{x_a x_b + y_a y_b + f^2}{\left| r_a \right| \cdot \left| r_b \right|} \qquad (4.46)$$

where $\left| r_a \right|$ and $\left| r_b \right|$ are the absolute values of the corresponding vectors, i.e.

$$\left| r_a \right| = (x_a^2 + y_a^2 + f^2)^{1/2} \qquad \text{and} \qquad \left| r_b \right| = (x_b^2 + y_b^2 + f^2)^{1/2}$$

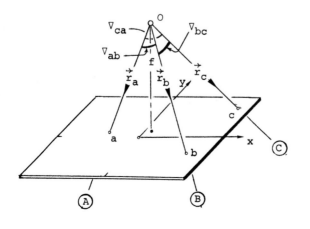

Fig. 4.7

Angular configuration
at perspective center

Similar expressions can be written for $\cos\nabla_{bc}$ and $\cos\nabla_{ca}$.

All parameters in Eqs 4.46 are known, either from camera calibration (f), or from observations (x, y photo coordinates; refined in view of various known distorsion corrections). With regard to the corresponding location vectors for the object points, considering coordinates in the object space,

$$\cos\nabla_{ab} = \cos\nabla_{AB}$$

$$= \frac{(X_A - X_o)(X_B - X_o) + (Y_A - Y_o)(Y_B - Y_o) + (Z_A - Z_o)(Z_B - Z_o)}{\left|R_A\right| \cdot \left|R_B\right|} \tag{4.47}$$

where $\left|R_A\right| = [(X_A - X_o)^2 + (Y_A - Y_o)^2 + (Z_A - Z_o)^2]^{1/2}$

and $\left|R_B\right| = [(X_B - X_o)^2 + (Y_B - Y_o)^2 + (Z_B - Z_o)^2]^{1/2}$.

Similar expressions can be written for $\cos\nabla_{BC}$ and $\cos\nabla_{CA}$ also. Depending on the circumstances, the angular relationship between the camera and object spaces can be utilized to solve various problems. One case is that of space resection where X_o, Y_o, Z_o coordinates of the perspective center are to be determined (Section 6.1.3). Another typical case is its application in camera calibration where all coordinates in the object space may be known but the camera focal length (f) and the associated lens distortion affecting observed photo coordinates are to be determined.

It may be pertinent to comment here on the relationship between the corresponding location vectors in the camera and object spaces, viz.,

$$\vec{r}_a = \lambda_a \cdot \vec{R}_A \; ; \; \vec{r}_b = \lambda_b \cdot \vec{R}_B \text{ and } \vec{r}_c = \lambda_c \cdot \vec{R}_C \tag{4.48}$$

where λ_a, λ_b and λ_c are scalar multipliers (scale factors) which are different, but have the same value only if the terrain is perfectly flat and if the photo plane is parallel to the other plane (i.e., no camera tilt).

Another form of Eq. 4.47 can be obtained by inserting the direction cosines for respective directions. For example, with regard to points A and B, Eq. 4.47 can be written as follows (cf. α, β and γ in Fig. 4.2)

$$\cos\nabla_{AB} = \cos\alpha_A \cos\alpha_B + \cos\beta_A \cos\beta_B + \cos\gamma_A \cos\gamma_B . \tag{4.49}$$

Similar amplifications can be made with respect to the camera space also.

4.5 CRITICAL GEOMETRY

The concept of critical geometry has one-, two- or three-dimensional implications in photogrammetry. One very well-known two-dimensional analogy is obtained from the problem of planimetric resection in surveying where if the observer's station (unknown) falls on a circle passing through three or more known stations, the solution for the observer's station is indeterminable. This is known as the *critical circle*. Such critical geometric circumstances may arise in photogrammetry even with an added spatial dimension and are known as *critical surfaces*.

Mathematically speaking, a critical condition arises when there exist dependent variables indicating correlations.

Note: *Mathematical dependency*: A matrix $Y = c_1 X_1 + c_2 X_2 + \ldots + c_m X_m$ is said to be a linear combination of the m matrices X_1, X_2, $\ldots X_m$ of the same order, where c_1, $c_2 \ldots c_m$ are scalars. If a linear combination, in which not all scalars are zero, is equal to the null matrix, then the matrices are said to be "linearly dependent", (see Faddeeva, 1959), i.e., when

$$c_1 X_1 + c_2 X_2 + \ldots + c_m X_m = \bar{0}$$

The significance of such linear dependency can be studied from a simple example of a set of linearized condition equations for two parameters:

$$[a_1 \ a_2 \ \ldots \ a_m]^T \cdot \delta X + [b_1 \ b_2 \ \ldots \ b_m]^T \cdot \delta Y = [c_1 \ c_2 \ \ldots \ c_m]^T \qquad (4.50)$$

A solution of these equations is possible by an arbitrary choice of one of the values (say, δX). A consistent solution of all equations is possible then by one appropriate but correspondingly incorrect value for δY. Therefore, a check in this respect for such dependencies will be of worthwhile significance. One such test would be provided through an analysis of $\dot{B}$ matrix for linearly dependent columns. In this respect, the Normal Equations provide a means for isolating critical geometries also. Consider, e.g., the above two-parameter problem. Assuming that normal equations are formed (X being the solution vector and U being the constant vector),

$$NX + U = \bar{0} \qquad (4.51)$$

Using Gaussian notations, $|N| = \begin{bmatrix} \Sigma aa & \Sigma ab \\ \Sigma ba & \Sigma bb \end{bmatrix}$

The test for singularity of N is: $|N| = 0$, in which case no solution of the normal equations is possible because N^{-1} is not defined. However, considering $ka = b$, where k is a scalar, one gets

$$|N| = (\Sigma aa)(\Sigma bb) - (\Sigma ab)(\Sigma ba) = (\Sigma aa)k^2(\Sigma aa) - (\Sigma aa)k(\Sigma aa)k = \bar{0} \quad (4.52)$$

Therefore, $|N|$ is singular for linearly dependent (condition) equations. Several representative examples are given below as illustrations.

A. *Single photo case (one-dimensional implication)*

Consider a vertical photo taken on a flat terrain, where the focal length (f) and the flying height (h) above ground, both, are not known. It would be apparent from Fig. 4.8 that if the same photo can be considered with respect to two different locations of the perspectibe center (O' and O"), and accordingly, two different focal lengths (f' and f") would correspond with two different flying heights (h' and h"). The perspective geometry would be maintained to give direct one-to-one correspondence between all points on each location of the photo and their respective ground locations. This indicates a correlation between f and h and indicates a direct dependency, f/h being a constant. The correct value of one of the two would remain indeterminable without the knowledge of the other. On the other hand, in so far as the 2D photo- or ground- coordinates are concerned, this correlation situation has no effect, f/h being the constant scale factor.

From the point of view of mathematical considerations, consider here the application of the collinearity condition (general projective) equation in the partial differential form giving the B matrix (i.e., the total array or partials with respect to unknown parameters). Since the photo is vertical, $\omega = \varphi = k = 0$. The flying height h corresponds to $(Z-Z_o)$. In this case, the elements of the B matrix are as in Table 4.2. The terrain being flat, $(Z-Z_o)$ is a constant. Table 4.2 indicates a strong correlation between f and $(Z-Z_o)$ to involve the factor $f/(Z - Z_o)$, a scalar multiple, whereby it will not be possible to separate x_o, y_o and f from X_o, Y_o and Z_o, respectively. In case the terrain is flat yet sloping, it may not change the fundamental geometry problem; however in this case the tilt (ω) may be considered to be exchanged for the slope and then $\omega \neq 0$), hence some correlations are avoidable. This demonstrates a fundamental problem in calibrating a camera with photographs taken over a test area of flat terrain. Part of the problem is avoided by tilting the camera heavily, but the best would be to use for the test range a terrain where $(Z - Z_o)$ is not constant since f remains a constant with a photogrammetric camera.

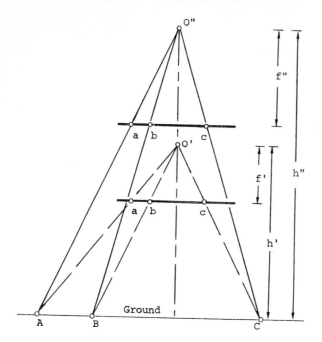

Fig. 4.8

Correlation between
focal length   and
flying height

Table 4.2

Elements of the coefficient matrix, B , of parameters

(Single photo resection)

	x_o	y_o	f	X_o	Y_o	Z_o
$f(x)$	-1	0	$\dfrac{(X - X_o)}{(Z - Z_o)}$	$\dfrac{f}{(Z - Z_o)}$	0	$-f\,\dfrac{(X - X_o)}{(Z - Z_o)^2}$
$f(y)$	0	-1	$\dfrac{(Y - Y_o)}{(Z - Z_o)}$	0	$\dfrac{f}{(Z - Z_o)}$	$-f\,\dfrac{(Y - Y_o)}{(Z - Z_o)^2}$

B.   *Arrangement of fiducial marks (two-dimensional implication)*

In one experiment on the use of additional fiducial marks towards improved
accuracy (McIntosh, 1972), the arrangement of eight fiducial marks was as in Fig.
4.9(a). Considering all significant terms, the resulting equations were:

$$\Delta x = a_0 + a_1 x + a_2 y + a_3 x^2 + a_4 y^2 + a_5 xy + a_6 x^2 y + a_7 xy^2 \left.\right\}$$

$$\Delta y = b_0 + b_1 x + b_2 y + b_3 x^2 + b_4 y^2 + b_5 xy + b_6 x^2 y + b_7 xy^2 \left.\right\}$$

where Δx, Δy are the differences between the 'known' x, y and the 'observed' x, y values.

and   a's and b's are the instrumental constants (coefficients).

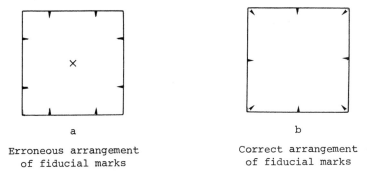

a

Erroneous arrangement
of fiducial marks

b

Correct arrangement
of fiducial marks

Fig. 4.9 Studies in arrangement of fiducial marks in excess

In this case, the least squares solution yielded a standard deviation of 122 μm which was considered unacceptable as the system was known to be capable of giving a standard deviation of $\simeq$ 2 μm. An analysis of the N^{-1} matrix in the adjustment revealed strong correlations, and thus proved to be unreliable due to instability. The cause of this was discovered to be that the fiducial points were on or nearly close to a circle with the origin at the center. This situation establishes the relationship $x^2 + y^2 = R^2$. Furthermore, in this case obviously, R^2 is a constant and establishes a dependency of terms. Such a problem could be avoided by one or both of the following two ways:

i) Consider the arrangement of fiducial marks as in Fig. 4.9 (b) such that they do not fall on the critical circle.

ii) Consider a ninth point (say, the centroid of all the eight points, indicated by a cross in Fig. 4.9 (a) and use this extra point in the least squares adjustment procedure.

C. *Relative Orientation (three-dimensional implication)*

Consider a dependent relative orientation (coplanarity condition) by using the elements of the right hand side camera expressed by

$$Py - dby_{II} + \frac{Y}{Z}dbz_{II} + Z(1 + \frac{Y^2}{Z^2})d\omega_{II} - \frac{(X - b)Y}{Z}d\varphi_{II} - (X - b)dk_{II} = 0$$

A solution of this equation requires Py (Y-parallax) observations at five points. There may arise a situation when the equations cannot be solved because of a constant ratio between at least two of the elements. Consider a point b (Fig. 4.10) in the middle of the model such that $Y_b = 0$ and $Z_b = Z_o$. For a point c at

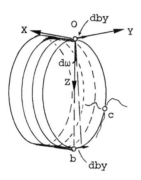

Fig. 4.10

Critical geometry

in a stereo-model

the edge of model, $Y_c = Y$ and $Z_c = Z$. Then with respect to the coefficient of dω, considering points b and c, we get:

$$Z_o = Z(1 + \frac{Y^2}{Z^2}) \text{ i.e., } Y^2 = Z_o Z - Z^2,$$

which is the equation of a circle in the Y-Z plane. The movement for the element by is applied at the perspective center (O) where Y = Z = 0 and this by-movement is in a direction tangential to a circle passing through points b, c and O on the Y-Z plane. If the terrain is formed in such sectional profiles containing circles, one would have a critical geometry with correlation between the elements dby and dω. The meaning of this critical geometry is that a parallax-free model surface can be obtained in such a situation without being able to correctly solve for elements (i.e., at the stereo-instrument, without being able to correctly set the particular elements). Thus, in such a case, the relative orientation is indeterminable. Such a sectional profile may extend into a critical surface for the stereo-model. Furthermore, such a surface may degenerate into a critical cylinder or a critical cone. For further interesting ideas on such surfaces, see Ghosh (1972). Real critical surfaces in nature are rare. However, a closeness to a critical surface may affect accuracy and should be avoided (see Brandenberger, 1947) with proper prior planning of the job, or certain possible manipulations during the process.

BIBLIOGRAPHY

American Society of Photogrammetry; *Manual of photogrammetry* (4th Ed.), (ASPRS,
    Fall Church, Virginia: 1980).

Brandenberger, A. J.; *Fehlertheorie der äusseren Orientierung von Steilaufnahmen*
    (Diss., ETH, Zürich: 1947).

Church, E. and A. Quinn; *Elements of Photogrammetry* (Syracuse University Press,
    Syracuse, N. Y.: 1944).

Coxeter, H. S. M.; *Introduction to Geometry* (John Wiley & Sons, Inc.: 1969).

Eshbach, O. W.; *Handbook of Engineering Fundamentals* (2nd Ed.) (John Wiley & Sons,
    Inc.: 1959).

Faddeeva. V. N.; *Computational Methods of Linear Algebra* (Dover Publications, Inc.:
    1959).

Ghosh, Sanjib K.; *Theory of Stereophotogrammetry* (2nd Ed) (Ohio State University
    Bookstores, Columbus, Ohio: 1972).

Ghosh, Sanjib K.; *Phototriangulation* (Lexington Books, Lexington, Mass: 1975).

Harris, W. D., G. C. Tewinkel and C. A. Whitten; *Analytic Aerotriangulation*;
    (Technical Bulletin No. 21, Corrected, U.S. Dept. of Commerce, C & GS: 1963).

Hirvonen, R. A.; *Adjustment by Least Squares* (F. Unger Publishing Co. N.Y.: 1971).

McIntosh, Bernard W., *Investigation of Aerial Film distortion Compensation
    Techniques Based on Fiducial Marks* (M.Sc. Thesis, Ohio State University: 1972).

Mikhail, E. M.; *Observations and Least Squares* (IEP-A Dun-Donnelley Publisher,
    N. Y.: 1976).

Pope, A. J.; *Some Pitfalls to be Avoided in the Iterative Adjustments of Nonlinear
    Problems* (Presented paper at annual convention, ASP: 1972).

Schut, G. H.; *An Introduction to Analytical Strip Triangulation With a Fortran
    Program* (Revised Ed) (NRC, Canada, Division of Physics, Publication No. NRC
    13148; Ottawa, Canada: 1973).

5

REFINEMENT OF PHOTO COORDINATES

At a photogrammetric measuring instrument the location of an image point is measured in a rectangular 2-D coordinate system having ranges in both directions which are sufficiently large to cover the entire photograph. The origin of this, instrument coordinate system, may be outside the photograph and, depending on the initial settings, is arbitrarily located.

Most of the analytical procedures require the photo coordinates with the *Principal* P*oint* as the origin. Therefore, such photo coordinates are to be obtained by subtracting the 'instrument coordinates' of the principal point from those of the image points. Various principal points used in practice may be noted (see also ASPRS Manual of Photogrammetry, 1980):

1. *Principal Point (photogrammetry):* The foot of the perpendicular from the interior perspective center to the plane of the photograph.

2. *Principal Point (optics):* The point on the optical axis where it intersects the principal plane (from principles of optics).

3. *Principal Point of Autocollimation:* The point where a ray which in the object space is perpendicular to the plane of the photograph intersects that plane (used by NRC, Cnada).

4. *Principal Point of Symmetry:* The point in the focal plane of the camera about which all lens distortions are symmetrical.

112

Usually, the principal point cannot be measured directly because it is not on the photogapah. Furthermore, the photographic coordinates need to be established in a system of reference, which is provided by the *fiducial marks*. The coordinates of the principal point are derived from those of the *fiducial center* (in the fiducial axes system) by way of using the camere calibration data. In practice, however, the fiducial center and the principal point are usually considered to be identical.

Corrections for comparator calibration effect (see Chap. 2) and for the réseau (discussed in Section 5.6) are to be applied before any other corrections due to all external influences are considered. Usually, these are contained in the transformation equations used for the reduction of the photo coordinates. The errors due to the approximations in the mathematical models applied at various stages may be significant at times. The physical sources inherent in the system are discussed in this chapter. Analogically applied corrections and the computational refinement of data should give appreciably correct photo coordinates. It is imperative that these corrections are applied sequentially in the order reverse to that of their occurrence during the data acquisition procedure.

5.1 EMULSION CARRIER

The emulsion and its carrier (film or glass) may be subjected to dimensional distortions, which are functions of the material, environment (e.g., temperature and humidity), aging and treatment (e.g., chemical processing). The effect may sometimes be complicated. Such dimensional distortions can be of three categories:

A. *Uniform (systematic) distortion:*

Shrinkage or expansion of uniform nature would produce a scale error, $d\ell/\ell$ = a constant, for a length ℓ measured on the photograph (see Fig. 5.1) in any direction. Such a distortion may be considered, for the sake of corrections, being radial from any point on the photo (say, the fiducial center). In the absence of a register glass with grid (réseau), measurement of the fiducial marks can give an indication of the distortion. The observed distances between such marks are compared with the corresponding true distances (obtained from the calibration information). This can be applied as a scale correction to all the observed coordinates.

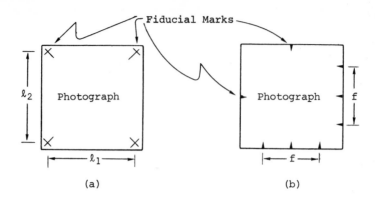

Fig. 5.1 Dimensional distortion checks in a photograph

B. *Differential (systemetic distortion):*

One may often notice one systematic distortion along the length of the film and
a different systematic distortion along the width of the film (note ℓ_1 and ℓ_2 in
Fig. 5.1), giving an affine deformation of the photograph. This can be compensated
by performing an affine transformation of the photocoordinates (see Section 3.3).
Unfortunately, most cameras have only four fiducial marks. That is not sufficient
for determination of non-linear dimensional distortion over the whole area of the
photograph. Additional fiducial marks (e.g., combining the patterns in Figs 5.1a
and 5.1b) or réseau photography are other possible answers to such a problem.

C. *Irregular (systematic) distortion:*

This may affect the photo-coordinates, being effected by various causes, e.g.,
varying elastic properties of the material, lack of flatness of the emulsion
surface or localized emulsion creep. Such errors can be complex and do not follow
any linear distribution pattern. These errors can be minimized only by using
réseau photography.

In using four fiducial marks and considering systematic distortions, the
effects can be compensated by using correction equations (after Keller and
Tewinkel, 1965) as below:

$$x' = x + a_1 + b_1 x + c_1 y + d_1 xy \left.\vphantom{\begin{matrix}1\\1\\1\end{matrix}}\right\}$$
$$y' = y + a_2 + b_2 x + c_2 y + d_2 xy$$

$$(5.1)$$

where x', y' are the corrected photo coordinates;

x , y are the observed photo coordinates;

and a's, d's are certain coefficients, to be determined.

These coefficients can correct for several effects at the same time, viz., provide the translations to the origin (a_1, a_2); accomplish rotation and affine scale-corrections (b_1, b_2, c_1, c_2); and provide a quadratic or curvilinear correction (d_1, d_2) for film (i.e., emulsion base) distortion.

In this connection, it will be good to notice that it is necassary for precision mensural work to have the image surface (surface of emulsion) absolutely flat. Lack of flatness may cause unsharpness or deviation or both. This, however, does not pose any great problem in the observational work if the instrument has an orthogonal (to the image surface) viewing. Furthermore, image unsharpness caused by movement of the camera during exposure (i.e., image smear) and the image quality parameters of the system (e.g., limiting resolving power) can be two causes of concern sometimes. While the former can be compensated by an appropriate Image Motion Compensation (IMC) device in the camera, the latter imposes limitation to the photogrammetric procedure. The difference in the sharpness of the two conjugate images comprising the stereoscopic model may contribute towards irregular pointing accuracies in the model. In jobs demanding very high precision, one has to consider all such factors very carefully.

5.2 LENS (OBJECTIVE) DISTORTION

All lenses in use now-a-days have measurable distortions and other optical defects (aberrations). The aberrations (viz., spherical and chromatic aberrations, coma, astigmatism and curvature of field) degrade the quality or the sharpness of image. Lens distortion, on the other hand, causes displacement of the image, which is unfavorable to precision measurements. It can have *radial* and *tangential* components. It is essential, therefore, that all camera objectives (lenses) be tested (calibrated) carefully. The *camera calibration* procedure determines the focal-length, the location of the principal point and all distortion parameters.

5.2.1 Radial Distortion

One must first assure the use of the intended principal point. The center of the perspective bundle of rays in the image space is considered along the perpendicular at the assumed principal point and at a distance equal to the calibrated focal length (f) from the photo plane. Let α be the field angle made by a ray with the perpendicular and let r be the distance of the image point from the principal point (Fig. 5.2). The radial distortion Δr is the radial distance between the actual and the ideal locations of the image point. This can be expressed by

$$\Delta r = r - f \cdot \tan\alpha \qquad (5.2)$$

Eq. 5.2 shows that the radial distortion is a function of the assumed value of the focal length. In practice, one determines that the value of the focal-length which makes the maximum difference between the values of the radial distortion and the standard reference values for the lens as small as possible. In case the reference values for the camera are not available, one determines that value of the focal length which makes the maximum value of the distortion as small as possible (by balancing the positive and the negative maximum values of Δr). This value is known as the Calibrated Focal Length. Consider the aberrations (Klein, 1970) and the following genaral hypotheses (after Conrady, 1919 and Washer, 1957):

    a.   The axial ray passes undeviated through the lens;

    b.   The distortion can be represented by a continuous function; and

    c.   The sense of the distortion should be positive for all outward displacement of the image.

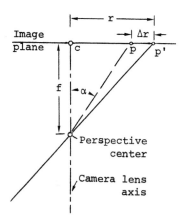

Fig. 5.2

Radial lens distortion

Accordingly, the following polynomial may be considered to approximate the radial lens distortion curve:

$$\Delta r = a_0 r + a_1 r^3 + a_2 r^5 + a_3 r^7 + a_4 r^9 + \ldots \qquad (5.3)$$

The 'a' coefficients define the shape of the curve. They may be
least squares curve fitting computation during the camera ca
The radial distortion is considered in terms of two componer

5.3). The radial distance (r) being equal to $\sqrt{(x^2 + y^2)}$
components are related to each other as follows:

$$\frac{\Delta r}{r} = \frac{\Delta x}{x} = \frac{\Delta y}{y}$$

The corrected photo coordinates (x', y') are given by

$$\left. \begin{array}{l} x' = x - \Delta x = x\left\{1 - \frac{\Delta r}{r}\right\} = x(1 - a_0 - a_1 r^2 - a_2 r^4 - \cdots) \\[2ex] y' = y - \Delta y = y\left\{1 - \frac{\Delta r}{r}\right\} = y(1 - a_0 - a_1 r^2 - a_2 r^4 - \cdots) \end{array} \right\} \quad (5.5)$$

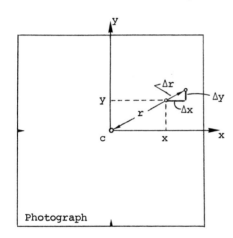

Fig. 5.3

Components of radial distortion

In using Eqs 5.5, at least five to six terms in the series can be taken to
express the correction adequately. In some organizations (see Harris et al. 1962),
such uniform lens distortion is corrected along with that for atmospheric
refraction through the use of Eqs 5.6, in which the terms k_1 and k_2 relate to
atmospheric refraction (see also Section 5.3):

$$\left. \begin{array}{l} x' = x\left\{1 + \frac{rd}{r^2} + k_1 + k_2 r^2\right\} \\[2ex] y' = y\left\{1 + \frac{rd}{r^2} + k_1 + k_2 r^2\right\} \end{array} \right\} \quad (5.6)$$

The value rd is obtained in the computer from tabulated values and interpolation based on r^2 as the independent argument as in Eqs 5.5. It may be recommended that the numerical precision of such data should be better than the precision obtainable from the consideration of the distortion alone. This is generally of the order of 0.1 μm with modern photogrammetric systems.

5.2.2 Decentering Distortion

This is due to imperfect centering of the lens components and other manufacturing defects in a compound lens. The consequences, occurring in many lenses, is roughly equal to the effect of adding a small prism to the lens. As a result, the distortion is asymmetric with respect to the principal point of autocollimation and the resulting effect is called *Tangential Distortion*. There is, however, always one radial line (called the axis of zero tangential distortion), which remains straight. Washer (1957) called it *Prism Effect*. The distortion can be referred to a different principal point. This implies that the center of the perspective bundle in the image space is shifted. As a result of this shift (also involving a rotation), the pattern of the distortion in the photo plane is changed. With narrow projective bundles, this shift of the principal point is very nearly the projective equivalent of a small tilt of the camera axis. This distortion pattern can be expressed (according to Brown, 1966; after Conrady, 1919) as below:

$$\Delta x = \{ P_1(r^2 + 2x^2) + 2P_2 xy \} \{1 + P_3 r^2 + P_4 r^4 + \ldots \}$$

$$\Delta y = \{ 2P_1 xy + P_2(r^2 + 2y^2) \} \{1 + P_3 r^2 + P_4 r^4 + \ldots \}$$

$$(5.7)$$

where $P_1 = -J_1 \cdot \sin\varphi_0$

$P_2 = J_1 \cdot \cos\varphi_0$

$P_3 = J_2 / J_1$

$P_4 = J_3 / J_4$

$\cdot$
$\cdot$
$\cdot$

J_1, J_2 etc. are the coefficients of the profile function of the decentering distortion.

φ_o is the angle subtended by the axis of maximum tangential distortion with the photo x-axis (see Figs 5.4 and 5.5).

and   P's   represent the tangential profile function, i.e., the tangential distortion at radial distance   r   along axis of maximum tangential distortion.

Decentering distortion can be effectively determined through calibration. But also it can be tolerated to the extent that it does not affect the accuracy to any considerable extent.

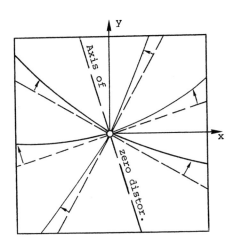

Fig. 5.4

Tangential distortion

pattern

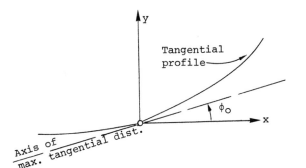

Fig. 5.5

Geometric significance

of tangential distortion

If one considers the shift and rotation (due to decentering distortion) made in such a way that the asymmetries in the radial distortion become as small as possible, the new principal point is called the principal point of best symmetry. If a shift of the perspective center parallel to a radial direction is $\underline{a}_1$, the rotation associated to it is $\underline{a}_1/f$, and the shift perpendicular to the plane of the photo is $\underline{a}_2$ (Fig. 5.6), the resulting radial shift of the point of intersection of a ray and the radial is

$$
dr = \underline{a}_1 - \frac{r^2 + f^2}{f^2}\,\underline{a}_1 + \frac{r}{f}\,\underline{a}_2 = \frac{r^2}{f^2}\,\underline{a}_1 + \frac{r}{f}\underline{a}_2 \tag{5.8}
$$

For two points at equal distances on opposite sides of the principal point, the shifts (dr) must cancel the radial distortions valid for the principal point of autocollimation. By definition, the radial distance (r) is always positive, while the radial distortion (dr) is positive in the direction away from the principal point. Therefore, for two such points (on opposite sides of the principal point), the required radial shifts dr_1 and $-dr_2$ give, by using Eq. 5.8:

$$
\left.
\begin{aligned}
dr_1 - dr_2 &= -2\,\frac{r^2}{f^2}\,\underline{a}_1 \\[2ex]
dr_1 + dr_2 &= 2\,\frac{r}{f}\,\underline{a}_2
\end{aligned}
\right\} \tag{5.9}
$$

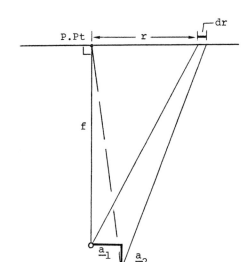

Fig. 5.6

Effect of change
in the choice of principal point
on radial distortion

The shifts $\underline{a}_1$ and $\underline{a}_2$ can thus be computed for each pair of radial distortions at equal distances on opposite sides of the principal point. The computation of the shifts can be performed for numerous point pairs on the two principal diagonals of the photo by using Eqs 5.9. This would help obtain the location of the principal point of best symmetry with regard to the previously used principal point. With most modern cameras, such shifts are seldom >10 μm. Some organizations (e.g., the National Research Council of Canada) maintain computer programs to provide such corrections.

The nature of asymmetry of radial distortion being complex, generally no effort is made in practice to compensate for the irregular part of such errors. This is particularly true of the tangential distortion, which is seldom more that one seventh of the radial distortion at the same point.

5.3 ATMOSPHERIC REFRACTION

5.3.1 Vertical Photography

On its path from the ground to the camera, a light ray passes through air of decreasing density. This causes a continuous bending of the ray due to refraction. It is a function of the refractive index of the air at all the points along the ray path. The refractive index depends on temperature, pressure and composition (humidity, dust, carbon-dioxide, etc.) of the atmosphere. Since these quantities cannot be measured along the entire ray, it is customary to generalize the path (see Fig. 5.7). The radial displacement (dr) corresponds to the angular deviation (ψ) of the ray path.

The light ray from the ground point (P) reaches the lens (at 0) as it passes through the atmosphere, which may be considered to be composed of numerous layers of refractive indices decreasing from the ground upwards. Between any two such successive layers, the angles of incidence and refraction are β_i and $\beta_i+d\alpha$, respectively. Their refractive indices are n_i+d_n and n_i, respectively (along the upward direction). According to the law of refraction,

$$(n_i + d_n) \cdot \sin\beta_i = n_i \cdot \sin(\beta_i + d\alpha).$$

The angle $d\alpha$ being very small, this gives, after appropriate generalization and simplification,

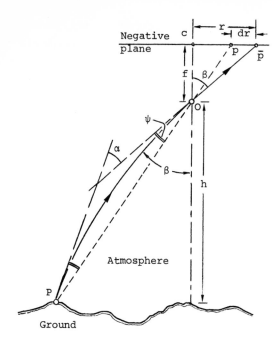

Fig. 5.7

Atmospheric refraction

in vertical aerial photography

$$d\alpha = \frac{dn}{n}\,\tan\beta \tag{5.10}$$

By integrating, from Eq. 5.10.

$$\alpha = \int_{\alpha_p}^{\alpha_0} d\alpha = \tan\beta \int_{n_p}^{n_0} \frac{dn}{n} = \tan\beta \cdot \ln(n)\Big|_{n_p}^{n_0} \tag{5.10a}$$

where   ln   indicates natural logarithm;

       0, P (subscripts) refer to the camera station (0) and the ground point (P).

   In view of the generalization,

$$\psi = \alpha/2 = K\cdot\tan\beta = K\cdot\frac{r}{f} \tag{5.11}$$

In these expressions, all variables except β are considered constant for a given photograph and contained in the factor K. Based on the derivations made (Bertram, 1969) with respect to the ARDC Standard atmosphere, for example,

$$K = \frac{1}{H_c - H_g} \left[I(H_c) - I(H_g) \right] - R(H_c) \qquad (5.11a)$$

where H_c and H_g are the camera and ground elevations, respectively;

ρ is the atmospheric density as a function of altitude;

$R = 226\rho;$

and $I(H) = 226 \int_0^H \rho \cdot dH.$

Bertram (1969) gives an example of calculating K, for H_c = 5 km and H_g = 1 km, where he obtains a value of K = 40.4 micro-radians. Using an abbreviated table and ρ for the ARDC Standard atmosphere (after Minzner et al, 1959), one gets the following values, for example:

H (km)	ρ	R	I
0	1.225	276.8	0
1	1.112	251.3	264.0
3	0.909	205.4	719.9
5	0.736	166.3	1090.8

Furthermore, the radial displacement (dr) of the image point is

$$dr = f \cdot \sec^2 \beta \cdot \psi$$

This gives, from aforementioned considerations,

$$dr = \frac{(r^2 + f^2)r}{2f^2} \left[\ln(n_0) - \ln(np) \right] \qquad (5.12)$$

where   r   is the radial distance of the point from photo center;
and   f   is the focal length of camera.
Note: The refractive index at any point in the atmosphere is given by

$$n = 1 + \frac{(n' - 1) B}{(1 + ta)760}$$

where   n' is the refractive index at 0°C temperature and 760 mm air pressure, and n' = 1.0002926;

a   is the expansion coefficient of air due to temperature;

t   is the temperature (in °C) at the location in question;

and   B   is the air pressure (in mm of mercury) at the location in question.

In normal practice, one of the various standard atmospheres is assumed, e.g.,

1.   The US Standard Atmosphere, 1962; of the US Committee on Extension to the Standard Atmosphere (obtainable from the US Government Printing Office);

2.   The ARDC Standard Atmosphere, 1959 (see Minzner et al, 1959); or

3.   The ICAO Standard Atmosphere, 1952 (see NASA Report 1235, 1955).

These three atmospheres are practically the same upto about 20 km height. In view of a standard atmosphere, a particular flying height and a particular focal-length, Eq. 5.12 can be simplified into a power series:

$$dr = k_1 r + k_2 r^3 + k_3 r^5 + \dots \qquad (5.12a)$$

where k_1, k_2, etc. are certain constants. In practice, the series is considered upto two terms (see Harris et al, 1962). dr, k_1 and k_2 can be pretabulated for a standard atmosphere with respect to the particular camera. A brief example, after Harris et al (1962) is given in Table 5.1.

The x and y components of such radial displacement (dr) are often obtained and applied as corrections to the photo coordinates along with the uniform radial lens distortion as indicated in Eqs 5.6.

5.3.2 Tilted Photography

If the camera is tilted, the image displacement due to refraction is different from that of the vertical case. The difference is maximum along the direction of the greatest tilt. Table 5.2 (after Schut, 1969) gives refraction errors for an exactly vertical photo and those along the direction of greatest tilt for a tilt of 2°. This table demonstrates that the error due to neglecting the tilt of an aerial photograph may, in practice, be negligibly small. Schut (1969) noted that the positional errors introduced by 'real' (as against 'standard') atmosphere can differ upto 10 per cent from those calculated with regard to a standard atmosphere. This, however, is a negligible quantity because of the small size of the refraction error itself.

Table 5.1

Radial image distortion due to atmospheric refraction (dr in μm
for a focal length of 153 mm and ICAO standard atmosphere;
after Harris et al, 1962)

Flying Ht in m	For Radial Distance r of Image Point from photo center, in mm									Coefficients	
	12	24	50	63	78	94	111	131	153	$k_1 \cdot 10^{-2}$	$k_2 \cdot 10^{-6}$
For ground elevation - 0 m above sea level											
3000	0.4	0.9	1.9	2.6	3.4	4.5	5.9	7.9	10.7	3.4	1.53
6000	0.7	1.5	3.3	4.4	5.9	7.7	10.1	13.5	18.3	6.1	2.50
9000	0.9	1.9	4.2	5.7	7.5	9.9	13.0	17.3	23.4	7.7	3.23
For ground elevation - 500 m above sea level											
3000	0.3	0.7	1.6	2.1	2.8	3.7	4.9	6.4	8.8	2.8	1.25
6000	0.7	1.3	3.0	4.0	5.3	6.9	9.1	12.2	15.4	5.4	2.30
9000	0.9	1.8	3.9	5.3	7.0	9.2	12.0	16.0	21.7	7.2	2.99
For ground elevation - 1000 m above sea level											
3000	0.3	0.6	1.3	1.7	2.2	2.9	3.9	5.1	6.9	2.2	0.99
6000	0.6	1.2	2.7	3.6	4.8	6.3	8.2	10.9	14.5	4.8	2.08
9000	0.8	1.6	3.6	4.9	6.5	8.5	11.2	14.9	20.1	6.7	2.76
For ground elevation - 1500 m above sea level											
3000	0.2	0.4	0.8	1.2	1.6	2.2	2.8	3.8	5.1	1.6	0.74
6000	0.5	1.1	2.4	3.2	4.2	5.5	7.3	9.7	13.1	4.2	1.87
9000	0.7	1.5	3.4	4.5	6.0	7.8	10.3	13.8	18.6	6.1	2.59

Interesting ideas on various aspects of refraction have been presented by numerous researchers, for example, Bertram (1966), Leijonhufvud (1953) and Saastamoinen (1972 and 1974).

In the case of excessive tilt, the consideration of atmospheric refraction as in a vertical photograph may not be adequately valid. Consideration of a fictious Instantaneous Equivalent Vertical Photograph (IEVP) would conveniently adapt to

Table 5.2

Radial atmospheric refraction errors in tilted photographs

(values in μm, after Schut, 1969)

Field Angle from camera axis	Standard Angle Camera Focal length: 152.4 mm Flying height: 6000 m		Super Wide Angle Camera Focal length: 88.2 mm Flying height: 6000 m	
	Tilt 0°	Tilt 2°$_{max}$	Tilt 0°	Tilt 2°$_{max}$
9°	1.5	1.8	0.9	1.0
18°	3.2	3.6	1.9	2.1
27°	5.7	6.2	3.3	3.6
36°	9.9	10.7	5.7	6.2
45°	17.9	19.2	10.4	11.1
59°	-	-	32.5	35.2

existing computer programs for such cases. The rotation matrix (M, see Chap.4) is assumed to have been known with some approximation, e.g., from a previous cycle of adjustment (or, iteration). The photo coordinates of the points in the 'real' photograph are projected to the IEVP by considering a unit focal length by way of utilizing Eqs 5.13.

$$
\left.
\begin{aligned}
x_F &= f' \frac{a_{11}x + a_{21}y + a_{31}f}{a_{13}x + a_{23}y + a_{33}f} \\
\\
y_F &= f' \frac{a_{12}x + a_{22}y + a_{32}f}{a_{13}x + a_{23}y + a_{33}f}
\end{aligned}
\right\}
\qquad (5.13)
$$

where x_F and y_F are the photo coordinates on the IEVP (by considering f' = 1)

x, y and f   refer to the real photograph;

and   the "a"   elements refer to the inverse of the orientation matrix for the real photo.

The coordinates of the IEVP may now be refined as with vertical photos to correct for the effects of atmospheric refraction. The final step then is to project from the IEVP back to the real (tilted) photo plane, also recognizing that f' = 1.

5.4 EARTH CURVATURE

If the photogrammetric work is performed in a rectangular three-dimensional coordinate system (e.g., universal geocentric or local space rectangular), the earth curvature effect as a contributing distortion does not exist. If conditions permit, this approach is to be preferred. If, however, the work is performed in a geodetic reference system or a plane coordinate system with respect to a reference surface, it may then be necessary to account for image distortion (apparent) caused by the curvature of the earth.

The aerial photograph is a central projection on a plane, but the points on the earth's surface are referenced to one or the other of the following reference surfaces:

Geoid: By definition, every point on the geoid is horizontal. Spirit leveling refers to the geoid.

Reference Ellipsoid: A regular ellipsoid of revolution; different ellipsoids are considered according to various assumptions.

Earth Sphere: The best fitting sphere, approximated, under various different considered criteria.

None of these reference surfaces can be portrayed by the photograph without any apparent distortion. The correction may be applied either to individual photos or to the stereo-models. While the latter is used traditionally in analogical (instrumental) work, the former may sometimes be more convenient in computational work.

The displacement (ds) due to earth curvature (p'p in Fig. 5.8) is negative by convention, being towards the photograph nadir point (n). Assuming the Earth Sphere, one obtains (see Ghosh, 1975):

$$ds \;=\; \frac{hs^3}{2Rf^2} \;=\; \frac{fs^3}{2Rh^2} \tag{5.14}$$

where h is the flying height above the ground nadir point;
          R is the radius of the earth sphere;
          s is the radial distance of image point from the nadir point on the photo;

S   is the distance of the ground point from the nadir point (N) along
     the earth sphere surface;

and   f   is the focal length of the camera.

The earth curvature displacement being radial with respect to the nadir point,
on a vertical photograph this correction may be added to the corrections due to the
radial lens distortion and atmospheric refraction.   Earth curvature correction, by
itself, may be of sizable dimension sometimes (see Table 5.3).   In case the photo
is not vertical, this effect may exceed other image errors.

If earth curvature correction is not applied, a strip triangulation will
develop an elevation misclosure corresponding to the difference in elevation
between the curved earth and a plane tangent to the earth at the nadir point of the
first photograph of the strip. Consider, as an example, a standard camera (f = 152
mm; format: 230 x 230 mm) and flying height of 6 km. Points in the corners of the
photograph are 3.2 m below the plane which is tangent to the earth sphere in the
center.   If the strip is 100 km long, points at the end of the strip are 800 m
below this plane. It follows that even for a single photograph this displacement
may not be negligible.   The direct transformation of the strip in such a case would
produce correct map coordinates and elevations only if it is preceded or
accompanied by a deformation of the triangulated strip that is identical with the
deformation in that system.

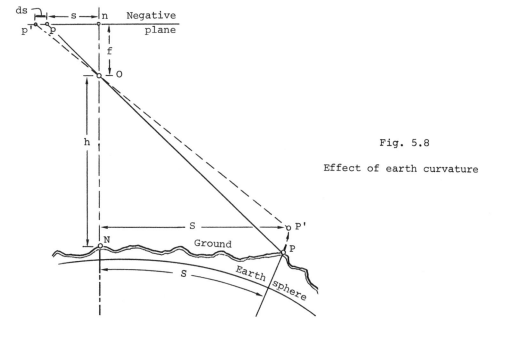

Fig. 5.8

Effect of earth curvature

Table 5.3

Radial displacement due to earth curvature

(Vertical photo, f = 150 mm; values, negative, in μm)

At s (mm)	For Flying Heights in km						
	0.5	1	2	4	6	8	10
10	0	0	0	0	0	0	0
20	0	0	0.1	0.1	0.2	0.2	0.3
40	0.1	0.2	0.4	0.9	1.3	1.8	2.2
60	0.4	0.8	1.5	3.0	4.5	6.0	7.6
80	0.9	1.8	3.6	7.2	10.8	14.3	17.9
100	1.8	3.5	7.0	14.0	21.0	28.0	35.0
120	3.1	6.0	12.1	24.2	36.3	48.4	60.5
140	4.9	9.6	19.2	38.4	57.6	76.8	96.0
160	7.1	14.3	28.6	57.2	85.7	114.3	142.9

5.5 IMAGE MOTION

Image motion of various types has been known to be one primary cause of degradation of the space or air photography (see NASA publication SP-193, 1969). It is most frequent and at the same time most damaging form of distortion likely to appear in images relating to the space exploration. Aircraft (or spacecraft) motion, rotation (roll, pitch or yaw) and vibration during the opening of the camera shutter may cause the image blur. This may result in resolution degradation and displacement of the image point. Camera magazines have been designed to provide film movement during exposure by using the Image Motion Compensation (IMC) device. Since the advent of jet aircrafts and the use of slow-speed, fine-grained, high resolution photographic emulsions, the need for IMC became more profound. As an example, consider vertical photography with a focal length of 152 mm, shutter speed 1/100 sec., aircraft speed of 800 km per hour, and flying height of 12 km. The image smear in this case will be 28 μm in the direction of flight.

There are three basic mothods of accomplishing IMC, viz., (a) By moving the platen-film assembly, (b) By moving the lens cone (tilting) and (c) By using a focal plane shutter. Often the third method is combined with the first or the second. Whereas the first or the second method tends to disturb the interior geometry of the camera system, the third one creates a situation somewhat similar to the strip camera (see Chapter 10), i.e., instead of giving a central perspective of a frame photograph, it represents an infinite number of line photographs with respect to a continously changing perspective center (a locus). Devices such as electro mechanical V/h sensor cam correlator have been successfully used in obtaining comparatively sharp images (e.g., in the Lunar Orbiter Systems, see NASA publication SP-193, 1969); although their intrinsic metric qualities are not yet fully assessed.

The aircraft vibration causes blur of another kind. The vibration can be internal to the camera (because of the required use of various devices associated with the camera) or can be external (due to the vehicle and the various mechanisms of the vehicle). Anti-vibration devices are used but a fully vibration-free system has not been developed.

Optical and photoelectric restoration of the images degraged by atmospheric turbulence have been attempted. The experiments have shown results that show sharp imagery, whose metric quality remains doubtful. In all these attempts, if the type of the error source is known from prior information, the quality of the image can be improved. But the post facto removal of the degradation is yet imperfect and is unworkable for high precision work. Improvements with somewhat successful results have been obtained with both digital and non-digital processing techniques (see, NASA, 1969 publication for details). However, considerable scope exists for further improvements in all these and motion degradation remains as one of the most important areas of concern in space photography. In normal use of vertical aerial photography for medium and large scale mapping, however, in most cases IMC may not be necessary at all. In special cases of high precision works, one may consider the image motion of two kinds, viz., (a) Due to linear motions and (b) Due to rotational motions.

5.5.1 Due to Linear Motions

With a constant flying height, a constant aircraft speed and no rotation of the camera, one may consider the following relations:

Speed of film $= v_F = \dfrac{fV}{h}$ and Speed of image $= v_I = \dfrac{fV}{(h-H)}$

where f is the camera focal length, h is the flying height above datum, H is the height of the ground above datum, and V is the ground speed of the aircraft. From these, the relative speed Δv may obtained,

$$\Delta v = f \cdot V \frac{H}{(h-H)h} \qquad (5.15)$$

If the effective exposure time is t_e, then the blurring (b), contributing an image error in the x direction (but nothing in the y direction) is:

$$\underline{b} = \Delta v \cdot t_e \qquad (5.16)$$

It may be pointed out that the IMC devices are meant to compensate for this kind of image blur in the regular photogrammetric cameras.

5.5.2 Due to Rotational Motions

The image velocities from rotational motions, roll, pitch and yaw (ω, φ and κ) for various cases are as in Table 5.4 (after Kawachi, 1965). One needs first to determine the rotational velocities from available data; next, these values are substituted into the appropriate equations (Table 5.4); next, the image velocity has to be multiplied by exposure time to get the approximate distance of blur due to rotational motions. This procedure assumes that there are no other sources of image motion. The image motion from other sources is often not readily known. In such a case, the loss of resolution, assuming that rotational motions are just the only causes of the blur, is the single information which may be estimated (or computed). Often, this information may be sufficient, because it may show that the rotational motions have either very large or very small effects. Table 5.5, after Kawachi (1965) gives an example of such possibilities.

The above approach, credited to Kawachi (1965), is applicable in refining the photo coordinates data. However, the formulas do not interconnect the image and the object spaces directly, which possibility exists by using the collinearity condition. Therefore, another approach, by the procedure of augmentation of the collinearity condition equation may be considered when a mathematical relationship incorporating direct connection between the object and image spaces is desired.

AP-K

Table 5.4

Image velocity from rotational motions, various cases (after Kawachi, 1965)

Special Case	Velocity from Aircraft		
	Roll Rate	Pitch Rate	Yaw Rate
Vertical Frame Camera	$\dot{x}_\omega = \frac{xy}{f}\dot{\omega}$ $\dot{y}_\omega = \left(\frac{f^2+y^2}{f}\right)\dot{\omega}$	$\dot{x}_\phi = \left(\frac{f^2+x^2}{f}\right)\dot{\phi}$ $\dot{y}_\phi = \frac{xy}{f}\dot{\phi}$	$\dot{x}_\kappa = y\dot{\kappa}$ $\dot{y}_\kappa = x\dot{\kappa}$
Forward Oblique Frame Camera	$\dot{x}_\omega = y\left(\sin\phi - \frac{x}{f}\cos\phi\right)\dot{\omega}$ $\dot{y}_\omega = \left[\left(\frac{f^2+y^2}{f}\right)\cos\phi + x\cdot\sin\phi\right]\dot{\omega}$	$\dot{x}_\phi = \left(\frac{f^2+x^2}{f}\right)\dot{\phi}$ $\dot{y}_\phi = \frac{xy}{f}\dot{\phi}$	$\dot{x}_\kappa = y\left(\cos\phi + \frac{x}{f}\sin\phi\right)\dot{\kappa}$ $\dot{y}_\kappa = \left[\left(\frac{f^2+y^2}{f}\right)\sin\phi - x\cdot\cos\phi\right]\dot{\kappa}$
Side Oblique Frame Camera	$\dot{x}_\omega = \frac{xy}{f}\dot{\omega}$ $\dot{y}_\omega = \left(\frac{f^2+y^2}{f}\right)\dot{\omega}$	$\dot{x}_\phi = \left[\left(\frac{f^2+x^2}{f}\right)\cos\omega + y\cdot\sin\omega\right]\dot{\phi}$ $\dot{y}_\phi = x\left(\sin\omega - \frac{y}{f}\cos\omega\right)\dot{\phi}$	$\dot{x}_\kappa = \left[\left(\frac{f^2+x^2}{f}\right)\sin\omega - y\cdot\cos\omega\right]\dot{\kappa}$ $\dot{y}_\kappa = x\left(\cos\omega + \frac{y}{f}\sin\omega\right)\dot{\kappa}$
Vertical Panoramic Camera	$\dot{x}_\omega = 0$ $\dot{y}_\omega = f\cdot\dot{\omega}$	$\dot{x}_\phi = \left(\frac{f^2+x^2}{f}\right)\cos\theta\cdot\dot{\phi}$ $\dot{y}_\phi = x\cdot\sin\theta\cdot\dot{\phi}$	$\dot{x}_\kappa = \left(\frac{f^2+x^2}{f}\right)\sin\theta\cdot\dot{\kappa}$ $\dot{y}_\kappa = x\cdot\cos\theta\cdot\dot{\kappa}$

Note: The symbols in this table are as follows (dots indicating velocities):

f : camera focal length;

x,y : photo coordinates, along and perpendicular to the flight direction;

ω : angle of roll, positive in the right-side direction;

ϕ : angle of pitch, positive in the forward direction;

κ : angle of yaw, positive in the right-handed sense;

$\dot{\omega},\dot{\phi},\dot{\kappa}$: respective angular velocities in radians per second; and

θ : sweep-angle of panoramic camera, positive in the left-side direction.

Table 5.5

Examples of resolution degradation due to

rotational motions, vertical camera (after Kawachi, 1965)

Focal length	Static resolution	Exposure time	Rotational velocity	Photo coordinates x	Photo coordinates y	Degradation
mm	lines/mm	sec	° per sec	mm	mm	%
152	20	1/500	1	0	0	0.6
			10	0	0	0.6
			10	115	115	50.0
		1/2000	1	0	0	0.0
			10	0	0	4.0

5.5.3 Augmentation of Collinearity Equations

Consider the collinearity condition equations (see Chapter 4) in the following

form:

$$
\left.
\begin{aligned}
x_p - x_o &= -f\left\{M_1(X_p - X_o) \,/\, M_3(X_p - X_o)\right\} \\
y_p - y_o &= -f\left\{M_2(X_p - X_o) \,/\, M_3(X_p - X_o)\right\}
\end{aligned}
\right\}
\qquad (5.17)
$$

where f is the calibrated focal length of the camera;

x_p, y_p are the photo coordinates of a point;

x_o, y_o are the coordinates of the principal point;

M_i is the ith row of the general rotation matrix M;

X_p is a vector of object space coordinates, i.e., $X_p = [X\ Y\ Z]_p^T$;

and X_o is a vector of coordinates representing the perspective center
(camera station), i.e., $X_o = [X\ Y\ Z]_o^T$

In view of a moving camera over a stationary object, photo point 1 is taken at
$X_o = X_o'$ and yields coordinates x_p', y_p' and photo point 2 is taken at $X_o = X_o''$ and

yields coordinates x_p'', y_p'' for the same object point represented by X_p. Assume the camera (photo platform) to move with a three-dimensional velocity V. This will give $X_o'' - X_o' = V \cdot \Delta t$, where Δt is the exposure time responsible for creating the blur. Therefore, altenative expressions for x_p'', y_p'' are:

$$
\left.
\begin{aligned}
x_p'' - x_o &= -f\left[M_1(X_p - X_o' - V\cdot\Delta t) \;/\; M_3(X_p - X_o' - V\cdot\Delta t)\right] \\[2mm]
y_p'' - y_o &= -f\left[M_2(X_p - X_o' - V\cdot\Delta t) \;/\; M_3(X_p - X_o' - V\cdot\Delta t)\right]
\end{aligned}
\right\}
\qquad (5.18)
$$

Then, the displacement of the image causing the blur may be computed as below:

$$
\begin{aligned}
\Delta x = x_p'' - x_p' &= -f\left[M_1(Xp - X_o' - V\cdot\Delta t) \;/\; M_3(Xp - X_o' - V\cdot\Delta t)\right] \\[2mm]
&\quad + f\left[M_1(Xp - X_o') \;/\; M_3(Xp - X_o')\right] \\[3mm]
\Delta y = y_p'' - y_p' &= -f\left[M_2(Xp - X_o' - V\cdot\Delta t) \;/\; M_3(Xp - X_o' - V\cdot\Delta t)\right] \\[2mm]
&\quad + f\left[M_2(Xp - X_o') \;/\; M_3(Xp - X_o')\right]
\end{aligned}
\qquad (5.19)
$$

The image velocities due to the translation of the perspective center can be obtained from the above expressions as

$$
v_x = \Delta x/\Delta t \qquad \text{and} \qquad v_y = \Delta y/\Delta t
\qquad (5.20)
$$

We shall next describe the velocities due to the rotational motions. We know,

$$
M = \begin{bmatrix} M_1 \\ M_2 \\ M_3 \end{bmatrix} = M_\kappa\, M_\varphi\, M_\omega.
$$

The corresponding augmented rotation matrix is

$$
N = M_{(\kappa + \dot\kappa\cdot\Delta t)}\; M_{(\varphi + \dot\varphi\cdot\Delta t)}\; M_{(\omega + \dot\omega\cdot\Delta t)}.
\qquad (5.21)
$$

This, by virtue of the 'double angle' formulas, gives,

$$N = \begin{bmatrix} N_1 \\ N_2 \\ N_3 \end{bmatrix} = M_\kappa \ M_{\dot{\kappa} \cdot \Delta t} \ M_\varphi \ M_{\dot{\varphi} \cdot \Delta t} \ M_\omega \ M_{\dot{\omega} \cdot \Delta t} \qquad (5.22)$$

where $\dot{\kappa}$, $\dot{\varphi}$ and $\dot{\omega}$ are the respective angular velocities in radians per second of time and Δt, as before, is the exposure epoch.

The general expressions for image coordinates of a moving system with respect to a defined epoch are, then,

$$\left.\begin{aligned} x_p - x_o &= -f \left[N_1(X_p - X_o - V \cdot \Delta t) \, / \, N_3(X_p - X_o - V \cdot \Delta t) \right] \\ y_p - y_o &= -f \left[N_2(X_p - X_o - V \cdot \Delta t) \, / \, N_3(X_p - X_o - V \cdot \Delta t) \right] \end{aligned}\right\} \qquad (5.23)$$

In a way similar to Eqs 5.19 obtained from Eqs 5.18 (for the translation case), one can obtain expressions for Δx and Δy, by differentiating which with respect to Δt, one gets the following expressions for the image velocities from rotational motions:

$$\begin{aligned} v_x = \dot{x}_p = -f &\left\{ \left[\dot{N}_1(X_p - X_o - V \cdot \Delta t) - N_1 V \right] \left[N_3(X_p - X_o - V \cdot \Delta t) \right] \right. \\ &\left. - \left[\dot{N}_3(X_p - X_o - V \cdot \Delta t) - N_3 V \right] \left[N_1(X_p - X_o - V \cdot \Delta t) \right] \right\} \\ &\cdot \left[N_3(X_p - X_o - V \cdot \Delta t) \right]^{-2} \\ v_y = \dot{y}_p = -f &\left\{ \left[\dot{N}_2(X_p - X_o - V \cdot \Delta t) - N_2 V \right] \left[N_3(X_p - X_o - V \cdot \Delta t) \right] \right. \\ &\left. - \left[\dot{N}_3(X_p - X_o - V \cdot \Delta t) - N_3 V \right] \left[N_2(X_p - X_o - V \cdot \Delta t) \right] \right\} \\ &\cdot \left[N_3(X_p - X_o - V \cdot \Delta t) \right]^{-2} \end{aligned}$$

where $\dot{N}_1 = dN_1/d\Delta t$; and $\dot{N}_2$, $\dot{N}_3$ are obtained similarly. $\qquad (5.24)$

Equations 5.24 are without restrictions as to the initial orientation of the camera, the terrain ruggedness, the time interval (Δt) or the magnitude of the rates of motion. The only restriction remains in the assumption that the rates are constant. It can be demonstrated by expanding the N and $\dot{N}$ matrices and using specific values that the expressions 5.24 would, by degeneration, yield the values as presented in Table 5.4. The idea has been further elaborated in Ghosh (1985).

5.6 RÉSEAU PHOTOGRAPHY

Réseau (focal plane grid) photography has been used for precision photogrammetric work for quite some time. Prior to the Second World War, the British mapping organizations used réseau in various aerial film camera applications (in the U.K., India and South Africa). In these, a grid plate (glass) was interposed between the lens and the emulsion at the focal plane and was used as a registration plate (see Lawrence method, chap. 2). More recent developments in various countries have taken basically two forms. Accordingly, those two types are discussed below.

5.6.1 Réseau Mounted in Focal Plane

This type (e.g., Wild Modified RC-8 Aviogon, Zeiss RMK-AR or Hasselblad 500 EL Data cameras) is similar to the British pattern but is somewhat modified. The modification is basically in the use of a plano-convex glass plate (with the convex side facing the camera lens), in order to reduce another source of distortion error due to the plate acting as a lens, as the film support. The réseau crosses are on the plane side of the plate. In this case, the coordinates of each réseau intersection are determined from camera calibration. These calibrated coordinates are referred to the principal point as origin and may be already corrected for lens distortion. There are three possibilities:

i) The simplest method of using them is to read the coordinates x_i, y_i of the réseau intesection nearest to each observed image point. Then the image point coordinates are given by:

$$
\left. \begin{array}{l} x' \;=\; x'_i + (x - x_i) \\[3mm] y' \;=\; y'_i + (y - y_i) \end{array} \right\}
\tag{5.25}
$$

where subscript i refers to the réseau point number;

x'_i , y'_i are réseau point coordinates obtained from calibration;

x , y   are the observed coordinates of the image point;

and x_i , y_i are the observed coordinates of the réseau point.

In this approach, it is assumed that the comparator axes are coinciding with the réseau axes during observations. The principal drawback here is that this procedure ignores any non-linear deformation within the réseau interval.

(ii) An alternate method is to read the four grid intersections around the image point. Then a projective transformation is applied by using the following equations:

$$x' = \frac{a_1 x + a_2 y + a_3}{c_1 x + c_2 y + 1} \qquad y' = \frac{b_1 x + b_2 y + b_3}{c_1 x + c_2 y + 1} \qquad (5.26)$$

where the a's, b's and c's are certain constants. By using the observed and calibrated coordinates of the four réseau points, one may obtain the eight constants. A variation of this approach would be to use an affine transformation,

$$x' = a_1 x + a_2 y + a_3 \qquad y' = b_1 x + b_2 y + b_3 \qquad (5.27)$$

Here one has six unknown constants; therefore, three grid points would be adequate. However, with four points, a least squares fit is pertinent.

(iii) A third alternative method will be to observe all réseau points on each photograph along with all of the image points. The differences between the calibrated coordinates and the observed coordinates are used to determine the coefficients in the polynomials which express the corrections to the measured coordinates as functions of the positions of the images on the photo,

$$\left.\begin{array}{l} x' = x + a_c + a_1 x + a_2 x^2 + a_3 y + a_4 y^2 + a_5 xy + a_6 x^2 y + \cdots \\[2mm] y' = y + b_o + b_1 x + b_2 x^2 + b_3 y + b_4 y^2 + b_5 xy + b_6 x^2 y + \cdots \end{array}\right\} \qquad (5.28)$$

The number of terms in the polynomials has to be decided upon separately in each case (arbitrarily, depending on factors such as desired precision, computer capability, etc.). This is, however, generally done without much basic understanding of scientific justifications. In case of redundant data, it would be appropriate to have a least squares adjustment.

5.6.2 Réseau from the Pressure Plate

In some cameras (like Faichild KC-6A camera) light coming through tiny holes arranged in a grid pattern in the pressure plate is superposed from the rear during the film exposure. In this case, the pressure platen cannot be expected to occupy precisely the same position for each exposure. This means that the relationship between the réseau and fiducial marks must be established freshly every time. The images of the fiducial marks, therefore, should be treated as other images and are corrected for film distortion according to the observed coordinates of the réseau. In this case, an orthogonal transformation (with or without any scale-change, i.e., affine may be applicable, e.g.,

$$
\left.\begin{array}{ll}
x' = a_1x + a_2y + a_3 & \quad x' = a_1x + a_2y + a_3 \\
\text{or,} & \\
y' = b_1x + b_2y + b_3 & \quad y' = a_2x - a_1y + a_3
\end{array}\right\} \qquad (5.29)
$$

Recently developed automatic réseau measuring equipment (see Roos, 1975) is also capable of reading coordinates with standard deviations below 1 μm. In such equipment, if at any time the accuracy becomes too low, a new calibration can be performed to obtain a new set of coefficients for using at the computer for subsequent operations/applications. The measurement of réseau points on a comparator means considerable extra work. The Oberschwaben Test (performed by OEEPE during the early 1970's) compared the results of final practical applications of non-réseau and réseau cameras. It revealed no significant difference between them. This can be interpreted as a definitive establishment of the fact that errors of interior (to camera) geometry after corrections are of secondary importance compared to the external influences. Perry (1978) concludes that backlighted réseau is not as accurate as the glass réseau. However, its low cost, ease of calibration and extreme flexibility outweigh its lower accuracy and it would be a useful tool in photogrammetry.

BIBLIOGRAPHY

American Society of Photogrammetry; *Manual of Photogrammetry* (4th Ed.) (ASPRS, Falls Church, Virginia: 1980).

Arthur, D. W. G.; *A Stereocomparator Technique for Aeral Triangulation* (Ordnance Survey Professional Paper, New Series No. 20, London: 1966).

Bertram, S.; "Atmospheric Refraction"; *PE* 35, No. 6 (1969).

Brown, D. C.; *The Simultaneous Determination of the Orientation and Lens Distortion of a Photogrammetric Camera* (Technical Report No. 33, RCA Data Reduction: 1956).

Brown, D. C.; "Decentering Distortion of Lenses"; *PE* 32, No. 3 (1966).

Conrady, A. E.; "Decentered Lens Systems" *Monthly Notices of the Royal Astronomical Society* 79, No. 5; London (1919).

Ghosh, Sanjib K.; *Phototriangulation* (Lexington Books, Lexington, Mass.: 1975).

Ghosh, Sanjib K.; "Image Quality Versus Metric Capability"; *PE* 39, No. 11 (1973).

Ghosh, Sanjib K.; "Image motion compensation through augmented collinearity equations"; *Optical Engineering* 24, No. 6 (1985).

Harris, W. D., G. C. Tewinkel and C. A. Whitten; *Analytic Aerotriangulation* (Technical Bulletin No. 21; US Department of Commerce, C & G S: 1968).

Kammerer, Joachim; "The Moon Camera and Its Lenses", *PE* 39, No. 1 (1973).

+ Kawachi, D. A.; "Image motion and its compensation for the oblique frame camera", *PE* 31. No. 1 (1965).

+ Kawachi, D. A.; "Image Motion Due to Camera Rotation", *PE* 31, No. 5 (1965).

Keller, M. and G. C. Tewinkel; *Aerotriangulation, Image Coordinate Refinement* (Technical Bulletin No. 25; US Department of Commerce, C & G S; 1965).

Klein, Miles V.; *Optics;* (John Wiley and Sons, Inc.: 1970).

Lampton, B. Frank; "Film Distortion Compensation", *PE* 31, No. 5 (1965).

Leijonhufvud, Axel; "On Photogrammetric Refraction", *Photogrammetria* 9, No. 3 (1953).

Minzner, R. A.; K. S. W. Champion and H. L. Pond; *The ARDC Model Atmosphere, 1969* (Air Force Surveys in Geophysics No. 115, USAF Cambrindge Research Center; 1969).

NASA; *Evaluation of Motion-Degraded Images* (Publication No. NASA SP-193: 1969).

Perry, Leslie H.; "An NOS-Developed Backlight Réseau and Its Effect on Coordinate Refinement"; *Proceedings of the ASP, Fall Technical Meeting* (1978).

Roos, Maurits; "The Automatic Réseau Measuring Equipement (ARME)", *PERS* 41, No. 9 (1975).

Saastamoinen, J,; "Refraction", *PE* 38, No.3 (1972).

Saastamoinen, J,; "Local Variation of Photogrammetric Refraction", *PE* 40, No. 3 (1974).

Schöler, Horst; "On Photogrammetric Distortion", *PERS* 41, No. 6 (1975).

Schut, G. H.; "Photogrammetric Refraction", *PE* 35, No. 1 (1969).

Trachsel, Arnold F.; "Réseau Techniques", *PE* 31, No. 5 (1965).

Trott, T.; "The Effects of Motion on Resolution", *PE* 26, No. 5 (1960).

US Standard Atmosphere Supplements (US Government Printing Office: 1966).

Van Roessel, J.; "Estimating Lens Distortion With Orthogonal Polynomials", *PE* 36, No. 6 (1970).

Vlcek, J.; "Systematic Errors of Image Coordinates", *PE* 35, No. 6 (1969).

Washer, F. E.; "Prism Effect, Camera Tipping and Tangential Distortion", *PE* 23, No.4 (1957).

Washer, F. E.; "Calibration of Airplane Cameras", *PE* 25, No. 5 (1957).

Wolfe, R. N. and R. L. Lamberts; "The Effects of Image Motion on Resolving Power", *PE* 11, No. 4 (1955).

Ziemann, H.; "Economics of Image Deformation Correction", *PE* 38, No.2 (1972).

6
OBJECT-PHOTO RELATIONSHIP

The fundamental relationship between the object and the corresponding photograph can be formulated by utilizing the geometry of the imaging process (Chap. 4). The related problems are considered as different, according to the parameters that are known directly from observations (measured data), those obtained from sources other than direct observations (accepted as known data) and those to be determined from the computational or other solution process (considered as unknown data). The corresponding conditions (equations) can thereby be established.

The most obvious and usually the simplest approach is to treat the image coordinates as the observed values. A number of standard problems (and the corresponding conditions) are listed in Table 4.1. If some of the known parameters are also observed quantities and are subject to observational errors, it is possible to incorporate them in the solution as constrained parameters. The techniques of considering such constraints are discussed in Chap. 9. Some practical uses of the geometric relations where the data are straightforward will be discussed in this chapter. These are the standard and most frequently solved problems. Other problems, which may be considered as extensions of the discussed ones, are easily derivable in view of the purposes under specific circumstances.

With ragard to a single photograph, its *exterior orientation* (with respect to the object space) consists of two easily separable sets of parameters. The first set involves *angular orientation data* whereby the attitude of the photograph (or, better, the camera axis) at the time of exposure is defined in terms of the angles of rotation (ω, φ and κ). The second contains the *positional data* of the exposure station in terms of the three-dimensional coordinates of the perspective center $(X_o, Y_o$ and $Z_o)$. The solution is known as *space-resection.*

With the knowledge of the exterior orientation parameters of two or more photographs taken of the same object, one may perform *space-intersection* to obtain the locations of unknown objects points.

Another typical problem is the *inverse problem* giving *fictitious photographs*, where the image coordinates are derived after the corresponding object point and the camera parameters are known. This may be found useful in various applications (for example, camera calibration, establishing the effects of atmospheric refraction, in handling some non-conventional imaging systems, etc.)

6.1 EXTERIOR ORIENTATION

6.1.1 Complete, By Use of Collinearity Equations

A method very frequently used in obtaining the exterior orientation data of one photograph is by applying the collinearity condition. Equations 4.8 provide the basis for this condition here. The unknown (required) data being six (viz., X_o, Y_o, Z_o , ω, φ and κ), one requires at least six equations, which are provided by three ground control points. In view of the non-linearity of the equations, linearized condition equations are necessary and the solution should, therefore, be iterative.

In Eqs 4.8 or Eqs 4.9, consider the first function as F_1 and the second one as F_2 (see also Appendix A). Starting with approximate (or estimated) values of the unknonw parameters and, thereafter, the terms of the partial derivatives with respect to the variables being added, one would establish the mathematical models concerning the corrected (or updated) photo-coordinates:

$$
\left.
\begin{aligned}
x_i &= \frac{\partial F_1}{\partial \omega}\Delta\omega + \frac{\partial F_1}{\partial \varphi}\Delta\varphi + \frac{\partial F_1}{\partial \kappa}\Delta\kappa - \frac{\partial F_1}{\partial X_o}\Delta X_o - \frac{\partial F_1}{\partial Y_o}\Delta Y_o - \frac{\partial F_1}{\partial Z_o}\Delta Z_o + F_1 \\[2mm]
x_i &= \frac{\partial F_2}{\partial \omega}\Delta\omega + \frac{\partial F_2}{\partial \varphi}\Delta\varphi + \frac{\partial F_2}{\partial \kappa}\Delta\kappa - \frac{\partial F_2}{\partial X_o}\Delta X_o - \frac{\partial F_2}{\partial Y_o}\Delta Y_o - \frac{\partial F_2}{\partial Z_o}\Delta Z_o + F_2
\end{aligned}
\right\}
\quad (6.1)
$$

The observations equations obtained from the above,, in general form, can be written as:

$$\left.\begin{array}{l} v_{x_i} = x_i - \underline{x}_i \\[2ex] v_{y_i} = y_i - \underline{y}_i \end{array}\right\} \qquad (6.2)$$

where $\underline{x}_i$, $\underline{y}_i$ are the observed photo coordinates and v_{x_i}, v_{y_i} are the discrepancies (or observational errors). Alternately, one may consider only the relevant terms of Eqs 4.14 for such a solution. Table 6.1 provides an example.

There are various ways of simplifying the process. With near vertical aerial photographs, one may consider the initial values of ω, φ and κ to be zero, which give the following M matrix:

$$M = \begin{bmatrix} 1 & 0 & 0 \\ 0 & 1 & 0 \\ 0 & 0 & 1 \end{bmatrix}$$

In order to compute Eqs 6.2, the partial derivatives must first be evaluated. These are given in Appendix A. The equations can be solved for ΔX_o, ΔY_o, ΔZ_o, $\Delta\omega$, $\Delta\varphi$ and $\Delta\kappa$. Next, they are iterated until the changes are minimized to acceptable values close to zero.

6.1.2 Angular Orientation Only

As indicated in Chapter 4, the collinearity condition (of vectors $\vec{r}$ and $\vec{R}$) establishes the exterior orientation of the photograph. The situation becomes simple when the coordinates of the perspective center (i.e., the camera station) are known along with an adequate number of ground stations whose photo coordinates are observed. The required (i.e., considered unknown) data here being the rotation angles only, the scalar multiple, k (i.e., the scale factor) need not be considered and one can work with unit vectors.

The unit vector $(\vec{r}^o)$ corresponding to $\vec{r}$ has 3 components in the photographic coordinate system, i.e.,

Table 6.1

Exterior orientation at Wild Aviolyt BC-1

Note : One step solution; NASA-USA Large Format Camera
f = 305.88 mm; Approximate flying height : 244.8 km.
Two photographs over littoral Morocco were used.
Points P1, P3, P11 and P13 are at sea level. Program PMO

Point No.	RESIDUALS ON							
	Photo coordinates (μm)					Ground coordinates (m)		
	DXL	DYL	DXR	DYR	PY	DXG	DYG	DZG
P1	-.0	-.9	-.1	.9	1.8			
P2	.0	-1.1	-.1	1.4	2.6			
P3	-.6	1.9	.7	-1.9	4.0	4.58	-9.71	3.70
P5	-.0	-1.6	.1	1.4	2.9			
P7	-.1	-1.9	-.2	1.9	3.7			
P9	2.7	1.8	-3.1	-2.1	7.0	-4.94	-18.98	-20.42
P10	-.1	.6	.0	-.7	1.3			-.01
P11	-.4	6.7	.2	-6.7	13.4			.44
P12	-.1	-.8	-.1	.8	1.7			
P13	-.2	-.6	.4	.7	1.4	.56	17.59	
P14	-.1	-3.3	.2	3.6	6.9	-13.97	12.73	
P15	-1.6	-.6	1.7	.5	3.5			14.05
P16	.0	1.8	.2	-1.9	3.6			
P18	.8	-1.8	-.3	1.4	3.4	33.18	5.50	
P20	-2.3	-.9	2.2	.9	4.9			19.42
P21	-.5	-1.3	.4	1.3	2.7			4.44
P22	1.8	1.7	-2.1	-1.4	5.0	-19.42	-7.09	-21.61
R.M.S.					4.1	16.93	12.95	13.66

Orientation elements and their standard deviations:

Photo No.	X_O	Y_O	Z_O	Omega	Phi	Kappa
CM1	491181.48	512759.98	244876.19	-.086	.120	-146.237
	82.46	79.50	42.14	.020	.021	.011
CM2	476158.37	484022.86	244737.94	.265	-.281	-146.229
	82.62	80.02	43.02	.020	.021	.011

Normalized standard deviation : 1.2 m.

Data redundancy : 25

$$\vec{r}^{\,O} = \left\{ \frac{(x_p - x_o)}{[(x_p - x_o)^2 + (y_p - y_o)^2 + f^2]^{1/2}} \right. ;$$

$$\frac{(y_p - y_o)}{[(x_p - x_o)^2 + (y_p - y_o)^2 + f^2]^{1/2}} ;$$

$$\left. \frac{-f}{[(x_p - x_o)^2 + (y_p - y_o)^2 + f^2]^{1/2}} \right\} \qquad (6.3)$$

However, each component can be expressed as a direction cosine of the vector $\vec{r}$, i.e., the unit vector can be expressed by:

$$\vec{r}^{\,O} = (\cos xp0 ; \cos yp0 ; \cos zp0) \qquad (6.4)$$

Similarly, the unit vector $\vec{R}^{O}$ corresponding to the vector $\vec{R}$ in the object space can be expressed by:

$$\vec{R}^{O} = (\cos XP0 ; \cos YP0 ; \cos ZP0) \qquad (6.5)$$

The unit vectors, $\vec{r}^{\,O}$ and $\vec{R}^{O}$, represent the same line. However, they have been defined above in two different coordinate systems; viz., $\vec{r}^{\,O}$ in the photographic system and $\vec{R}^{O}$ in the object space system. Therefore, in order to provide the correspondence, one must be rotated to coincide with the other, i.e.,

$$M^T \cdot \vec{r}^{\,O} = \vec{R}^{O} \qquad (6.6)$$

where the rotation matrix M is the same as the one expressed in Eq. 4.2. This matrix has nine terms. Consequently, three control points must be known for determning all the terms. Consider, therefore, three known objects points, P_1, P_2 and P_3 corresponding to which the photo points are p_1, p_2 and p_3, respectively. Then Eq. 6.6 can be expresssed as:

$$M^T \cdot [\vec{r}_1^{\,O} \quad \vec{r}_2^{\,O} \quad \vec{r}_3^{\,O}] = [\vec{R}_1^{O} \quad \vec{R}_2^{O} \quad \vec{R}_3^{O}] \qquad (6.7a)$$

i.e.,

$$
\begin{bmatrix} m_{11} & m_{12} & m_{13} \\ m_{21} & m_{22} & m_{23} \\ m_{31} & m_{32} & m_{33} \end{bmatrix}
\begin{bmatrix} \cos xp_1 0 & \cos xp_2 0 & \cos xp_3 0 \\ \cos yp_1 0 & \cos yp_2 0 & \cos yp_3 0 \\ \cos zp_1 0 & \cos zp_2 0 & \cos zp_3 0 \end{bmatrix}
$$

$$
= \begin{bmatrix} \cos XP_1 0 & \cos XP_2 0 & \cos XP_3 0 \\ \cos YP_1 0 & \cos YP_2 0 & \cos YP_3 0 \\ \cos ZP_1 0 & \cos ZP_2 0 & \cos ZP_3 0 \end{bmatrix} \tag{6.7b}
$$

From this, the orientation matrix (M) can be solved:

$$
M = [\vec{R}_1^O \quad \vec{R}_2^O \quad \vec{R}_3^O]^{-1} \ [\vec{r}_1^O \quad \vec{r}_2^O \quad \vec{r}_3^O] \tag{6.8}
$$

The angles of rotation in the object space can, next, be individually obtained from the elements of this rotation matrix (see Eq. 3.18 for the details).

6.1.3 Space Resection Only

Several different approaches to this problem are in use. One very frequently used method only will be discussed here. This method uses the angular relationship criterion (see Chap. 4).

Consider Fig. 4.7 which illustrates the situation. The known ground control points A, B and C have the corresponding image points a, b, and c. Consider also that the camera focal length (f) is known. The purpose here is to obtain the coordinates of the perspective center (X_O, Y_O and Z_O) in the object (ground) system.

As has been discussed in Chapter 4 (see Eq. 4.47), the angles subtended by the point location vectors in the camera space must be equal to the corresponding angles in the object space, i.e.,

$$
\left.
\begin{aligned}
\cos \nabla_{ab} &= \cos \nabla_{AB} \\
\cos \nabla_{bc} &= \cos \nabla_{BC} \\
\cos \nabla_{ca} &= \cos \nabla_{CA}
\end{aligned}
\right\} \tag{6.9}
$$

Expanding the first one, for example (see Eqs 4.46 and 4.47), one gets:

$$
\frac{x_a \cdot x_b + y_a \cdot y_b + f^2}{\left| r_a \right| \cdot \left| r_b \right|}
$$

$$
= \frac{(X_A - X_o)(X_B - X_o) + (Y_A - Y_o)(Y_B - Y_o) + (Z_A - Z_o)(Z_B - Z_o)}{\left| R_A \right| \cdot \left| R_B \right|} \tag{6.10}
$$

The other two relations can be expanded similarly. In these, whereas all parameters in the camera space are known either through observation (photo coordinates) or from a priori knowledge (focal length from camera calibration data), the expressions for the object space contain the unknowns $(X_o, Y_o$ and $Z_o)$. However, a direct solution of these unknowns in this case is difficult because of the non-linear nature of these equations. Therefore, usually a Newton method of approximation is applied. This is done by first assuming:

$$
\left.
\begin{aligned}
X_o &= X_o' + \Delta X \\[2mm]
Y_o &= Y_o' + \Delta Y \\[2mm]
X_o &= X_o' + \Delta X
\end{aligned}
\right\} \tag{6.11}
$$

where X_o', Y_o', Z_o' are the initial approximate coordinates of the exposure station (e.g., estimated from an available map and flight data);

and ΔX, ΔY, ΔZ are the corrections to the initial approximate values.

A set of approximate values of the angles, V_{AB}', V_{BC}' and V_{CA}', can be obtained by using these approximate coordinates. Subsequently, one can write, for example:

$$
\cos V_{ab} = \cos V_{AB}' + \frac{\partial \cos V_{AB}'}{\partial X} \Delta X' + \frac{\partial \cos V_{AB}'}{\partial Y} \Delta Y' + \frac{\partial \cos V_{AB}'}{\partial Z} \Delta Z' \tag{6.12}
$$

It may be noted that $\Delta X'$, $\Delta Y'$ and $\Delta Z'$ here are approximate values in view of the differentiation. Similar expressions can be written for $\cos V_{bc}$ and $\cos V_{ca}$. Now, rearranging these equations,

$$\left. \begin{array}{c} \cos V_{ab} - \cos V'_{AB} = \Delta_1 \\[2ex] \cos V_{bc} - \cos V'_{BC} = \Delta_2 \\[2ex] \cos V_{ca} - \cos V'_{CA} = \Delta_3 \end{array} \right\} \qquad (6.13)$$

in which

$$\left. \begin{array}{l} \Delta_1 = \dfrac{\partial \cos V'_{AB}}{\partial X'} \Delta X + \dfrac{\partial \cos V'_{AB}}{\partial Y} \Delta Y' + \dfrac{\partial \cos V'_{AB}}{\partial Z} \Delta Z' \\[3ex] \Delta_2 = \dfrac{\partial \cos V'_{BC}}{\partial X'} \Delta X' + \dfrac{\partial \cos V'_{BC}}{\partial Y} \Delta Y' + \dfrac{\partial \cos V'_{BC}}{\partial Z} \Delta Z' \\[3ex] \Delta_3 = \dfrac{\partial \cos V'_{CA}}{\partial X'} \Delta X' + \dfrac{\partial \cos V'_{CA}}{\partial Y} \Delta Y' + \dfrac{\partial \cos V'_{CA}}{\partial Z} \Delta Z' \end{array} \right\} \qquad (6.14)$$

and

These three unknowns, $\Delta X'$, $\Delta Y'$ and $\Delta Z'$, can now be obtained by solving Eqs 6.14. Accordingly, the coordinates of the camera station after the initial corrections are:

$$X''_O = X'_O + \Delta X' ; \qquad Y''_O = Y'_O + \Delta Y' \quad \text{and} \quad Z''_O = Z'_O + \Delta Z' \qquad (6.15)$$

This approach implies an iterative procedure because of the computations of V'_{AB} etc. and the involved defferentiations. Therefore, such computations must be continued through successive iterations, each time with updated values and executed until corrections are acceptably small and close to zero. For example, after the second iteration, one obtains:

$$\left. \begin{array}{c} X'''_O = X''_O + \Delta X'' \\[2ex] Y'''_O = Y''_O + \Delta Y'' \\[2ex] Z'''_O = Z''_O + \Delta Z'' \end{array} \right\} \qquad (6.16)$$

In order to compute ΔX, ΔY nd ΔZ from Eq. 6.14, the partial derivatives are to be evaluated. By using Eq. 4.47 (which expresses the cosine function of the subtended angle as a function of ground coordinates), the partials are:

$$\frac{\partial \cos\nabla_{AB}}{\partial X} = \frac{(X_A - X_o)}{|R_A|} \left\{ \frac{1}{|R_B|} - \frac{1}{|R_A|} \cos\nabla_{ab} \right\}$$

$$+ \frac{(X_B - X_o)}{|R_B|} \left\{ \frac{1}{|R_A|} - \frac{1}{|R_B|} \cos\nabla_{ab} \right\}$$

i.e.,

$$\frac{\partial \cos\nabla_{AB}}{\partial X} = \cos\alpha_A \left\{ \frac{1}{|R_B|} - \frac{1}{|R_A|} \cos\nabla_{ab} \right\} + \cos\alpha_B \left\{ \frac{1}{|R_A|} - \frac{1}{|R_B|} \cos\nabla_{ab} \right\}$$

$$(6.17a)$$

Further, similarly

$$\frac{\partial \cos\nabla_{AB}}{\partial Y} = \cos\beta_A \left\{ \frac{1}{|R_B|} - \frac{1}{|R_A|} \cos\nabla_{ab} \right\} + \cos\beta_B \left\{ \frac{1}{|R_A|} - \frac{1}{|R_B|} \cos\nabla_{ab} \right\}$$

$$(6.17b)$$

and

$$\frac{\partial \cos\nabla_{AB}}{\partial Z} = \cos\gamma_A \left\{ \frac{1}{|R_B|} - \frac{1}{|R_A|} \cos\nabla_{ab} \right\} + \cos\gamma_B \left\{ \frac{1}{|R_A|} - \frac{1}{|R_B|} \cos\nabla_{ab} \right\}$$

$$(6.17c)$$

The other derivatives may be obtained similarly. The partial derivatives may be evaluated also as follows:

$$\frac{\partial \cos\nabla_{AB}}{\partial X} = (X_A - X_o)T_{BA} + (X_B - X_o)T_{AB}$$
$$(6.18a)$$

where

$$T_{AB} = \left\{ 1 - \frac{|R_A|\cdot\cos\nabla_{ab}}{|R_B|} \right\} \Big/ |R_A|\cdot|R_B|$$

and

$$T_{BA} = \left\{ 1 - \frac{|R_B|\cdot\cos\nabla_{ab}}{|R_A|} \right\} \Big/ |R_A|\cdot|R_B|$$

Similarly,
$$\frac{\partial \cos V_{AB}}{\partial Y} = (Y_A - Y_o)T_{BA} + (Y_B - Y_o)T_{AB} \qquad (6.18b)$$

$$\frac{\partial \cos_{AB}}{\partial Z} = (Z_A - Z_o)T_{BA} + (Z_B - Z_o)T_{AB} \qquad (6.18c)$$

and so on.

This approach requires at least three known ground control points. In case there are more than three points, the least squares method of adjustment by using observation equations may be applied to obtain unique solutions. An observation equation based on Eqs 6.12 may be written as follows:

$$v_{ij} = \frac{\partial \cos V_{IJ}'}{\partial X'} \Delta X' + \frac{\partial \cos V_{IJ}'}{\partial Y'} \Delta Y' + \frac{\partial \cos V_{IJ}'}{\partial Z'} \Delta Z' - (\cos V_{ij} - \cos V_{IJ}') \qquad (6.19)$$

where ij or IJ   refers to the point-pair subtending angle at the perspective center (capital letter subscripts refer to the object space and lower case letters refer to the camera space);

and v_{ij} is the deviation between the cosines of the corresponding angles in the image (camera) and object spaces.

These deviations (v_{ij}) should be minimized by the Least Squares adjustment. Considering unit weight in the observations, this means Σvv = a minimum. However, the real observations being the photo coordinates, one may consider that the use of these v's is unrealistic. In practice, however, in view of desirable assessment of the quality of the work, this is permissible even though this assessment could be interpreted as being indirect.

6.2 SPACE INTERSECTION

The problem of spatial intersection will be discussed here in terms of three different approaches. In the first case, the camera station coordinates and the orientation angles are treated as measured (known) quantities and may be regarded as fixed. The second case is based on the collinearity equations, which can be combined with the space resection program, resulting in a unified, resection-cum-intersection solution. In the third case, simplified approaches with regard to terrestrial photography are studied to illustrate the needs of various parameters in view of various modes of obtaining data.

6.2.1 Direct Solution

The goal is to obtain three-dimensional coordinates of points on the object. The situation is illustrated in Fig. 6.1 where P is an intersected point, whose coordinates X, Y, Z are unknown. The known quantities are two orientation matrices M_1 and M_2 for the two overlapping photos. The camera station (i.e., perspective center) coordinates for both photographs are also known either from space resection or from direct meaurements, i.e., X_{o1}, Y_{o1}, Z_{o1}, X_{o2}, Y_{o2} and Z_{o2} are known. The observed quantities are the photo-coordinates (x_1, y_1 and x_2, y_2). The focal length (f) is also known, say, from the camera calibration data.

The location vectors in the camera spaces for the two photographs are $\vec{r}_1$ and $\vec{r}_2$, their corresponding vectors in the object space being $\vec{R}_1$ and $\vec{R}_2$. The relationships between the respective unit vectors are (as Eq. 6.6):

$$M_1^T \cdot \vec{r}_1^{\,o} = \vec{R}_1^{\,o} \qquad \text{and} \qquad M_2^T \cdot \vec{r}_2^{\,o} = \vec{R}_2^{\,o} \qquad (6.20)$$

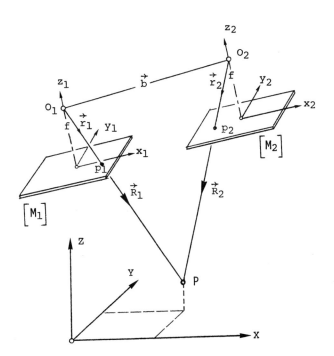

Fig. 6.1

Space intersection

The equations of the $\vec{R}_1$ and $\vec{R}_2$ lines can be written (after Eq. 6.5 in the pattern of Eq. 6.3) as:

$$\frac{X - X_{o1}}{\cos XPO_1} = \frac{Y - Y_{o1}}{\cos YPO_1} = \frac{Z - Z_{o1}}{\cos ZPO_1}$$

and

$$\frac{X - X_{o2}}{\cos XPO_2} = \frac{Y - Y_{o2}}{\cos YPO_2} = \frac{Z - Z_{o2}}{\cos ZPO_2}$$

$$(6.21)$$

The three unknown coordinates (X, Y, Z) of the intersected point P can be obtained from these equations. A practical procedure will be to first solve for only X and Y coordinates by using the portions of Eq. 6.21 involving X and Y, i.e.,

$$\frac{X - X_{o1}}{\cos XPO_1} = \frac{Y - Y_{o1}}{\cos YPO_1} \quad \text{and} \quad \frac{X - X_{o2}}{\cos XPO_2} = \frac{Y - Y_{o2}}{\cos XPO_2} \qquad (6.22)$$

Thereafter, by substituting the values of X and Y in the rest of Eqs 6.21, one can obtain two separate values of Z for the same point. This provides a check on the computations and the difference between the two values would provide an assessment of the quality of the worrk.

There can be other interesting applications of Eqs. 6.21. For example, if the Z coordinate of a point is known from a ground survey or otherwise, its X and Y coordinates can be determined from a single photograph by using one equation in parts:

$$X = X_{o1} + (Z - Z_{o1}) \frac{\cos XPO_1}{\cos ZPO_1} \quad \text{and} \quad Y = Y_{o1} + (Z - Z_{o1}) \frac{\cos YPO_1}{\cos ZPO_1} \qquad (6.23)$$

Furthermore, in such a case, if two or more photographs containing the same points are available, a Least Squares solution will be appropriate.

6.2.2 Use of Collinearity Equations

The collinearity equations (Eq. 4.8) contain three groups of parameters for the space exterior to the camera, viz., rotation elements (contained in the rotation matrix), the coordinates of the camera station, and the coordinates of the ground point. Consequently, if the first two groups of parameters are known, the third group (i.e., the ground coordinates) can be obtained by using the collinearity equations. Equations 4.8 can be rearranged for any point i as follows:

$$x_i \{(X_i - X_o)m_{31} + (Y_i - Y_o)m_{32} + (Z_i - Z_o)m_{33}\}$$

$$= -f\{(X_i - X_o)m_{11} + (Y_i - Y_o)m_{12} + (Z_i - Z_o)m_{13}\} \tag{6.24}$$

$$y_i \{(X_i - X_o)m_{31} + (Y_i - Y_o)m_{32} + (Z_i - Z_o)m_{33}\}$$

$$= -f\{(X_i - X_o)m_{21} + (Y_i - Y_o)m_{22} + (Z_i - Z_o)m_{23}\}$$

In these, X_i, Y_i and Z_i are the unknowns (being the coordinates of point P, see Fig. 6.1). The rest are known quantities, either through direct observations (x_i, y_i photo coordinates), or otherwise (f, focal length from camera calibration data; X_o, Y_o, Z_o and the m's from, say, space resection or phototriangulation). In view of the unknowns, Eqs 6.24 can be rearranged with respect to one photograph:

$$X_i(x_i m_{31} + f \cdot m_{11}) + Y_i(x_i m_{32} + f \cdot m_{12}) + Z_i(x_i m_{33} + f \cdot m_{13})$$

$$= x_i(X_o m_{31} + Y_o m_{32} + Z_o m_{33}) + f(X_o m_{11} + Y_o m_{12} + Z_o m_{13}) \tag{6.25}$$

$$X_i(y_i m_{31} + f \cdot m_{21}) + Y_i(y_i m_{32} + f \cdot m_{22}) + Z_i(y_i m_{33} + f \cdot m_{23})$$

$$= y_i(X_o m_{31} + Y_o m_{32} + Z_o m_{33}) + f(X_o m_{21} + Y_o m_{22} + Z_o m_{23})$$

With two photographs of known exterior orientations, one gets two sets (i.e., four) of Eqs 6.25, where all the parameters except X_i, Y_i and Z_i for the specific point are known. Any suitable computational solution can be used, e.g., the method of determinant or of the Least Squares. It may be pertinent to mention here that a similar arrangement of the Collinearity equations can also be applicable to the problem of Exterior Orientation. This may be found to be, in some case, simpler than the approach discussed in Section 6.1.1 earlier.

6.2.3 Simple Intersection With Terrestrial Photos

For the sake of simplicity and convenience in work, photographs with terrestrial cameras (like photo-theodolites or stereometric cameras or even amateur cameras) would be planned so that the horizontal collimating (fiducial) line in each photo remains horizontal while the vertical collimating line may not always remain vertical due to the inherent tilt. A point on ground (object) is defined in terms of 3-D coordinates, X, Y, Z while the corresponding points in the photographs are in terms of their photo-coordinates, x', y' for point p' on the left side photograph and x", y" for point p" on the right side photograph (see Fig. 6.2).

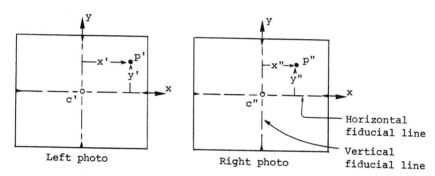

Fig. 6.2 Coordinate determination on terrestrial stereophotos

The ground coordinates (X, Y, Z,) are in a system for which the perspective center of the left side camera is the origin and the left side camera axis (assumed horizontal) indicates the direction of the Y axis in a right-handed system with the X-axis pointed in the general direction of the camera base (see Figs 6.3 and 6.4).

Two typical cases can be studied, viz, (1) the normal case where both camera axes are parallel and perpendicular to the terrestrial (camera) base (case A) and (2) the camera axes are arbitrarily convergent (case B).

Case A: Normal Case
This is illustrated in Fig. 6.3.

The photo coordinates, x', y' and x", y" are measured quantities. The horizontal projection of the camera base ($\bar{b}$) is assumed known and so is the focal length (f). The following relationship can be established from simple geometric consideration:

$$\frac{\bar{b}}{x'' - x'} = \frac{Y_p}{f} \qquad \text{i.e.} \qquad Y_p = \frac{\bar{b} \cdot f}{P_x} \qquad (6.26)$$

where $\quad P_x = x'' - x' =$ the x-parallax

Similarly, $\quad X_p = - \dfrac{Y_p \cdot x'}{f}$

with substitution from Eq. 6.26,

$$X_p = - \frac{\bar{b} \cdot x'}{P_x} \qquad (6.27)$$

and $\qquad Z_p = Z_{o'} - \dfrac{Y_p \cdot y'}{f} = Z_{o'} - \dfrac{\bar{b} \cdot y'}{P_x} \qquad (6.28)$

where $Z_{o'}$ is the elevation of the camera position O' for the left photograph.

An expression similar to Eq. 6.28 can be written also where $Z_{o''}$ of the right side camera position is used. It is interesting to note here that Eqs 6.27 and 6.28 i.e., expressions for X and Z coordinates of the ground point are independent of the focal length in this, Normal case. A normal case would be the simplest and is recommended if the situation permits.

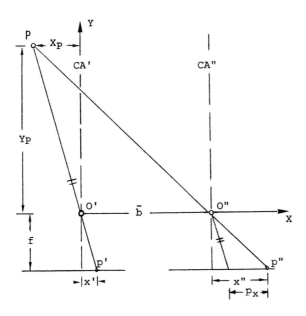

Fig. 6.3

Intersection with terrestrial
photos, Normal case

Case B: Convergent Case

This is illustrated in Fig. 6.4 where, as the Normal Case, $\bar{b}$ is the horizontal projection of the camera base.

The angles ψ' and ψ'', the angles subtended by the camera axes with the directions of the perpendiculars to the camera base on the horizontal planes, define the convergence of the left and right camera, respectively. These two angles of convergence are assumed known as are $\bar{b}$ and f. Consider the horizontal distance of a ground point P from the left camera position, $O'P = d$. The photo coordinates x', y' and x'', y'' are measured quantities. Consider α' and α'' being the directions to the point P with regard to the respective camera axes (CA' and CA"). Furthermore,

$$\alpha' = \text{arc tan} \left(- \frac{x'}{f}\right) \text{ and } \alpha'' = \text{arc tan} \left(- \frac{x''}{f}\right).$$

Then; $\delta = (\psi' - \psi'' + \alpha' - \alpha'')$

also, from sine conditions in triangle O'PO",

$$\frac{d}{\bar{b}} = \frac{\sin(90° + \psi'' + \alpha'')}{\sin \delta}$$

i.e. $$d = \frac{\bar{b} \cdot \cos (\psi'' + \alpha'')}{\sin (\psi' - \psi'' + \alpha' - \alpha'')}$$

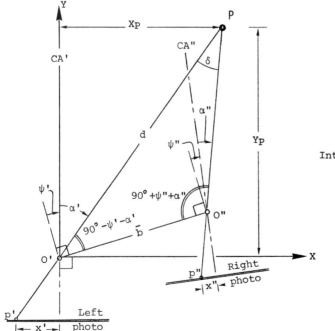

Fig. 6.4

Intersection with terrestrial

photos, Convergent case

These give , $\quad Y_p = d \cdot \cos \alpha' = \dfrac{\bar{b} \cdot \cos (\psi'' + \alpha'') \cos \alpha'}{\sin(\psi' - \psi'' + \alpha' - \alpha'')}$ $\hspace{2cm}$ (6.29)

Now, $\qquad\qquad X_p = -\dfrac{Y_p \cdot x'}{f}$ $\hspace{4.5cm}$ (6.30)

and $\qquad\qquad Z_p = Z_{0'} - \dfrac{Y_p \cdot y'}{f}$ $\hspace{4cm}$ (6.31)

Similar expression can be written with regard to $Z_{0''}$.

If $\psi' = \psi''$ one obtains a case with no convergence but a case with camera axes turned and parallel to each other. On the other hand if $\psi' = -\psi''$ one obtains a case of symmetrical convergence. In these two cases the situations become somewhat less complex and are recommended if the Normal case cannot be worked out adequately.

6.3 INVERSE PROBLEM

In case the three-dimensional ground coordinats of certain points and the camera orientation data (both Interior and Exterior) are known, one would be able to obtain the corresponding photo coordinates of those points. These would represent the theoretically obtained locations of those image points. In case the photographic coordinates of those points are also measured, the difference between the measured (actual) and computed (theoretically correct) locations are obtained. Such information can be of help in various problems. For example, assuming that such differences are due to the (unaccounted for) lens distortion, one could use this in calibrating the camera.

One way of doing this will be by using the collinearity equations (Eqs 4.8) directly. In this, all parameters in the right hand side of the equations being known, the photo-coordinates (x, y) are computed directly.

Alternately, in view of Eqs 6.4, 6.5 and 6.6, with respect to the corresponding unit vectors, $\vec{r}^{\,0}$ and $\vec{R}^{\,0}$,

$$\begin{bmatrix} \cos xp0 \\ \cos yp0 \\ \cos zp0 \end{bmatrix} = M \cdot \begin{bmatrix} \cos XP0 \\ \cos YP0 \\ \cos ZP0 \end{bmatrix} \hspace{2cm} (6.32)$$

This gives the direction cosines within the camera space. The equation of the line
from the image point to the perspective center (camera station) is :

$$\frac{x_p - x_o}{\cos xpO} = \frac{y_p - y_o}{\cos ypO} = \frac{-f}{\cos zpO} \tag{6.33}$$

Now, assuming that the coordinates of the principal point are $x_o = y_o = 0$, one
obtains simple expressions for the photo-coordinates:

$$x_p = -f \frac{\cos xpO}{\cos zpO} \quad \text{and} \quad y_p = -f \frac{\cos ypO}{\cos zpO}. \tag{6.34}$$

For further ideas, see Chapter 10 (concept of IEFP).

BIBLIOGRAPHY

Brown, Duane C.; *A Solution to the General Problem of Multiple Station Analytical Stereo-Triangulation* (R.C.A. Data Reduction Technical Report, No. 43: 1958).

Keller, M. and G. C. Tewinkel; *Space Resection in Photogrammetry* (ESSA Technical Report, C & G S Bulletin No. 32, U.S. Department of Commerce: 1966).

Merritt, E. L.; *Analytical Photogrammetry* (Pittman Publishing Company, New York,: 1958).

Rapp, R. H.; "Comparison of Space Resection Adjustment"; *Journal of the Surveying and Mapping Division*, ASCE 92 (1966).

Tewinkel, G. C.; *Analytical Absolute Orientation in Photogrammetry*; (C & G S Technical Bulletin No. 19, U.S. Department of Commerce: 1962).

7
DESIGN OF PROJECTS

Technological, circumstantial and competitive factors interact in a very complicated fashion in today's economy. It is not easy to design a project that is both realistic and economical. Another reason for complexity is that sometimes the organizations may pursue inconsistent goals. The responsibility for making decisions may be diffused often. There is often no clear line of demarkation between the work of the photogrammetrist and that of the user of photogrammetric data. Such an user can be from any field, e.g., space science, industrial engineering, metallurgy, surgery, etc. Because of such diversities, the photogrammetrist cannot always follow any standard procedure. Moreover, there are generally several ways to approach any problem. Therefore, careful planning and designing of any project is necessary.

A project development may become ineffective and inefficient if its cost-effectiveness is inadequate. Cost-effectiveness considerations are also complex (for an introduction to this, see Ghosh, 1976). This book emphasizes the technical aspects only and, therefore, the socio-economic aspects will not be discussed. However, the working photogrammetrist must keep in mind that decisions concercing the utilization of the end product of photogrammetry are often economic rather than technical.

Some basic and fundamental yet important technical considerations necessary for designing and/or evaluating any project will be discussed in this chapter. There are some differences between aerial (also spatial) and terrestrial applications and yet there are aspects common to every case. In view of these, the discussions will be made in general terms. The reader will be able to apply the concepts easily to the specific cases.

159

7.1 SCALE AND CAMERA CONSIDERATIONS

For topographical mapping, most of the countries in the world are switching from graphical (by direct tracing) mapping to instrumental and automated (analytic) map compilation. Analytical/computational generation of control data to assist such map compilations is also pursued extensively now. Between the aerial photograph and the finished map, there are two operational steps involving possibilities of changing the scales. In this respect, one considers Photo-, Model-, Compilation- (at instrument), and Map-Publication-Scales. These are symbolized by M_B, M_M, M_K' and M_K, respectively. The specific values of such scale factors are valid for a certain stage (operational step) for specific man-machine-technique combination in order to meet certain tolerances of mensural qualities. The computational part being only a portion of the entire operation, one can not ignore the other implications. The general aspects have been broadly discussed by Ghosh (1971 and 1987). For general planning, however, the photogrammetrist may consider the two extremes, viz., M_B and M_K. Based on the currently available hardware and expertise, one may consider their relationships as presented in Fig. 7.1. This figure is based on 1980 data collected under the UN auspices and as reported by Brandenberger and Ghosh (1983). Here the upper line corresponds to the best possible situation, i.e., when excellent cameras and instruments (best precision) are used. The lower line corresponds to average situations such as are available to almost all mapping organizations. Most cases are expected to stay within the ranges indicated by the two lines. The central line indicates the optimum on the average for cadastral and topographic mapping in general. The graph is limited to Map Scales 1:500 and 1:100,000. This is because in common practice, direct mapping (as against derived mapping) from aerial photographs is done within this range. Both scales being logarithmic (used for the sake of convenience), the figure indicates linear relationships.

Associated with the above is the problem of selecting the camera and the mode of its use. This is governed by two basic aspects, viz., (1) the ground coverage (for overall economy, see Fig. 7.2), which is inversely proportional to the focal length; And (2) the geometry of intersection (discussed in Section 7.2), which is associated with the stereo-coverage (for overall obtainable accuracy). The two, however, are not always compatible. With a wider field-angle of the camera, one would expect fewer stereo models which would require fewer control points and, in some cases, would give better intersection geometry. On the other hand, this may cause stereo-gaps on rugged (mountainous) terrain or may have masking effects locally.

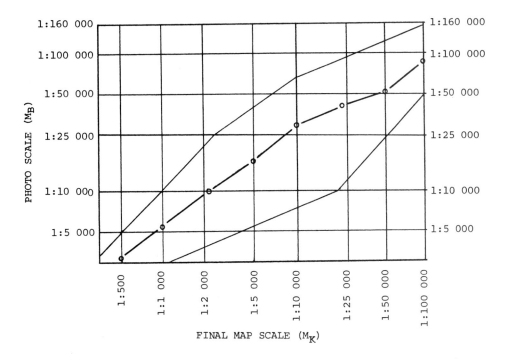

Fig. 7.1   Reasonable photo-to-map scale relations

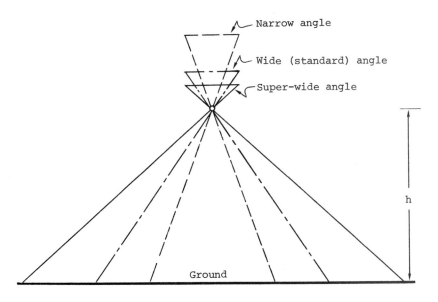

Fig. 7.2   Comparison of ground coverage with different camera angles

Further points to consider in these regards are whether or not the photography is meant to be used in other jobs (e.g., orthophotography, mosaicing, etc.); whether or not unusual lack of flatness of the emulsion/ film is expected; whether or not critical geometry is involved, etc.

In general, unless economy at the expense of some accuracy (in spite of some other problems) is desired, it will be advisable to use a camera with smaller field angle, provided sufficiently large intersection angle is obtained.

7.2 GEOMETRIC CONSIDERATIONS

Three-dimensional mensuration is essentially dependent on the quality of the spatial intersection of the conjugate rays. In order to establish formulation for assessing the quality of such intersection, one can consider a two-dimensional analogy from ground survey (see Fig. 7.3). Consider an intersected point (P) of two rays, 1P and 2P, originating from stations 1 and 2, respectively. Here γ is the angle of intersection (parallactic angle, b is the base (distance between the stations, α's are included angles at the stations, ν's are the azimuths, and d's are the distances from the stations. The subscripts refer to the specific points or directions. One can state, for the coordinates of the intersected point (P),

$$\left.\begin{array}{l} X = X_1 + d_1 \cdot \sin\nu_{1P} \\[2ex] Y = Y_1 + d_1 \cdot \cos\nu_{1P} \end{array}\right\} \tag{7.1}$$

also,

$$\left.\begin{array}{l} \gamma = 180° - (\alpha_1 + \alpha_2) \\[2ex] \nu_{1P} = \nu_{12} - \alpha_1 \\[2ex] d_1 = (\sin\alpha_2 / \sin\gamma)\, b \end{array}\right\} \tag{7.2}$$

Considering Eqs 7.2 and substituting appropriate values, one gets from Eqs 7.1:

$$\left.\begin{array}{l} X = X_1 + \dfrac{b \cdot \sin\alpha_2 \cdot \sin(\nu_{12} - \alpha_1)}{\sin(\alpha_1 + \alpha_2)} \\[3ex] Y = Y_1 + \dfrac{b \cdot \sin\alpha_2 \cdot \cos(\nu_{12} - \alpha_1)}{\sin(\alpha_1 + \alpha_2)} \end{array}\right\} \tag{7.3}$$

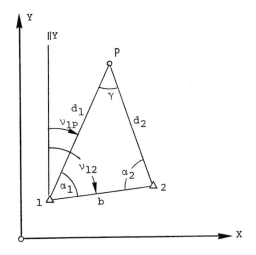

Fig. 7.3

Geometry of intersection

Equations 7.3 contain information obtainable from the two base stations and the base length. The partial derivatives of Eqs. 7.3 give:

$$\frac{\partial X}{\partial \alpha_1} = -\frac{b \cdot \sin\alpha_2 \cdot \sin(\nu_{12} - \alpha_2)}{\sin^2\gamma} \tag{7.4a}$$

$$\frac{\partial X}{\partial \alpha_1} = \frac{b \cdot \sin\alpha_1 \cdot \sin(\nu_{12} + \alpha_1)}{\sin^2\gamma} \tag{7.4b}$$

$$\frac{\partial Y}{\partial \alpha_2} = \frac{b \cdot \sin\alpha_2 \cdot \cos(\nu_{12} - \alpha_2)}{\sin^2\gamma} \tag{7.4c}$$

and,
$$\frac{\partial Y}{\partial \alpha_2} = -\frac{b \cdot \sin\alpha_1 \cdot \cos(\nu_{12} + \alpha_1)}{\sin^2\gamma} \tag{7.4d}$$

The standard error in planimetry of intersection at point P can be expressed:

$$m_s^2 = m_X^2 + m_Y^2 \tag{7.5}$$

where
$$m_X^2 = \left(\frac{\partial X}{\partial \alpha_1}\right)^2 m_{\alpha_1}^2 + \left(\frac{\partial X}{\partial \alpha_2}\right)^2 m_{\alpha_2}^2$$

$$\left.\begin{array}{c}\\ \\ \\ \\ \end{array}\right\} \tag{7.6}$$

and
$$m_Y^2 = \left(\frac{\partial Y}{\partial \alpha_1}\right)^2 m_{\alpha_1}^2 + \left(\frac{\partial Y}{\partial \alpha_2}\right)^2 m_{\alpha_2}^2$$

AP-M

Considering that the angles are obtained with equal reliability (in consideration of the same instrument, same observer, etc.), i.e.,

$$m_{\alpha_1} = m_{\alpha_2} = m_\alpha$$

one gets from Eqs 7.5 and 7.6;

$$m_s^2 = \left\{ \left(\frac{\partial X}{\partial \alpha_1} \right)^2 + \left(\frac{\partial X}{\partial \alpha_2} \right)^2 + \left(\frac{\partial Y}{\partial \alpha_1} \right)^2 + \left(\frac{\partial Y}{\partial \alpha_2} \right)^2 \right\} \cdot m_\alpha^2 \qquad (7.7)$$

From the above, with appropriate substitutions and rearrangements,

$$m_s^2 = \frac{d_1^2 + d_2^2}{\sin^2\gamma} m_\alpha^2 \qquad (7.8)$$

Considering that the working system is constant, the mensural reliability of all angles will be the same. Hence, consider m_α as unity (or, a constant). This gives the expression of the weight or degree of reliability of the planimetry of the intersection (P_s being the weight):

$$Ps \propto \frac{1}{m_s^2} = \frac{\sin^2\gamma}{d_1^2 + d_2^2} \qquad (7.9)$$

The above analogy from land surveying can be appropriately applied to a stereomodel where the perspective centers are the "stations" for the originating rays and the intersections are in the epipolar planes (i.e., these are spatial intersection cases), the perspective centers being the epipoles. Equation 7.9 can be expressed in terms of 'model' data (see Ghosh, 1972):

$$Ps \propto \frac{\sin^2\gamma}{d_1^2 + d_2^2} = \frac{b^2 (R^2 - X^2)}{R^2 (R^2 + b^2 - 2bX)(2R^2 + b^2 - 2bX)} \qquad (7.10)$$

where γ is the space-angle of intersection (parallactic angle);

d_1, d_2 are the distances of the model point from the perspective centers;

b is the model base;

$R^2 = X^2 + Y^2 + Z^2$

and X, Y, Z   are the model coordinates of the point in the International
                   system of coordinates (the left side perspective center being
                   the origin, the system being right handed with X-axis coinciding
                   with the base and the Z-axis pointing downwards).

Equation 7.10 can be used in principle in designing or planning a
photogrammetric project consisting of stereo models, in one way or the other.

The denominator in Eq. 7.10 (i.e., $d_1^2 + d_2^2$) will give, generally speaking,
better values when the object distances are smaller, which also corresponds to
larger scale photographs. The numerator indicates that the best possible situation
with regard to the angle of intersection is when $\gamma = 90°$. However, from practical
considerations, this is not always realistic. Usually, if the parallactic angle is
very large, stereo vision may be difficult. Unless the instrument is equipped with
continuously zooming optics, there could be serious problems in stereo observation.
In extreme cases, detail point identification may be impossible.

For planning purposes, it is customary to express the parallactic angle in
terms of base-distance ratio (or, base-height ratio in the aerial case). This, at
the middle of the model (considering $d_1 = d_2$) is: $b/Z = 2\tan(\gamma/2)$. The
obtainable accuracy of coordinates in the stereo model (expressed in terms of
error-ellipsoids or variance-covariance matrix, see Ghosh, 1972) can be related to
the average of all base-distance ratios in the model or the average parallactic
angle for the purpose of designing a project. The actual values may be obtained
empirically with regard to the camera, photograph material, instrument, etc. An
example is illustrated in Fig. 7.4, where a standard photography situation (i.e.,
f = 15 cm, 23×23 cm format) has been used. The standard errors of measuring the Z

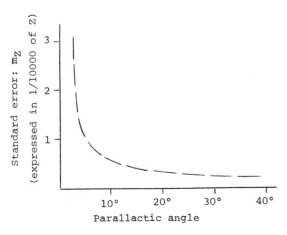

Fig. 7.4

Relation between height error
and parallactic angle
Note: Z is the projection distance

coordinates (m_z) were obtained at a Wild A7 Autograph instrument with precision grid stereo models.

An earlier study by Harpe (1965) with Zeiss Stereoplanigraph C8 instrument also gave similar results. Such graphs can be used for successful planning of a project. The optimum with regard to required accuracy and suitable stereo coverage of the object can be decided upon very easily.

7.3 TARGET DESIGN

Photogrammetric precision work often demands pre-signalization of points. The particular situation of the camera relative to the object would influence the shape and size of such targets. Other influencing factors are the imaging quality of the camera, the capability of the instrument (size of measuring marks, in particular), resolving capacity of the photographic material and the scale of the photograph. Targets must be provided in cases where lack of good stereo vision (say, due to extreme geometry) or lack of desirable natural features pose identification problems.

Because of the involved perspectivity, the targets may appear irregularly distorted in shape and in varying sizes on different photographs taken over the same object area in a stereo or multiple image situation. The resulting problems of image matching and accurate pointing are considerably minimized (practically eliminated) if symmetrical shaped targets (e.g., circles, concentric rings, crosses, triangles, or squares) are designed for use. The center of the target should, of course, refer to the point to be located and measured. Fortunately, all measuring instruments have symmetrical (usually circular) shaped measuring marks. The placement of such marks on the target image can be made with great reliability if the target appears larger than the measuring mark. In this light, considering a circular target, its minimum apparent diameter should not be smaller than that of the measuring mark. This would depend on the photo-scale. Accordingly, the following relationship holds:

$$d_{min} = \frac{d'}{M_B} = \frac{D \cdot d'}{f} \eqno(7.11)$$

where   d and d'   are the diameters of the circular target and the measuring
                    mark, respectively;

f   is the focal length of the camera;

D   is the object distance from camera base (flying height in aerial);

and M_B is the photo scale.

On the other hand, if the target appears as unusually large, placement of the measuring mark may not be made with sufficient reliability. In practice, therefore a very logical maximum diameter of such a target may be suggested:

$$d_{max} = \frac{2D \cdot d'}{f} \tag{7.12}$$

In terrestrial work, one may expect D to vary considerably. Therefore, careful individual designing of such targets is imperative. In general, targets of concentric rings giving several contrasty bands are favored. These seem to be universal in their applications.

Often one may require targets/marks used for identification purpose only and not for measurements. These have no consequences on the mensural accuracy; hence are not discussed here. However, mensural targets can always be used in such jobs.

7.4 REQUIRED ACCURACIES AND RESULTS

Each job being different from any other, its accuracy requirements need to be separately specified at the time of planning/designing with due consideration of the final objectives. Accordingly, on the completion of the project, the results should be assessed to see if the accuracy specifications are realized. For this also there should be acceptable criteria (of standards and specifications) and testing procedures.

Standard accuracy specifications and testing criteria can be and usually are established for standard (regular) jobs. Topographical mapping is one good example of such standard work. However, even in topo-mapping, accuracy specifications and testing procedures cannot be so clear and without controversy that they would give only one answer to the problem of evaluating the accuracy of a given map! . Furhtermore. a map may pass or fail, according to how the accuracy specifications are applied or interpreted.

The United States National Map Accuracy Standards, as drawn up by the Congress and issued by the office of Management and Budget (formerly, the Bureau of the Budget) in June 1947 states, among other points:

1. *Horizontal Accuracy.* For maps on publication scales larger than 1:20,000, not more than 10 percent of the points tested shall be in error by more than 1/30 inch, measured on the publication scale; for maps on publication scales of 1:20,000 or smaller, 1/50 inch. These limits of accuracy shall apply in all cases to positions of well defined points only. "Well defined" points are those that are easily visible or recoverable on the ground, such as the following: monuments or markers, such as bench marks, property boundary monuments; intersection of roads, railroads, etc.; corners of large buildings or structures (or center points of small buildings); etc. In general what is "well defined" will also be determined by what is plottable on the scale of the map within 1/100 inch. Thus while the intersection of two roads or property lines meeting at right angles would come within a sensible interpretation, identification of the intersection of such lines meeting at an acute angle would obviously not be practicable within 1/100 inch. Similarly, features not identifiable upon the ground within close limits are not considered as test points within the limits quoted, even though their positions may be scaled closely upon the map. In this class would come timber lines, soil boundaries, etc.

2. *Vertical Accuracy,* as applied to contour maps on all publications scale, will be such that not more than 10 percent of the elevations tested shall be in error more than one-half the contour interval. In checking elevations taken from the map, the apparent vertical error may be decreased by assuming a horizontal displacement within the permissible horizontal error for a map of that scale.

3. *The accuracy of any map* may be tested by comparing the positions of points whose locations or elevations are shown upon it with corresponding positions as determined by surveys of a higher accuracy. Tests shall be made by the producing agency, which shall also determine which of its maps are to be tested, and the extent of such testing.

Similar specifications are existing or are being developed in other countries and organizations. They indicate several important aspects, viz.,

(a) There is a general agreement on the desirability of using "standard deviation (or error)" or "root mean square error", directly or indirectly to express accuracy.

(b) In estimating accuracy on a map there is a widespread agreement of separating planimetry (X and Y coordinates being combined) from elevation (Z coordinates); i.e., horizontal (planimetric) accuracy from vertical (height) accuracy.

(c) For planimetry, it is debatable whether its accuracy should be expressed as a univariate or a bivariate (i.e., consisting of two variables, X and Y) entity.

(d) Another question remains, whether correct statistical theory is used in such expressions; e.g., whether or not the 90 percent rule is appropriate in evaluating topo maps.

7.4.1 Accuracy in Planimetry

In keeping with common practices, the linear standard errors for planimetric parameters are expressed as below:

$$\sigma_X = \left\{ \frac{\sum\limits_{i=1}^{n} (\Delta X_i)^2}{n} \right\}^{1/2} \quad \text{and} \quad \sigma_Y = \left\{ \frac{\sum\limits_{i=1}^{n} (\Delta Y_i)^2}{n} \right\}^{1/2} \quad (7.13)$$

where ΔX_i and ΔY_i are the coordinate discrepancies between accepted (as true or absolutely correct) and mapped positions at each test point;

and   n   is the total number of points used for checking.

Note: It is debatable if n (or, rather n−1) should be used in the denominators. For large values of n, the difference is not significant.

The planimetric standard error (σ_p) is expressd by:

$$\sigma_p^2 = \sigma_X^2 + \sigma_Y^2 \tag{7.14}$$

Some, however, favor using in such cases the *two-dimensional* (i.e., circular or elliptical) *standard error*, which is the error in a quantity defined by two random variables. With a fundamental assumption that planimetric errors are expected with equal probability in any direction with equal magnitude, the circular standard error concept is popular in many quarters. The circular standard error (σ_c) would represent the bivariate distribution level of 39.35 percent probability.

A comparative study made by Crombie (1967), reported in Thompson and Rosenfield (1971), of three approximate methods against the exact solution for determining the radius of a 90 percent probability circle indicates that the radius that most closely approximates the correct values under all conditions of $\sigma_{min}/\sigma_{max}$ where σ_{min} is the smaller linear standard error of the two, gives:

$$\sigma_c = \left\{ \frac{\sigma_X^2 + \sigma_Y^2}{2} \right\}^{1/2} = \frac{\sigma_P}{\sqrt{2}} \tag{7.15}$$

7.4.2 Accuracy in Elevation

The elevation accuracy in a map may be expressed by using the Koppe (1905) formula directly or indirectly. This formula, expressed for any point on a contour line is:

$$\sigma_{HC} = \sigma_{H'} + \sigma_p \cdot \tan\alpha \tag{7.16}$$

where σ_{HC} is the standard error in the elevation of a point on the contour line;

$\sigma_{H'}$ is the standard error of the determination of she spot height of a point (a measure of the working system and procedure);

σ_p is the standard planimetric error of a point (also a measure of the system and procedure);

and α is the local slope of the terrain.

This formula is usually adapted for expressing permissible elevation accuracy of points in a map:

$$\sigma_{\overline{H}} = 0.3 \cdot \overline{C} + \sigma_p \cdot \tan\alpha \qquad (7.17)$$

where $\sigma_{\overline{H}}$ is the permissible standard error in elevation;

$\overline{C}$ is the contour interval;

and σ_p, α are as above.

In practice, this can be applied when the ground slope is uniform over the entire area. In case there is considerable ruggedness, the formula should be applied point by point. This means that, for test points, the formula needs to be somewhat modified and rewritten (after Thompson, 1979):

$$\sigma_h = 0.3 \cdot \overline{C} \qquad (7.18)$$

where

$\sigma_H = \left\{ \dfrac{\sum e_{\overline{H}}^2}{n} \right\}^{1/2}$ = permissible standard error in elevation (or, height) based on residual errors at each point;

$e_{\overline{H}} = e - \sigma p \cdot \tan\alpha$ = residual error at each point;

and e is the elevation error before horizontal shift allowance.

7.4.3 Contour Interval

The choice of a contour interval, the obvious expression of the form of a surface is not an easy task. The contour intervals are practically always equal-step sequences.

The contour interval depends basically, on two considerations, viz., the map-scale and the amount of relief. In areas of high relief, the interval needs to be large because primarily of the inability to accomodate numerous lines in a small space. The same argument holds with regard to smaller map-scales. Smaller intervals would mean more work and thus certainly a factor of economic reality

also.   On the other hand, in order to depict landform in the best possible way one
would use the smallest possible interval. This has also a direct relation to the
permissible tolerances in the vertical accuracy desired of the map. The contour
interval represented on a map should be consistent with the map scale and the
intended use of the map.

Based on UN Studies (1983) a study of the frequency of contour intervals with
regard to specific map scales was made by Ghosh (1987). In view of this, one can
make a list of recommended contour intervals (Table 7.1).

Associated with the contour-intervals vis-a-vis the map-scale is the
consideration of elevation accuracy. Following the practice in the U.S.A. and most
of the NATO countries the à posteriori standard height error (m_H) required in most
countries is that 90% of the elevations tested should be accurate within half the
contour interval. On the other hand, the obtainable accuracy in photogrammetric
mapping depends on the photography, the camera, the intersection geometry (overlap)
and the instrument used, amongst others. Assuming a good quality wide angle
(standard) aerial camera, 60% forward overlap and a precision plotter, one would
expect m_H to be always better than 0.1% of the flying height. These two accuracy
criteria often do not agree in the results.

In view of the above, certain confusion exists with the people involved in
planning for topographical mapping. In particular, since the obtainable accuracy
depends on the ground control, it is the accuracy desired of such ground control
that is often of immediate concern to the planner. In this regard, a list of
reasonable average elevation accuracies for ground control as provided in Table 7.1
can be suggested.

With regard to contour intervals (C.I.) one of the most authoritative ideas was
presented by Imhof (1965) suggesting the following equation, irrespective of the
accuracy requirements:

$$\text{C.I.} = n.\log n. \text{tg } \alpha \tag{7.19}$$

where $n = \sqrt{\dfrac{K}{100} + 1}$

             α = slope of terrain

and K = map scale number.

Table 7.1

Reasonable contour intervals and elevation accuracies

Map scale M_K	Recommended in general (UN study)	According to Imhof			Standard error at control pts: m_H (in metre)
		Contour intervals (in metre)			
		Mountainous terrain ($\alpha = 45°$)	Medium terrain ($\alpha = 26°$)	Flat terrain ($\alpha = 9°$)	
1:500	0.5	1	0.46	0.15	± 0.15
1:1 000	1	1	0.5	0.25	± 0.30
1:2 000	2	2	1	0.5	± 0.40
1:5 000	5	5	2	1	± 0.60
1:10 000	5,10	10	5	2	± 0.70
1:20 000	10,20	20	10	2.5	± 0.80
1:25 000	10,20	20	10	2.5	± 1.00
1:50 000	10,20,40	20,30	10,20	5	± 1.25
1:100 000	20,50	50	25	5,10	± 2.00

Large-scale group: 1:500 – 1:20 000

Small-scale group: 1:25 000 – 1:100 000

Note: Usually the cost of mapping varies inversely as the square of m_H for the same map-scale. Therefore, accuracy requirements should be established with care.

Imhof considered in general $\alpha = 45°$ to represent highly mountainous terrain (for example, in countries like Nepal, Switzerland or Equador), $\alpha = 26°$ for medium mountainous terrain (for example, in countries like Burma or Greece) and $\alpha = 9°$ for flat terrain (for example in countries like Bangladesh, Egypt or Holland). For the sake of technical interest, Imhof's ideas may be studied against the values recommended here (Table 7.1).

There is also a current tendency, however, to promote variable contour intervals in a map, this based on the terrain ruggedness and some demands made from the map. Even contour intervals combined with shading has been attempted. These indicate newer tendencies. The future would show the possibilities. However, these are beyond the scope of this book.

For further interesting ideas with respect to contour lines and contour intervals, see Richardus (1973).

In assessing test data, one must avoid blunders. An appropriate and statistically acceptable method of detecting blunders (so that one can eliminate them) should be used. Furthermore, in most organizations, coordinatographs are used for reading map coordinates as necessary in such assessments. The positional accuracy of points is evaluated by measurements of graticule (or map grid) marks or lines and well-defined points. In this respect, the use of a calibrated precision coordinatographs is imperative. The use of an on-line computer would allow the evaluation as a real-time operation.

The map grid or graticule points need to be evaluated first in accordance with the used map-projection since the grid represents the geometric foundation of the map. The plan positions of the grid points must be corrected first according to the coordinatograph calibration. The corrected data are then to be fitted by an acceptable transformation (with due consideration of the Least Squares adjustment). The residuals of this adjustment (of grid points) would give an idea of the overall reliability of the map. Only after an evaluation of the map grid points should one work for the evaluation of the detail points for both planimetry and elevation.

Two other tables (Tables 7.2 and 7.3) are presented here with a view to providing answers to other remaining questions with regard to the control on which such map compilations are based. These two tables were prepared in 1967 by the ASP Photogrammetry for Highway Commitee. It is, however, assumed that with improving technology one would expect to improve on the presented 'specifications'.

Table 7.2

Specifications for basic control in aerial surveys and mapping

(Maximum error of closure for basic ground control)

| Order of accuracy | Unadjusted horizontal distances | Unadjusted horizontal angles | | | Unadjusted vertical distances |
| | | Traverse | Triangulation | | |
			Average	Maximum	
First	1:25 000	2" √N	1"	3"	4.0mm √K
Second	1:10 000	10" √N	3"	5"	8.4mm √K
Third	1: 5 000	30" √N	5"	10"	12.0mm √K
Fourth	1: 2 500	60" √N	15"	30"	120.0mm √K

Note: N is the number of stations in the traverse circuit

and K is the number of kilometres in the level circuit.

[After the Highway Committee, ASP, 1967]

Table 7.3

Specifications for error tolerances in control extension

by photo-triangulation

| Classification | | Absolute error as a fraction of flying height | | |
| | | Planimetry | | Elevation |
		X	Y	Z
Maximum[±]	(1)	1:2 700	1:2 700	1:1 800
	(2)	1:2 100	1:2 100	1:1 500
Average	(1)	1:18 000	1:18 000	1:12 000
	(2)	1:14 000	1:14 000	1:10 000
Standard	(1)	1:9 000	1:9 000	1:6 000
(rms)	(2)	1:7 000	1:7 000	1:5 000

Note: (1) refers to Super-wide-angle (f ≃ 9cm) photography

(2) refers to Standard-angle (f ≃ 15cm) photography

[After the Highway Committee, ASP, 1967]

Individual organizations would consider their own criteria with regard to specific work circumstances. Therefore, the ideas presented in this chapter should be taken in the spirit of a broad guiding outline, of which details could not be provided here.

BIBLIOGRAPHY

American Society of Photogrammetry; *Manual of Photogrammetry,*(4th Ed.) (ASPRS, Falls Church, Virginia: 1980).

Crombie, M. A.; *Note on Circular Errors*(Unpublished, Autometric Operations, Raytheon Corporation: 1967).

Ghosh, Sanjib K.; "Photo/Model/Map Scales", *PE* 37, No. 11 (1971).

Ghosh, Sanjib K.; *Theory of Stereophotogrammetry* (The Ohio State University Bookstores; Columbus, Ohio: 1972).

Ghosh, Sanjib K.; "Economic Aspects in Special Applications of Photogrammetry"; *ISP Archives (Invited Paper)* Helsinky Congress; Helsinky, Finland (1976).

Ghosh, Sanjib K.; "Some thoughts on Photo-scale, Map-scale and Contour intervals in topographic mapping"; *Photogrammetria* 42; No. 1   (1988).

Harpe, R. W.; "Experiments with Minimum to Optimum Base-Height Ratios" *Proceedings of ASP Semi-Annual Convention*; Dayton, Ohio (1965).

Imhof, Eduard; *Kartographische Gelände-Darstellung* (Walter de Gruyter & Co., Berlin: 1965).

Richardus, P.; "The Precision of Contour Lines and Contour Intervals of Large and Medium Scale Maps"; *Photogrammetria* 29, No. 3 (1973).

Thompson, M. M. and G. H. Rosenfield; "On Map Accuracy Specifications"; *Surveying and Mapping* 31, No. 1 (1971).

Thompson, M. M.; *Maps for America* (US Geological Survey: 1979).

United Nations (Brandenberger, A. J. and Ghosh, S. K. for the UN); *World Cartography* (Vol. 16, UN Sales No. E.83.I [No. ST/ESA/SER.L/17]: 1983).

MULTIPLE-PHOTO APPLICATIONS

The utilization of more than two photographs is nothing but the synthesis of certain photogrammetric principles that are applied to a single photo or simple extension of stereophotogrammetric principles. The user of photogrammetric services can be from various fields of science and engineering. Nevertheless, one major use of analytical photogrammetry has been in the field of control provision for topographic mapping. This is known as *Photo-triangulation* (or Aerial Triangulation). There are numerous phototriangulation procedures depending on the instrumental or computational solutions of various involved operations (Ghosh, 1975). These are illustrated in figs 8.1 and 8.1a. Depending on the extent of use of an instrument or a computer, one may consider a particular procedure as *analogical* or *analytical*.

There are usually many ways to approach a problem. It is not easy to prepare a schedule that is both economical and realistic. With regard to data acquisition and data processing, problems related to single photos or stereo models have been presented in Chaps 3, 4 and 5. Multiple photographs pose different and unique data-handling procedures and may even require supplementary mathematical modeling. In this chapter will be discussed only the computational procedures where the instrumental work is limited to the reading of only the x, y photo coordinates, the rest being done at a computer, on-line or off-line. These would illustrate certain procedures which are utilized with success in various organizations.

It may be noted that multiple photographs may also be used in applications other than control extension, like in self-calibration (Chaps 9, 10) or in enhancing intersection accuracies. The triangulation procedures are grouped in two categories, sequential and simultaneous.

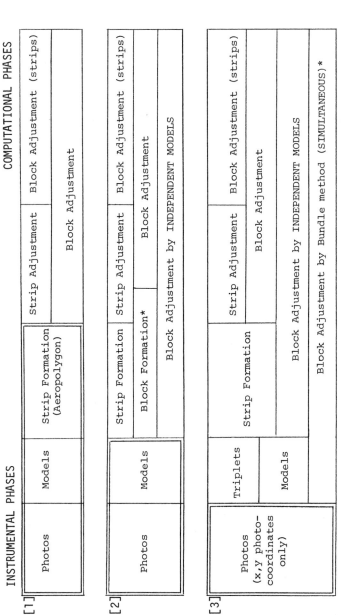

Fig. 8.1 Outline of phototriangulation procedures : [1] Analogical procedures;
[2] Semi-analytical procedures; and [3] Analytical procedures

*Program in the Appendix of book PHOTOTRIANGULATION (Ghosh, 1975)

8.1 SEQUENTIAL PROCEDURE

This procedure can be visualized as analogous to the instrumental process of photo-triangulation. It consists of the following three computational steps:

(a) Relative Orientation of individual basic units in arbitrary coordinate systems (Note: A basic unit cas be a stereo-pair, a triplet or a sub-block of limited number of photographs);

(b) Assembly of the basic units to form the full block (of all the photographs);

(c) Adjustment of the assembled block to known control.

There are two variations in this approach:

1. *Aeropolygon:* The procedure somewhat follows the routine of an analog steroeplotter by performing co-orientations (relative orientation by dependent method in second and subsequent models) in each strip. Next, without affecting the co-orientation, the resulting model's scale (say, by utilizing the scale restraint condition) is adjusted to that of the preceding model. One strip is formed and possible adjusted initially. Other strips are subsequently formed, adjusted and connected one after the other (sequentially) to form the block which is finally adjusted to the ground control. The method of Independent Models (see Ackermann et al, 1973; Ghosh, 1975), in principle is basically this approach, performed also with analog stereo plotters.

2. *Three-photo (Triplet) Analytic:* In this procedure, all six orientation elements of the photograph are computed simultaneously (by applying the Collenearity condition) and, in the presence of redundant observations, adjusted by utilizying the principles of Least Squares. For points which are common with the preceding stereo pair, the condition of intersection with the corresponding ray from the first photograph in that model is used for adjusting all exterior elements (see details given later).

In these procedures, in spite of using more than one common point between models, the deformation of one model (Ghosh, 1972)   may cause the next and other subsequent models to deform also. Consequently, the results of the triangulation would depend on the initial model (or the basic unit) and the propagation of error through the strip.

AP-N

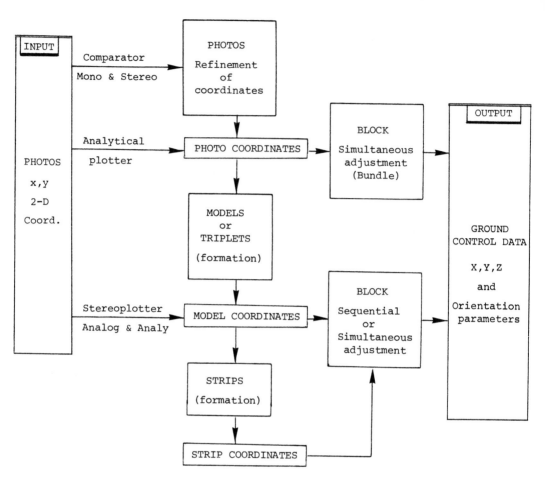

Fig. 8.1a Flowchart showing various possibilites of analytical

phototriangulation

A typical example of the various stages of a sequential method of triangulation
is as follows (as practiced at the NOS; see Keller and Tewinkel, 1967):

Phase I: Data Acquisition

1.   Photo preparation and stereo marking of necessary points;

2.   Coordinate measurements of all points on the photographs;

Phase II   Date Processing:

   1.   Coordinate refinement

        a.   Correction for comparator calibration (Chap. 2);
        b.   Correction for film distortion with reduction to perspective center
             (Chap. 5);
        c.   Correction for lens distortion (Chap. 5);
        d.   Correction for atmospheric refraction (Chap. 5);
        e.   Correction for Earth's curvature (Chap. 5.), if applicable;
        f.   Correction for image motion and réseau (Chap. 5) as may be
             applicable;

   2.   Solution

        a.   Iterative coorientations (or three-photo orientations, explained
             later);
        b.   Cantilever assembly (with or without scale restraint, Chap. 4);
        c.   Earth curvature correction, if applicable and not performed earlier;
        d.   Strip (or Block) transformation to the ground control system (Chap.
             3);

   3.   Solution refinement

        a.   Further transformation as necessary (e.g., to Geocentric system);
        b.   Block adjustment (explained later) in case necessary.

   Most strip triangulations would terminate at Phase II2b (Keller and Tewinkel,
1967). However, depending on the degree of required accuracy, one may continue
with the subsequent steps. Step IIa, alternately, may be performed by (i) Relative
orientation using coplanarity condition (Chap. 4) and (ii) scale-transfer, by using
the scale-restraint condition (Chap. 4). Some of these steps are elaborated
briefly below:

ITERATIVE COORIENTATION: This is entirely independant of any ground control data.
Three-photo orientation is also coorientational. At the end of the strip, one
obtains the positions of all pertinent points in a three-dimensional coordinate
system at the approximate photo scale (unless a particular scale is considered).

The residual errors can be analyzed at this stage with the help of a computer. Data with blunders may be removed to obtain 'clean' data for subsequent work.

STRIP TRANSFORMATION TO GROUND SYSTEM: This is the transformation of model coordinates into the prevailing ground control by fitting, through the application of polynomials (see Ghosh, 1975). The principle of Least Squares may be applicable here also. The result of this step is a set of provisional three-dimensionl coordinates of all points in the strip. Large residual discrepancies may be detected by human inspection to provide another step of freeing the data of blunders prior to entering the solution refinement program.

BLOCK ADJUSTMENT: This would involve: (a) Simultaneous solution of the parameters of absolute orientation (viz., dX_o, dY_o, dZ_o, $d\omega$, $d\varphi$ and $d\kappa$) for all the photos; and (b) Corrections to the provisional coordinates (X, Y, Z) of all the points. In the US National Oceanic Survey prectice (Keller and Tewinkel, 1967), this consists of three stages:

1. *Space Resection*. It starts with reading into storage the known ground coordinates (duly weighted) of control points and also the provisional ground coordinates of all points. The space resection routine fits the image coordinates data from each photograph to the corresponding provisional groung data in order to determine the initial exterior orientation parameters. This leads to the solution of the sets of equations (one set for each photograph) having the six incremental corrections to the unknown parameters and solving iteratively until further corrections are insignificant (see also Chapters 4 and 6).

2. *Block Orientation*. The solution of absolute orientation of all the photographs and the obtaining of the ground coordinates (final) of each point. The output of this stage contains:

   a. The maximum angular correction required by each program pass;
   b. The ground coordinates of all *pass points* used in relative orientation;

   Note: Pass points are of two types: (1) *Transfer points*, used for connecting adjacent models in the same strip; and (2) *Tie* or *Wing points*, used for connecting adjacent or crossing strips (Ghosh, 1975).

c. The misfits at the weighted control points;

d. The residual descrepancies of all photo coordinates on each photograph
    and the standard (RMS) values for the entire block;

e. The sine and cosine values of the final rotation angles $(\omega, \varphi, \kappa)$ of
    each photograph; and

f. The final three coordinates of each camera station (X_o, Y_o, Z_o).

3. *Object Intersection.* This gives the points other than pass points and the
    control points for which accurate ground coordinates are to be computed
    (e.g., the points for low-flown models from high-flown photographs).
    Because these points are non-uniformly distributed, they are generally not
    included in the stage of orientation, since their very presence could
    weight the solution unduly in view of their locations. An unlimited number
    of points may be determined in this stage because of their separate
    treatments.

THREE-PHOTO ANALYTIC (or, TRIPLET) METHOD: One requires only two photographs for a
relatibe orientation. The use of three photographs, combining aspects of relative
orientation and scale transfer in a simultaneous solution, may be considered as a
computational advantage towards a stronger geometry. The scheme is set for basic
unit of three photographs (hence the name, Triplet), e.g., 1-2-3, 2-3-4, 3-4-5, and
so on. Each triplet is oriented separately. By using three photographs in the
triple overlap area, one obtains a double check on the y-parallax (relative
orientation) and a check on the x-parallax (scale transfer). This scheme is
illustrated in Fig. 8.2. This arrangement helps tie one stereopair (say 3-4) to
the adjacent ones (say, here, 2-3 and 4-5) with considerable strength. This is
because one has a complete stereopair consisting of two rows of pass-points for

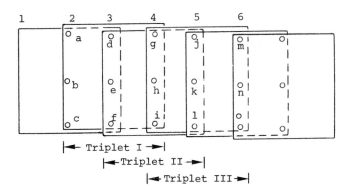

Fig. 8.2 Schematic arrangement of triplets

connecting adjacent triplets (e.g., in Fig. 8.2, points d, e, f and g, h, i are common to the triplets I and II). The working procedure is to consider the middle photograph of a triplet as fixed and the adjacent photographs are tied to it simultaneously on both sides. Also, a value for one stereo base (bx) is assigned initially. For example, one may consider the following in triplet I:

Photo #1: $X_{o1} = 0$ and ω_1, φ_1, κ_1, Y_{o1}, Z_{o1} are assumed to be zero initially.

Photo #2: $X_{o2} = 1$ and $\omega_2 = \varphi_2 = \kappa_2 = Y_{o2} = Z_{o2} = 0$ kept fixed; and

Photo #3: X_{o3}, Y_{o3}, Z_{o3}, ω_3, φ_3 and κ_3 are assumed to be zero initially.

Each photograph having six exterior orientation elements, this scheme gives seven out of the total eighteen elements as fixed initially. In order to avoid negative values, for practical convenience, it is advisable to consider $X_{o1} = 0$ and $X_{o2} = 1$. This means that, in this triplet, in view of one collinearity equation for each photo coordinate, and the standard pass points, the following situation exists:

Photo No.	Number of Points	Number of Unknowns	Number of Equations
1	6	5	12
2	9	0	18
3	6	6	12

Thus, in this triplet, there are 11 unknowns and 42 observation equations, which can be reduced to eleven normal equations (in order to solve for the eleven unknowns by applying the principles of Least Squares). The method of obtaining model coordinates of points and the associated details are discussed in Ghosh (1975).

When triplet II is connected to triplet I, the Z values at points d, e, f are first taken from triplet I; at points g, h, i are taken from triplet II; while the X and Y values are cheked together from both triplets. This procedure follows to the end of the strip. Circumstances permitting, two-directional (i.e., along X- and Y-axes) triplets are of considerable help in block formation and adjustment.

The basic condition equations in this case are of the form of Eqs 4.8 for photographs 1 and 3 (2 being fixed), by linearizing which the set of observation equations of the form of Eqs. 4.14 is obtained:

For the first steroegram (i.e., photo pair 1-2):

$$
\begin{aligned}
v_{x1j} = P_{11} &+ P_{12}d\omega_1 + P_{13}d\varphi_1 + P_{14}d\kappa_1 - P_{15}dX_{o1} - P_{16}dY_{o1} \\
&- P_{17}dZ_{o1} + P_{15}dX_{1j} + P_{16}dY_{1j} + P_{17}dZ_{1j}
\end{aligned}
$$

$$
\begin{aligned}
v_{y1j} = P_{21} &+ P_{22}d\omega_1 + P_{23}d\varphi_1 + P_{24}d\kappa_1 - P_{25}dX_{o1} - P_{26}dY_{o1} \\
&- P_{27}dZ_{o1} + P_{25}dX_{1j} + P_{26}dY_{1j} + P_{27}dZ_{1j}
\end{aligned}
$$

$$(8.1)$$

For the second stereogram (i.e., photo pair 2-3):

$$
\begin{aligned}
v_{x3j} = Q_{11} &+ Q_{12}d\omega_3 + Q_{13}d\varphi_3 + Q_{14}d\kappa_3 - Q_{15}dX_{o3} - Q_{16}dY_{o3} \\
&- Q_{17}dZ_{o3} + Q_{15}dX_{3j} + Q_{16}dY_{3j} + Q_{17}dZ_{3j}
\end{aligned}
$$

$$
\begin{aligned}
v_{y3j} = Q_{21} &+ Q_{22}d\omega_3 + Q_{23}d\varphi_3 + Q_{24}d\kappa_3 - Q_{25}dX_{o3} - Q_{26}dY_{o3} \\
&- Q_{27}dZ_{o3} + Q_{25}dX_{3j} + Q_{26}dY_{3j} + Q_{27}dZ_{3j}
\end{aligned}
$$

$$(8.2)$$

Where the coefficients $P_{11} \ldots P_{27}$ and $Q_{11} \ldots Q_{27}$ are derived by partial differentiation of the basic pairs of equations of the form of Eqs 4.8. Subscript j refers to the point, subscripts x and y refer to the respective photo coordinates, and subscripts 1, 2 and 3 refer to the respective photographs. The coefficients obtained in this way have initially only preliminary values, which are changed in the iterative procedure of computation to add corrections to the respective variables.

The unknown parameters here are of two groups, viz, (a) The Exterior orientation parameters, $d\omega$, $d\varphi$, $d\kappa$, dX_o, dY_o and dZ_o, all of which remain constant for one photograph; and (b) The Model coordinates, dX_j, dY_j and dZ_j, each of which differ for each point. Because X, Y, Z are variables that differ with each photograph, an elimination of these variables is necessary for the solution of Eqs

8.1 and 8.2. This can be done by substituting their values in terms of the variables that are fixed in value for every photograph (i.e., ω, φ, κ, X_o, Y_o and Z_o). For interesting ideas on these, see Harris et al (1963), Anderson and McNair (1966), and Ghosh (1975).

The most used sequential procedure is not fully computational. It may be considered as a variation where the relative orientation of the stereo models is performed at a stereo plotter (can be an analytical plotter), simply because of convenience and overall efficiency. In this procedure, model connection, scale-transfer, strip or block formation and adjustments are subsequently performed at a computer. Because of this combination of analytical and analogical processes, often this is called a "Semi-analytical" method of photo triangulation.

Some specific methods of sequential photo-triangulation procedure as currently available in the world are listed below:

1. *The Ohio State University Method*: For strip or block triangulation at a stereo plotter or an analytical plotter by the collection of Independent Models (see Ghosh, 1975 for details and the computer programs). Philip (1973) made an interesting error study of this method and Strahle (1971) made a comparative study of this method by utilizing an analytical plotter.

2. *National Research Council of Canada Method*: For strip triangulation, with a possobility of extension into a block by using only comparator data. In this the basic unit is the stereo model. See Schut (1973) for details.

3. *National Oceanic Survey of the USA Method*: For strip or block triangulation by using triplets as basic units and by utilizing only comparator data. See Harris et al (1963), Keller and Tewinkel (1966, 1967) for details and various aspects of the procedure.

4. *University of Stuttgart Method*: For strip of block triangulation with Independent Models with a stereo plotter or a comparator, the basic unit being the stereo model. See Ackermann et al (1973) for details. The software contains a simultaneous adjustment of models in the block.

5. *Rapid Analytical Block Aerial Triangulation System (RABATS) Method*: This is a comprehensive strip or block triangulation software package developed by J. F. Kenefick, Photogrammetric Consultant, Inc., Florida, USA. The

basic unit here is a stereo model formed either at a stereo plotter or with comparator data. Private communications with the author indicates that this has various features; e.g., as a by-product of fully analytical solutions, relative and absolute orientation elements are calculated for a number of stereo plotters. A group of 'support' programs are provided for computation peripheral to the aerial triangulation solution itself. An auxiliary program allows readjustment of a provisional horizontal solution for a strip or block to independently measured distances and azimuths. Some interesting features of this methos are also presented in Ghosh (1975).

8.2 SIMULTANEOUS PROCEDURE

This procedure (also known as "Bundle" solution) offers another approach whereby the desired parameters are also adjusted as a result of one simultaneous least squares solution of all the photographs by an iterative method. The iteration is involved because of the fact that the associated condition equations are non-linear. However, one can also form non-linear 'normal equations', in which case the solution can be considered as 'direct'. From a theoretical point of view, such a simultaneous procedure should provide the most accurate results.

The fundamental requirements in this procedure are the estimates of the exterior orientation parameters. Furthermore, depending on the specific approach taken, the estimates for coordinates of all pass points may also be needed. Thus, a simultaneous procedure should include a feasible method of obtaining the necessary estimated (approximate) values initially.

The basic equations used in this are the ones establishing the collinearity condition (Eqs 4.8, 4.9 and 4.10). These are non-linear functions relating the parameters (unknowns) to the observed and given (known) data:

$$f(L) \ = \ F(O,X) \eqno(8.3)$$

where   L   represents the observed (x,y) photo coordinates, already refined for all systematic distortions;

           O   represents the exterior orientation parameters;

and   X   represents the object space coordinates.

Considering that the observation data (albeit refined) may have discrepancies or residual errors (represented by V), one gets:

$$L + V = F(O_o + \Delta O, \quad X_o + \Delta X) \tag{8.4}$$

where O_o, X_o are the approximate values;

and ΔO, ΔX are the successive corrections.

Linearization of Eq. 8.4 by Taylor expansion would give:

$$f(L) + \frac{\partial f}{\partial L} \Delta L = F(O_o, X_o) + \frac{\partial F}{\partial O}\Delta O + \frac{\partial F}{\partial X}\Delta X \tag{8.5}$$

This, compactly stated and utilizing the commonly used notations, with respect to the image point j on photograph i, is:

$$\underset{(2,1)}{V_{ij}} + \underset{(2,6)}{\dot{B}_{ij}} \quad \underset{(6,1)}{\dot{\delta}_{i}} + \underset{(2,3)}{\ddot{B}_{ij}} \quad \underset{(3,1)}{\ddot{\delta}_{j}} = \underset{(2,1)}{\varepsilon_{ij}} \tag{8.6}$$

where

$$V_{ij} = [v_x \quad v_y]_{ij} \qquad = \quad \text{residuals of measured photo-coordinates;}$$

$$\dot{B}_{ij} = \begin{bmatrix} a_1 & a_2 & \cdots & a_6 \\ b_1 & b_2 & \cdots & b_6 \end{bmatrix}_{ij} = \quad \text{coefficient matrix, in which the}$$

elements are partial differentials of the collinearity equations with respect to the unknown, exterior orientation, parameters of the photograph;

$$\dot{\delta}_{i} = [\delta_\omega, \delta_\varphi, \cdots Z_o]_{i} \qquad = \quad \text{corrections to estimates for the unknown}$$

exterior orientation paremeters;

$$\ddot{B}_{ij} = \begin{bmatrix} a_7 & a_8 & a_9 \\ b_7 & b_8 & b_9 \end{bmatrix}_{ij} = \quad \text{coefficient matrix, in which the}$$

elements are partial differentials of the collinearity equations with respect to the unknown, object point, coordinates;

$$\overset{..}{\delta}_j \;=\; [\Delta X \;\; \Delta Y \;\; \Delta Z \;]_j \qquad = \quad \text{corrections to estimates for the unknown, object point coordinates;}$$

and $\quad \varepsilon_{ij} \;=\; [f(x) \;\; f(y)\;]_{ij} \qquad = \quad$ the values of Eq. 8.3 with estimated values being substituted for the unknown parameters.

Equivalently, $\qquad\qquad\qquad \bar{V} + \bar{B}\cdot\bar{\delta} \;=\; \bar{\varepsilon}$ $\qquad\qquad\qquad$ (8.7)

Equations 8.6 or 8.7 are the 'condition' equations, from which the 'Normal' equations (see for example, Mikhail, 1976) are formed:

$$N\cdot\delta \;=\; c \qquad\qquad (8.8)$$

where $\qquad N \quad = \quad \bar{B}^T P \, \bar{B}$

$\qquad\qquad c \quad = \quad \bar{B}^T P \, \bar{\varepsilon}$

and $\qquad P \quad$ is the weight (inverse of the covariance) matrix.

The solution of the normal equations is expressed by:
$$\delta \;=\; N^{-1}c \qquad\qquad (8.9)$$

Further consideration of the comparative reliability of various parameters can be made in the adjustment procedure by enforcing "weight constraints" (discussed in Chap. 9.). The weight matrices of the exterior orientation parameters and of the object point coordinates can be determined. Their utilization in a simultaneous solution of a block of aerial photographs (after Brown, 1974, 1976) modifies the set of the normal equations (Eq. 8.8), by making use of partitioning, to give:

$$\begin{bmatrix} \dot{N} + \dot{P} & \bar{N} \\ \bar{N}^T & \ddot{N} + \ddot{P} \end{bmatrix} \begin{bmatrix} \dot{\delta} \\ \ddot{\delta} \end{bmatrix} = \begin{bmatrix} \dot{c} - \dot{P}\dot{\delta} \\ \ddot{c} - \ddot{P}\ddot{\varepsilon} \end{bmatrix} \qquad (8.10)$$

in which, for a block of m photographs containing n object points, the respective dimensions are as given below:

$$\dot{\delta} : 6m \times 1 \qquad \dot{P} : 6m \times 6m \qquad \dot{\varepsilon} : 6m \times 1$$
$$\ddot{\delta} : 3n \times 1 \qquad \ddot{P} : 3n \times 3n \qquad \ddot{\varepsilon} : 3n \times 1$$

Note, as before, single dots refer to the exterior orientation paremeters and double dots refer to the object point coordinates. $\dot{P}$ and $\ddot{P}$ are the inverse covariance matrices. $\dot{\varepsilon}$ and $\ddot{\varepsilon}$ are the vectors of discrepancies between a priori (or, observed) values of exterior orientation parameters and object point coordinates, respectively, and their corresponding values used in linearization of projective equations. $\dot{N}$, $\ddot{N}$, $\bar{N},\dot{c}$ and $\ddot{c}$ are the contributions to normal equations resulting from the observed (and refined) photo-coordinates of the points.

The feasibility of a solution in practice depends on the augmentation of the weight matrices, their becoming diagonal matrices of dimension 6 × 6 for each photograph. This hinges on the assumption that the exterior orientation elements of different photographs are uncorrelated. Likewise, the coordinates of different object points are also assumed to be uncorrelated. For those paremeters which are treated as completely unknown, the appropriate positions of the augmented weight matrices are filled with zero elements. The augmented supplementary discrepancy vectors $\dot{\varepsilon}$ and $\ddot{\varepsilon}$ also would contain zero elements in the appropriate locations for the unknown quantities. Thus, $\ddot{P}_j$ and $\ddot{\varepsilon}_j$ for points used in relative orientation for example, would reduce to null matrices.

SOLUTION OF NORMAL EQUATIONS

It will be of interest to note that the normal equations of the form given below (Eq. 8.11) are indeterminate if one holds the working assumption that all of the three coordinates of each of the ground points as well as six of the exterior orientation parameters of each photograph, both, are unknowns unless some other additional considerations (as in self-calibration) are made. The matrices are defined directly by the linearized pair of projective equations (Eq. 8.6).

$$
\begin{bmatrix} \dot{N}_{ij} & \bar{N}_{ij} \\ (6,6) & (6,3) \\[2em] \bar{N}^T_{ij} & \ddot{N}_{ij} \\ (3,6) & (3,3) \end{bmatrix}
\begin{bmatrix} \dot{\delta}_i \\ (6,1) \\[2em] \ddot{\delta}_j \\ (3,1) \end{bmatrix}
=
\begin{bmatrix} \dot{c}_{ij} \\ (6,1) \\[2em] \ddot{c}_{ij} \\ (3,1) \end{bmatrix}
\qquad (8.11)
$$

where $\dot{N} = \dot{B}^T P \dot{B}$; $\ddot{N} = \ddot{B}^T P \ddot{B}$; $\bar{N} = \dot{B}^T P \ddot{B}$

$\dot{c} = \dot{B}^T P \dot{\varepsilon}$; $\ddot{c} = \ddot{B}^T P \ddot{\varepsilon}$;

and P is the weight matrix of the measured photo coordinates.

This difficulty of indeterminacy can be removed by deleting from this system each row and column corresponding to a known quantity. Furthermore, whenever a point (j) fails to appear on a photo (i), the weight matrix (P) can set to a zero matrix. This yields two alterations of the general normal equations, viz., (a) all corresponding $\bar{N}_{ij}$ submatrices become null matrices; and (b) all indicated summations along the principal diagonal are limited either to the points appearing on a given photograph (upper semi-diagonal) or to the photographs containing a given point (lower semi-diagonal).

In view of above, for an aerial block triangulation, the overall $\bar{N}$ submatrix tends to be rather sparse in the final structure. This is illustrated in Fig. 8.4, which shows the structure of the coefficient matrix of the general system of normal equations generated from the photo block schematically presented in Fig. 8.3.

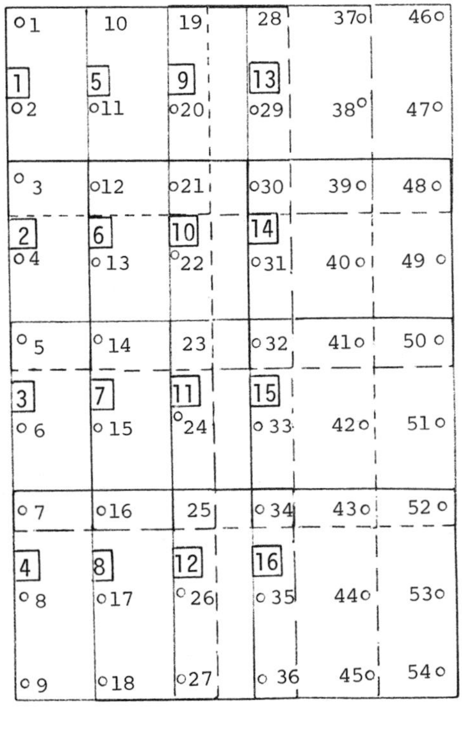

Fig. 8.3 Schematic diagram of a block of 4×4 photographs
(with cross-strip ordering of points and photographs, after
Brown, 1976)

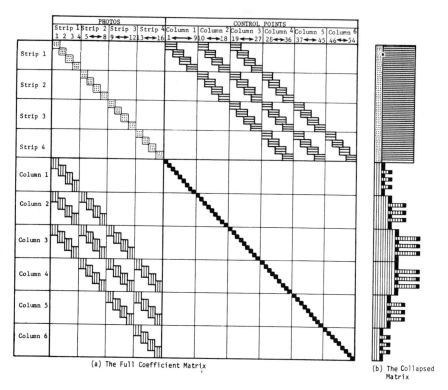

(a) The Full Coefficient Matrix

(b) The Collapsed Matrix

Fig. 8.4   Structure of general normal equations for simultaneous
adjustment of the block shown in Fig. 8.3 (after Brown, 1976)

Brown et al (1964), in taking advantage of the sparseness characteristics of
the matrix, utilized the indirect method of *Block Successive Over-Relaxation*
(BSOR).   The unique characteristic of this approach lies in the use of an indexing
scheme whereby, (a) only non-zero submatrices of the normal equations would be
formed, and (b) these would be stored and operated on in a collapsed form (see Fig.
8.5b).   This process drastically reduces storage requirements in the computer and
facilitates the formation and solution of the normal equations.   Davis (1966)
demonstrated the effectiveness of this approach.   The BSOR approach is somewhat
sensitive to the number and distribution of absolute control points in the block.
If there are more control points, the convergence of the solution is faster (i.e.,
fewer iterations).   In the extreme cases of very sparse control, the slowness of
convergence may create confusion in otherwise satisfactory reduction fo data.
Another drawback of this approach is that it does not produce the inverse of the
coefficient matrix of the normal equations.   Thus, the assessment of the quality of
the adjustment (in terms of computations of the covariance matrices of triangulated
coordinates) is not accomplished efficiently.

The shortcomings of the BSOR reduction are avoided by utilizing an algorithm called *Recursive Partitioning*, first published by Gyer (1967). This is performed by exploiting the banded structure of the reduced normal equations generated in the block triangulation with appropriately ordered photographs (see Fig. 8.4, note the $\bar{N}$ matrix for example, conforming to the cross-strip ordering scheme of Fig. 8.3). With cross-strip ordering, all non-zero elements of the coefficient matrix are confined to a diagonal band. The width of the band depends on the number of strips forming the block, but is independent of the number of photographs in the strips.

Recursive partitioning is also applicable to banded-bordered systems as illustrated in Fig. 8.5, which shows one N×N coefficient matrix having bandwidth q and borderwidth r. Following Brown (1976), one may start with the quadruply partitioned banded-bordered system as illustrated in Fig. 8.5. The number of elements in the first partition (s) is arbitrary except that $s \le q$. In the second partition, the number of elements correspond to the bandwidth q. The third partition containts $t = N - (s + q + r)$ and the fourth partition is equal to the borderwidth r. In view of this partitioning, the submatrices N_{13} and N_{13}^T are both composed of zeroes.

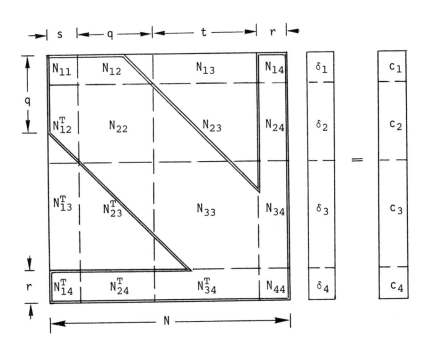

Fig. 8.5 An example of N×N banded-bordered coefficient matrix with bandwidth q and borderwidth r (after Brown, 1976)

Furthermore, the subvector δ_1 is eliminated by applying the method of partitioning. This process gives the system (mathematical model) as expressed in Eq. 8.12.

$$\left\{ \begin{bmatrix} N_{22} & N_{23} & N_{24} \\ N_{23}^T & N_{33} & N_{34} \\ N_{24}^T & N_{34}^T & N_{44} \end{bmatrix} - \begin{bmatrix} N_{12}^T \\ N_{13}^T \\ N_{14}^T \end{bmatrix} N_{11}^{-1} \begin{bmatrix} N_{12} & N_{13} & N_{14} \end{bmatrix} \right\} \begin{bmatrix} \delta_2 \\ \delta_3 \\ \delta_4 \end{bmatrix}$$

$$= \begin{bmatrix} c_2 \\ c_3 \\ c_4 \end{bmatrix} - \begin{bmatrix} N_{12}^T \\ N_{13}^T \\ N_{14}^T \end{bmatrix} N_{11}^{-1} c_1 \tag{8.12}$$

The N_{13} and N_{13}^T matrices being zero matrices, Eq. 8.12 reduces to:

$$\begin{bmatrix} N_{22} - N_{12}^T N_{11}^{-1} N_{12} & N_{23} & N_{24} - N_{12}^T N_{11}^{-1} N_{14} \\ N_{23}^T & N_{33} & N_{34} \\ N_{24}^T - N_{14}^T N_{11}^{-1} N_{12} & N_{34}^T & N_{44} - N_{14}^T N_{11}^{-1} N_{14} \end{bmatrix} \begin{bmatrix} \delta_2 \\ \delta_3 \\ \delta_4 \end{bmatrix} = \begin{bmatrix} c_2 - N_{12}^T N_{11}^{-1} c_1 \\ c_3 \\ c_4 - N_{14}^T N_{11}^{-1} c_1 \end{bmatrix} \tag{8.13}$$

This reduced system (Eq. 8.13) would demonstrate the following:

1. The original banded-bordered form is preserved with the same band- and border- widths (viz., q and r, respectively in Fig. 8.5);

2. N_{11} N_{12} and N_{12}^T are eliminated with their contributions absorbed into N_{22};

3. N_{14} and N_{14}^T are eliminated with their contributions absorbed into N_{24}, N_{24}^T and N_{44};

4. The remainder, N_{34} and N_{34}^{T} remain unaltered; and importantly enough,

5. There is no change in the basic structure of the coefficient matrix
    although the dimensions are reduced from N×N to (N–s)×(N–s).

The obove indicates a simple repetitive reduction process which can be formulated as one recurring, and thus the name *Recursive Partitioning*. The number of arithmetic operations required in the reduction of an N×N bandes–bordered system is much reduced. With a bandwidth q and a borderwidth r, assuming q >> r (which is the case in practice), the number of arithmetic operations required in reducing one N×N system is approximately proportional to $(q+r)^{2}N$ as against N^{3} in a conventional reduction by Gaussian elimination procedure. This indicates considerable computational efficiency when (q+r) << N, which is common with aerial photo block–triangulation. Further interesting ideas on these can be obtained in the publicaitons of Gyer (1967) and Brown (1976). Mikhail and Helmering (1973) have presented interesting discussions on the applications of recursive methods in photogrammetric data reduction in general.

Some specific examples of simultaneous procedure of photo–triangulation programs as currently available in the world are briefly discussed below:

1. *The Ohio State University Method*: Coded FORTBLOCK (Fortran Block–triangulation) consists of the main section and five sub-routines as follows:
    (a) MAIN program has all of the storage allocated for those arrays whose size is data dependent. It arrays documentation.
    (b) BLKTN (for block) subroutine handles actual numerical computation in three steps; viz., (i) Formation of normal equations, (ii) Call subroutine COFEI to compute partials with respect to exterior orientation and survey coordinate parameters, and (iii) Residuals of photo cooidinates are computed and printed prior to adjustment.
    (c) COFEI subroutine computes partials with respect to elements and survey coordinates as mentioned above.
    (d) MATINV subroutine computes inverse of a matrix by using a bordering technique.
    (e) MERGE subroutine receives control and forms the data base to be used. It provides a means to combine the input data (e.g., exposure station, survey coordinates, etc.) into a form acceptable to the BLKTN subroutine.
    (f) OUTPOS subroutine computes the elements of the rotation matrices.

Note: A simpler version of this program has been presented in Ghosh (1975).

2. *SAPGO* (an acronym for Simultaneous Adjustment of Photogrammetric and Geodetic Observations) *Method*: It was developed by Wong and Elphingstone (1972) and gives a solution to include geodetic measurements such as distances, horizontal angles, Laplace azimuths, longitudes, latitudes and elevations. It has been coded in Fortran IV language and has been tested for both strips and blocks. The SAPGO package consists of separate programs as follows:

(a) Image refinement: for correcting the image coordinates for lens distortion, atmospheric refraction and film shrinkage;

(b) The Principal program: for performing photo triangulation; and

(c) Error Propagation program: for computing the standard deviations of the computed ground coordinates. The inverse of the normal equations matrix is stored on disc for use in this program.

3. *MUSAT* (an acronym for Multiple Station Analytical Triangulation) *Method*: It was developed by the US Army Engineer Topographic Laboratories (see Matos, 1971) and provides a technique for the triangulation and adjustment of a model, strip or block of aerial photographs in a single computer run. Two variations of the MUSAT program have been completed by the Raytheon Corporation under contract of the US-ATL. The first, called MUSAT, employs the coplanarity condition for forming the stereo pairs; and the second, called Expanded MUSAT, uses the collinearity condition. This latter version also includes data editing, blunder elimination, and a technique for rapid solution and invertion of large system of normal equations. The MUSAT programs are coded to run in the IBM 7094 with Fortran IV language. They have also been coded to run in the UNIVAC 1108 computer. The programs are capable of some statistical analyses of results and propagation of errors. The Expanded MUSAT is claimed to be capable of triangulating up to 2000 photos in one run. Position data output may be in UTM (Universal Transverse Mercator), Geographic, Geocentric or Local coordinate systems. The program has been recently modified to include the functional constraints of air and ground distance measurements to supplement required standard ground control.

4. *Schmid Method*: It is based on the work of Schmid (1959). It uses the so called "bundles" of rays in each photograph simultaneously. A program

documented by Schenk (1972) was written in Fortran IV language for the CDC 6400/6500 computer. The initial program can handle upto 500 photographs in the block to a maximum of 49 points per photograph and to a maximum of 2048 points in the block. The method, however, somewhat resembles the system developed at the US National Oceanic Survey as discussed by Keller and Tewinkel (1967).

5. *Brown Method*: It has been developed by the DBA System Inc., Melbourne, Florida. The solution is based on a pair of collinearity condition equations for each point as in the other methods. In the words of Brown "In the solution, a duality exists between all quantities associated with the unknown coordinates of the control points. Hence, there exist two forms of the solution, depending upon the interpretation assigned to the primary matrices and their associated indices". The solution is iterative as the other programs and provides a simultaneous adjustment of an entire strip or block. Brown claims considerable versatility in the entire program, which was originally written for the CDC 1604-B computer complex of the Rome Air Development Center of the US Air Force. It consists of a direct formation of the "collapsed" system of normal equations and utilization of the iterative method of "Block Successive Overrelaxation". For the initial program, which is understood to have been considerably modified since then, see Brown et al (1964).

6. *BUNDLE REFINEMENT AERIAL TRIANGULATION SOLUTION (BRATS) Methods*: Developed by J. F. Kenefick, Photogrammetric Consultants, Inc., Florida. Nearly all of BRATS input data are collected from files generated by RABATS (see Chap. 8.1). Like RABATS, it is comprised of a series of program modules. BRATS is a fully rigourous bundle solution in which individual control points may be appropriately weighted. All BRATS modules contain their own data validation checks and it is possible to edit data or even to iterate the solution which is not often required.

It has been demonstrated during the 1980s that Block Triangulation (by Bundle method even without self-calibration or by the Independent Model method) can reach a precision level of 3 μm or better for image coordinates. This is indicative of the high geometrical quality fidelity of modern aerial photography and measuring instruments. The efficiency, however, depends also on sequential algorithm, required computer facilities, methods of analyses and degree of interactions in the computation procedures (Gruen, 1985; Julia, 1986).

An interesting study by Forstner (1985) supports the views given in Ghosh (1975) to emphasize good preparation and project planning for Block Aerotriangulation. Such a project planning should consists of appropriate choice of block parameters like overlap and of the distribution of control and pass points. These would lead to not only a homogeneous precision but also to a high reliability of such a triangulation.

These ideas can be extended to imagery other than direct aerial or spatial photography. McGlone and Mikhail (1985) obtained very satisfactory results with aircraft multispectral scanner data by using modified collinearity equations, constrained segmentation of strips, a priori weighting of parameters and constraints, and editing and evaluation statistics.

Camera orientation data and all other supplementary data available from modern computer controlled systems for photo-flight navigation provide extended auxiliary data, the processing of which in simultaneous block adjustment would permit considerable reduction of ground control (Ackermann, 1984).

BIBLIOGRAPHY

Ackermann, F.; "Utilization of Navigation Data for Aerial Triangulation", *ISPRS Archives Commission III* (15th Congress, Rio-de-Janeiro, Brazil: 1984).

Ackermann, F., H. Ebner and H. Klein; "Block Triangulation With Independent Models", *PE* 39, No. 9 (1973).

Ackermann, F.; "Results of Recent Experimental Investigations in Aerial Triangulation", *Proceedings of the 40th Annual Meeting of ASP*; St-Louis, Mo. (1974).

Anderson, James M. and A. J. McNair; "Analytic Aerotriangulation - Triplets and Sub-Blocks", *Photogrammetria* 21, No. 6 (1966).

Antipov, I. T.; "Automated System of Processing Photogrammetric Measurements", Presented Paper, *ISP Archives, Commission III*, 13th Congress; Helsinki, Finland (1976).

Brown, D. C., R. G. Davis and F. C. Johnson; *The practical and Rigorous Adjustment of Large Photogrammetric Nets* (Publication No. RADC-TRD-64-092; Rome Air Development Center; Rome, New York: 1964).

Brown, D. C.; "Evolution, Application and Potential of the Bundle Method of Photogrammetric Triangulation", Presented Paper, *Proceedings of ISP Commission*

III Symposium; Stuttgart, West Germany (1974).

+ Brown, D. C.; "The Bundle Adjustment – Progress and Prospects", Invited Paper, *ISP Archives, Commission III*, 13th Congress; Helsinki, Finland (1976).

Davis, R. G.; "Analytical Adjustment of Large Blocks", *PE* 32, No. 1 (1966).

Förstner, Wolfgang; "The Reliability of Block Triangulation", *PERS* 51, No. 6 (1985).

Ghosh, Sanjib K.; *Theory of Stereophotogrammetry* (2nd Ed) (The Ohio State University Bookstores; Columbus, Ohio: 1972).

Ghosh, Sanjib K.; *Phototriangulation* (Lexington Books; Lexington, Mass. 1975).

Gruen, A. W.; "Algorithm Aspects in On-Line Triangulation", *PERS* 51, No. 4 (1985).

+ Gyer, M. S.; *The Inversion of the Normal Equations of Analytical Aerotriangulation by the Method fo Recursive Partitioning* (Publication No. RADC-TR-67-69; Rome Air Development Center; Rome, New York: 1967).

Harris, W. D., G. C. Tewinkel and C. A. Whitten; *Analytical Aerotriangulation* (Technical Bulletin No. 21 [corrected]; US Department of Commerce, C & GS, Washington, D.C.: 1963).

Inghilleri, G., and R. Galetto; "Further Developments of the Method of Aerotriangulation by Independent Models", *Photogrammetria 22*, No. 1 (1967).

Julia, J. E.; "Developments with the COBLO Block Adjustment program", *PR* 12, No. 68 (1986).

+ Keller, M. and G. C. Tewinkel; *Three-photo Aerotriangulation* (Technical Bulletin No. 29; US Department of Commerce, C & GS, Washington, D. C.: 1966).

+ Keller, M. and G. C. Tewinkel; *Block Analytic Aerotriangulation* (Technical Bulletin No. 35; US Department of Commerce, C & GS, Washington, D. C.: 1967).

Kenefick, J. F.; Personal Communications (1985).

Kratky, V.; "On the Solution of Analytical Aerotriangulation by Means of an Iterative Procedure", *Photogrammetria 22*, No. 5 (1967).

Lobanov, A. N.; Analytical Aerotriangulation and its Application in the U.S.S.R.; Presented Paper, *ISP Archives, Commission III*, 13th Congress; Helsinki, Finland (1976).

McGlone, J. C. and E. M. Mikhail; "Evaluation of Aircraft MSS Analytical Block Adjustment", *PERS* 51, No. 2 (1985).

Mikhail, Edward M.; *A New Approach to Analytical Aerotriangulation – Two Directional Triplets in Sub-block (PH.D Thesis, Cornell University: Ithaca, New York: 1963).*

Mikhail, Edward M. and R. J. Helmering; "Recursive Methods in Photogrammetric Data Reduction", *PE* 39, No. 9 (1973).

Mikhail, Edward M.; *Observations and Least Squares* (IEP-A Dun-Donnelley Publishers, New York: 1976).

Matos, Robert A.; "Multiple Station Analytical Triangulation", *PE* 37, No.2 (1971).

Philip, Aldwyn; *Independent Model Aerial Triangulation Refinement and Error Studies* (Ph.D Dissertation, The Ohio State University, Columbus, Ohio: 1972).

Schmid, Hellmut H.; *A General Analytical Solution to the Problem of Photogrammetry* (US Ballistic Research Laboratories Report No. 1065; Aberdeen Proving Ground, Maryland: 1959). (Also, Bildmessung und Luftbildwesen, Heft 4 (1958) und Heft 1 (1959).

Schenk, Anton; *Fortran Program for Photogrammetric Block Triangulation with the Bundels Method* (Institut für Geodasie und Photogrammetry; E.T. H., Zurich, Switzerland: 1972).

Schut, G. H.; *Adjustment of Bundles* (National Research Council of Canada, Publication No. P-PR-47; Ottawa, Canada: 1978).

╋ Schut, G. H.; *An Introduction to Analytical Strip Triangulation with a Fortran Program* (National Research Council of Canada Publication No. P-PR-44; Ottawa, Canada: 1973).

Strahle, John A.; *Comparison of Semi-analytical and Aeropolygon Stereo-triangulation on the Analytical Stereoplotter AP/C* (M.Sc. Thesis, The Ohio State University; Columbus, Ohio: 1971).

Wong, K. W. and G. Elphingstone; "Aerotriangulation by SAPGO", *PE* 38, No.8 (1972).

Wood, R.; "Analytical Aerial Triangulation with Angular Measurments", *PR* 6, No. 36 (1970).

9

SELF-CALIBRATION AND CONSTRAINTS

Thus far, the universality of the projective equations has been established. These equations are amenable to practically any case of photogrammetry, aerial, spatial or terrestrial. These imply also, in a sense, completely rigorous techniques. Most of these techniques are limited to cases where the camera and the object related parameters are either exactly known of completely unknown.

In some cases, however, some unknown parameters are hidden and may be computationally derivable, whereas in others, some parameters may be known with unequal reliability and it may be advisable to use the known parameters directly or indirectly in the adjustment procedure. The concept of self-calibration addresses itself to the former cases, while the utilization of constraints is applicable to the latter cases. Such constraints are meant to enforce the measuring-adjusting process to conform to some functional or geometric relationships or to conform to the degree of reliability as defined by "weighting".

The value of such considerations lies in the ability to utilize the information to the greatest extent in reducing the number of unknowns or in reducing the magnitude of error propagations. It may be pertinent to express here that for any given problem, more than one least squares solutions are theoretically possible in view of the various 'forms' the mathematical model can assume. It is in the formulation of the mathematical model that one can exercise imaginative skill and improvisation. It has been demonstrated (Chapters 4 and 5, for example) that in developing mathematical models, one can often eliminate or introduce parameters or can simplify by manipulationg the observation/condition equation. It is in this philosophical context that the following discussions are presented.

9.1   SELF-CALIBRATION

One of the most interesting applications of the collinearity equations was made by Brown (1968) when he developed an analytical calibration technique which admits an infinite number of frames to a solution for a single set of interior orientation parameters and lens distortion coefficients presumed common to all frames. This, *Simultaneous Multi-Frame Analytical Calibration* (SMAC), assumes photography over a precisely surveyed test range, thereby eliminating the need to consider the coordinates of the ground control points as variables. We have noticed, however, significant errors in certain ranges, at least at individual points.

Furthermore, there are cases (e.g., close-range and micro-range applications) where a test range does not exist, or exterior/interior geometry parameters are not fully known. Such problem cases prompted the development of the Self-calibration technique.

The basis of this approach can be found in Brown et al (1964), the formulation in which permitted introduction of a priori constraints on one or more of the exterior orientation parameters and/or object points by treating the a priori knowledge as direct observations of these parameters. Some developments (e.g., Kenefick et al, 1972) specifically provide for the interior orientation parameters also. One may view this as a photogrammetric procedure in which the calibration parameters are recovered analytically, without the necessity for absolute three-dimensional control in the object space. This is accomplished by introducing an error model for the specific parameters in the computation procedure.

Kenefick et al (1972) reported on the use of this technique for inflight calibration of a camera used on a space flight around the Moon, for which there was no control in the object space. They had, however, certain orbital information, some camera paremeters (from camera calibration) and convergence angles as known values. Maune (1973) and Adiguzel (1985) used this technique in calibrating electron microscopes by using two-dimensional grids (for the test range) and sets of highly convergent micrographs.

Consider the case of 'complete' calibration of a camera. The collinearity equations provide the basis for such an analytical calibration scheme. The equations may be augmented with the parameters of 'interior' orientation as follows:

$$\bar{x}_{ij} + F(K) \cdot \bar{x}_{ij} + F(P) \left\{ P_1 (r_{ij}^2 + 2\bar{x}_{ij}^2) + P_2 (2\bar{x}_{ij}\bar{y}_{ij}) \right\}$$

$$= f_x \frac{(X_j - X_{oi})A_i + (Y_j - Y_{oi})B_i + (Z_j - Z_{oi})C_i}{(X_j - X_{oi})A_i'' + (Y_j - Y_{oi})B_i'' + (Z_j - Z_{oi})C_i''}$$

$$(9.1)$$

$$\bar{y}_{ij} + F(K) \cdot \bar{y}_{ij} + F(P) \left\{ P_2 (r_{ij}^2 + 2\bar{y}_{ij}^2) + P_1 (2\bar{x}_{ij}\bar{y}_{ij}) \right\}$$

$$= f_y \frac{(X_j - X_{oi})A_i' + (Y_j - Y_{oi})B_i' + (Z_j - Z_{oi})C_i'}{(X_j - X_{oi})A_i'' + (Y_j - Y_{oi})B_i'' + (Z_j - Z_{oi})C_i''}$$

where subscripts refer to: o   for the perpective center,

i   for the photograph, and

j   for the object (ground) point;

$$\bar{x}_{ij} = x_{ij} - x_c$$ x_{ij}, y_{ij} being the observed photo-coordinates of the image points, and

$$\bar{y}_{ij} = y_{ij} - y_c$$ x_c, y_c being the observed photo-coodinates of the principal point, assumed constant;

$$r_{ij}^2 = (\bar{x}_{ij}^2 + \bar{y}_{ij}^2)$$

$$F(K) = K_o + K_1 r_{ij}^2 + K_2 r_{ij}^4 + K_3 r_{ij}^6 + \dots$$

= function of symmetrical radial distortion (see Eq. 5.5), assumed constant over all photographs;

$$F(P) = 1 + P_3 r_{ij}^2 + P_4 r_{ij}^4 + \dots$$

= function of tangential distortion (see Eq. 5.7), also assumed as constant over all photographs;

P_1, P_2 are correction coefficients for decentering distortion (see Eq. 5.7), also assuemd constant over all photograph;

f_x, f_y are effective focal lengths, in the x- and y-directions, respectively, seperate in view of affine deformation in photo, assumed constant over all photographs;

A, B, C
A', B', C'   are the elements of the orthogonal orientation matrix M of the
A", B", C"   photograph, functions of three rotational angles (cf. Eq. 4.8);

and M_i = $\begin{bmatrix} A_i & B_i & C_i \\ A_i' & B_i' & C_i' \\ A_i'' & B_i'' & C_i'' \end{bmatrix}$.

Such an expression can be expanded to include other necessary parameters; e.g., Maune (1973) included spiral distortion parameters as contributors to the interior geometry of the SEM system. The equations are linearized by Taylor expansion about the measured quantities x_{ij}, y_{ij} and initial approximate values of the unknown parameters. If all linearized equations are collected, they may be written in matrix notations as below (cf. Eq. 8.6):

$$V + \dot{B} \dot{\delta} + \ddot{B} \ddot{\delta} = \varepsilon \qquad (9.2)$$

where, considering m number of photographs and n number of object points, and that all points appear on all photographs (note, this is nothing but a simultaneous multi-photo solution),

$\underset{2mn,\ 1}{V}$ is the vector of residuals of measured photo coordinates;

$\underset{2mn,9+6m}{\dot{B}}$ $\underset{2mn,3n}{\ddot{B}}$ are the matrices of the partial derivatives of Eq. 9.1, evaluated with measured quantities and the current values of the unknowns;

$\underset{9+6m,\ 1}{\dot{\delta}}$ $\underset{3n,\ 1}{\ddot{\delta}}$ are the vectors of cerrections to the current values of the parameters;

and $\underset{2mn,\ 1}{\varepsilon}$ is the discrepancy vector.

Note: In view of customary practices (see Ghosh, 1975), single dotted matrices here are those associated with parameters of interior and exterior orientations, whereas double dotted ones are associated with the object point coordinates. In some practices (e.g., Halim Munji, 1986) the parameters may be grouped into three or more categories, like interior orientation elements, exterior orientation elements and object point coordinates or other convenient number of categories. Such considerations would naturally lead into additional **B** matrices and associated δ vectors of corrections as well.

Kenefick et al (1972) suggested to consider supplemental observation equations arising from a priori knowledge regarding any of the parameters in Eqs 9.1. Such supplemental equations may be grouped according to the subset of parameters involved just for convenience,

$$\dot{v} - \dot{\delta} = \dot{\varepsilon} \left.\begin{array}{c} \\ \\ \end{array}\right\} \tag{9.3}$$

$$\ddot{v} - \ddot{\delta} = \ddot{\varepsilon}$$

where

$9+6m, \dot{\delta}_1 \quad 3n, \ddot{\delta}_1 \quad$ are vectors of observational corrections to the parameters;

and

$9+6m, \dot{\varepsilon}_1 \quad 3n, \ddot{\varepsilon}_1 \quad$ are discrepancy vectors, between observed values and current (in iterative solutions) values of the parameters.

The entire set of observation equations (Eqs 9.2 and 9.3) can be merged into one expression:

$$\bar{V} + \bar{B}\bar{\delta} = \bar{\varepsilon} \tag{9.4}$$

where $\quad {}_{k,1}\bar{V} = (v, \dot{v}, \ddot{v})^{T} ;$

$${}_{k,\ell}\bar{B} = \begin{bmatrix} \dot{B} & \ddot{B} \\ -I & 0 \\ 0 & -I \end{bmatrix} , \quad {}_{\ell,1}\bar{\delta} = (\dot{\delta}, \ddot{\delta})^{T} ;$$

and

$${}_{k,1}\bar{\varepsilon} = (\varepsilon, \dot{\varepsilon}, \ddot{\varepsilon})^{T}$$

Further, $k = 2mn + 9 + 6m + 3n$ and $\ell = 9 + 6m + 3n$

The covariance matrix associated with the merged observation equation is:

$$
\underset{k, k}{\overline{\Sigma}} \;=\; \begin{bmatrix} \Sigma & 0 & 0 \\ 0 & \dot{\Sigma} & 0 \\ 0 & 0 & \ddot{\Sigma} \end{bmatrix}
$$

where

$\underset{2mn, 2mn}{\Sigma}$ is the covariance matrix for the observed photo coordinates, 2×2 block diagonal when coordinates are assumed uncorrelated;

$\underset{9+6m, 9+6m}{\dot{\Sigma}}$ is the covariance matrix for the interior and exterior orientation parameters;

and

$\underset{3n, 3n}{\ddot{\Sigma}}$ is the covariance matrix for the object point coordinates, 3×3 block diagonal where coordinates are assumed uncorrelated.

The general form of the 'normal' equations, as formed from the 'condition' equations (Eq. 9.4) is:

$$N\delta = c \tag{9.5}$$

where $N = \overline{B}^T P \overline{B}$; $c = \overline{B}^T P \varepsilon$;

and P is the weight (inverse of covariance) matrix.

After appropriate operations, the general form of the normal equations, partitioned (after Brown, 1960), in this case is:

$$
\begin{bmatrix} \dot{N} + \dot{P} & \overline{N} \\ \hline \overline{N}^T & \ddot{N} + \ddot{P} \end{bmatrix} \cdot \begin{bmatrix} \dot{\delta} \\ \hline \ddot{\delta} \end{bmatrix} = \begin{bmatrix} \dot{c} - \dot{P}\dot{\varepsilon} \\ \hline \ddot{c} - \ddot{P}\ddot{\varepsilon} \end{bmatrix} \tag{9.6}
$$

where

$\underset{9+6m,\ 9+6m}{\dot{N}} \;=\; \dot{B}^T P \dot{B}$ $\underset{9+6m,\ 1}{\dot{c}} \;=\; \dot{B}^T P \varepsilon$

$$\ddot{N} \quad = \ddot{B}^T P \ddot{B} \qquad\qquad \ddot{c} \quad = \ddot{B}^T P \varepsilon$$

3n, 3, $\qquad\qquad\qquad\qquad$ 3n, 1

$$\bar{N} \quad = \dot{B}^T P \ddot{B}$$

9+6m, 3n

and $\qquad P = \Sigma^{-1} \qquad\qquad \dot{P} = \dot{\Sigma}^{-1} \qquad\qquad \ddot{P} = \ddot{\Sigma}^{-1}$

This concept has been applied with great success to Block Triangulation by the 'Simultaneous' method (also known as 'Bundle Adjustment') in order to increase the final overall accuracy (see Ebner, 1976). In such applications, however, two problems persist. The first one involves the proper choice of the additional parameters (photo-, strip- or block-dependent). A general concept for the choice of such parameters has yet to be agreed upon in the scientific community for works on specific problems. The second problem arises from highly correlated or insignificant parameters which may cause comparative instability in the adjustment procedure and create somewhat critical geometry.

Somewhat unusual but interesting extension of the self-calibration technique as applicable to Bundle Block Adjustment has been suggested by Ebner (1976) in which additional parameters to consider systematic image (film) deformation (two-dimensional) and model deformation (three-dimensional) are included. Computationally, these could be handled by *stochastic mathematical models* (by treating the additional parameters as free unknowns) or by treating them as *Collocation* problems (see Moritz, 1973) in terms of prediction and filtering of noise and signals. Skeptics may scoff at some of these attempts, which indicate the scientists' yielding to the mighty computer without really justifying the natural science. These, however, do point out the unlimited scopes of the modern analytical photogrammetric procedures. The technique of 'In Flight' calibration discussed by Anderson and Lee (1975) also follows the same general concept.

A recent development of the concept by Schlöler (1986) seems to be specially practicable in close-range applications. The basic idea is to derive individual data of interior orientation for a photograph from depth differences between control points around the perimeter of an object. On the other hand, if a suitable pattern of ground control can be established, it would be possible to perform a complete field calibration (along with radial and tangential distortions) of aerial or terrestrial cameras.

The method of self-calibration has seen considerable development during the last decade, leading to operational computer programs and practical applications in various conventional and unconventional approaches in photogrammetry. The method used in block adjustment of photo-triangulation can easily yield a consistent precision level of σ_o < 3 μm for image coordinates provided instrumental errors (for both reading and point transfer) are negligible, as has been reported by Ackermann (1984).

A computer program for self-calibration is appended to the book (Appendix C). This program is flexible enough to be used in conventional (aerial or satellite imaging) as well as unconventional (like X-ray or electron micrographic imaging) systems as has already been used successfully at Laval.   Photo-coordinates of the desired points (along with certain points in adequate number on the original negatives read at a precision comparator or an analytical plotter) are directed to a micro-computer using this program, which makes calculations of the positional as well as interior orientation parameters of the cameras (or, the same camera for two or more photos).   This permits to establish and ensure the involved parameters necessary for precision measurements.   Thereafter, the 3-D coordinates of points are calculated by spatial intersection, through the same program.

To give an example, four different cameras were used in a project (2 above and 2 below a transparent glass plate on which were placed the objects to be studied and mapped).   These are amateur cameras (Minolta SRT-100) with B&W film (ASA 400). Average object distance was around 1 m.   Photo-coordinates were obtained at the Wild STK-1 stereocomparator.   An IBM-PC micro-computer was used.   Final precision obtained was better than ±0.5 mm on the objects.

9.2 CONSTRAINTS

9.2.1 Weight Constraint

Comparative reliability amongst various parameters can be enforced by utilizing the constraint of weight.   This is done by using the standard deviations of various parameters in the condition equations.   As an example, consider that the standard deviations of the perspective center coordinates (X_{oi}, Y_{oi}, Z_{oi}) in the working system are known or can be approximated from previous or from some auxiliary data sources.   The covariance matrix of the camera stations coordinates then is:

$$\Sigma_i = \begin{bmatrix} \sigma^2_{X_{oi}} & \sigma_{X_{oi}Y_{oi}} & \sigma_{X_{oi}Z_{oi}} \\ \\ \sigma_{X_{oi}Y_{oi}} & \sigma^2_{Y_{oi}} & \sigma_{Y_{oi}Z_{oi}} \\ \\ \sigma_{X_{oi}Z_{oi}} & \sigma_{Y_{oi}Z_{o}} & \sigma^2_{Z_{oi}} \end{bmatrix} \tag{9.7}$$

in which each off-diagonal element, for the sake of convenience and simplification, may be considered in practice as zero. This means that they can safely be considered as diagonal matrices, thereby assuming that there is no correlation between coordinates.

Note: Some recent studies (for example, Maarek, 1973) suggest that mathematical correlation between coordinates, in practice, can be neglected at all times without causing any appreciable change in the results.

Furthermore,

$$P_i = \Sigma_i^{-1} \tag{9.7a}$$

Similarly, the weight matrices of the other exterior orientation parameters, object point coodinates or the interior orientation parameters can be determined. In order to utilize such weight matrices in the solution, the partitioned normal equations take the form as expressed in Eq. 9.6. Case (1961) is known to be the first to discuss the subject of constraints in photogrammetry.

Schmid and Schmid (1965) discussed a general procedure for the method of Least Squares, where all elements of the mathematical model are considered as observation data; the burden of classification being on the 'weight matrix'. The relative strengths of $\dot{P}$ and $\ddot{P}$ will have significant influence on the final results of Eq. 9.6. As an extreme case, for example, consider $\ddot{P}$ to be infinity. This is when the object point coordinates are fully known and are unchangeable (one may call it *Absolute Constraint*). This makes it a case of *Space Resection*. The case where $\dot{P}$ is infinity would, accordingly, correspond to *Space Intersection*, the case of the other extreme.

9.2.2 Functional Constraint

The functional relationships between various parameters would provide the functional constraints, which may be applied to the interior or exterior orientation parameters, or even to the object point coordinates. Consider an example case in which the perspective center coordinates (X_{oi}, Y_{oi}, Z_{oi}) are functions of parameters s, t and u:

$$X_{oi} = F_1(s,t,u) ; \quad Y_{oi} = F_2(s,t,u) \quad \text{and} \quad Z_{oi} = F_3(s,t,u) \tag{9.8}$$

Note here, as before, i refers to photos and j refers to points. Furthermore, $\dot{\delta}$ can be considered in two parts, viz., $\dot{\delta}'$ for the perspective center parameters and $\dot{\delta}''$ for the rest of interior and exterior orientation parameters.

By considering the differentials, then

$$\dot{\delta}_i' = \begin{bmatrix} \delta X_{oi} \\ \delta Y_{oi} \\ \delta Z_{oi} \end{bmatrix} = \begin{bmatrix} \dfrac{\partial X_{oi}}{\partial s} & \dfrac{\partial X_{oi}}{\partial t} & \dfrac{\partial X_{oi}}{\partial u} \\ \dfrac{\partial Y_{oi}}{\partial s} & \dfrac{\partial Y_{oi}}{\partial t} & \dfrac{\partial Y_{oi}}{\partial u} \\ \dfrac{\partial Z_{oi}}{\partial s} & \dfrac{\partial Z_{oi}}{\partial t} & \dfrac{\partial Z_{oi}}{\partial u} \end{bmatrix} \begin{bmatrix} \delta s \\ \delta t \\ \delta u \end{bmatrix} = U_i' \, \dot{\delta}' \tag{9.9}$$

In order to utilize the functional constraints in this case, one merely substitutes the relationships of Eqs 9.8 and 9.9 in the applicable places of the basic condition equation (Eq. 9.2), which becomes

$$V_{ij} + \dot{B}_{ij}(\dot{\delta}_i'' + U_i'\dot{\delta}') + \ddot{B}_{ij} \ddot{\delta}_{ij} = \epsilon_{ij} \tag{9.10}$$

where $\qquad \dot{\delta}_i'' = \begin{bmatrix} \delta x_c, & \delta y_c, & \delta f_x, & \delta f_y, & \delta\omega, & \delta\varphi, & \delta\kappa \end{bmatrix}_i^T$

and, naturally, σ_{ij} is a function of s, t and u (indirectly) rather than directly of X_{oi}, Y_{oi} and Z_{oi}. The most likely corrections δs, δt and δu to the current (initially assumed) values of s, t and u are determined as a result of the solutions of Eq. 9.10. In such a case, an alternate solution of obtaining the final values of X_{oi}, Y_{oi} and Z_{oi} can be made by substituting the adjusted values of s, t and u in Eq. 9.8, directly. Such functional constraints may be utilized to reduce the number of unknown parameters in the condition equations. In the case of correlated parameters, if one or more of the original parameters are unknown, use of such constraints becomes of considerable help.

Apart from giving interesting theoretical ideas, Case(1961) has discussed some examples of various types of such constraints. Interesting ideas on the procedures of Least Squares solutions in the presence of various constraints can be obtained from the works of Mikhail (1970, 1976). It is, however, expected that by adding constraints to any system, the residuals (indicated by V'PV matrix) should generally increase.

BIBLIOGRAPHY

Ackermann, F.; "Report on activities of Working Group III-1 during 1980-84"; *ISPRS Archives for 25th Congress,* Rio-de-Janeiro (1984).

Adiguzel, M.; *Problems Related to Three Dimensional Mapping with Electron Micrographs* (Ph.D Thesis, Laval University, Quebec:1985).

Anderson, James M. and Clement Lee; "Analytical In-Flight Calibration", *PERS* 41, No. 11 (1975).

Brown, D. C.; "Results in Geodetic Photogrammetry", *PE* 26, No. 3 (1960).

Brown, D. C., R. G. Davis and F. C. Johnson; "The Practical and Rigorous Adjustment of Large Photogrammetric Nets", *Report on US Air Force Contract No. Af-30(602)-3007;* DBA System, Inc., Florida (1964).

Brown, D. C.; Advanced Methods for the Calibration of Metric Cameras", *Report on US Army contract No. DA-44-009-AMC-1457 (X);* DBA System, Inc., Florida (1968).

Case, James B.; "The Utilisation of Constraints in Analytical Photogrammetry", *PE* 27, No. 5 (1961).

Ebner, H.; "Self-Calibrating Block Adjustment", *Bildmessung und Luftbildwesen,* Heft 4 (1976).

Ghosh, Sanjib K.; *Phototriangulation* (Lexington Books, Lexington, Mass.: 1975).

Halim Munjy, Raidh A.; "Self-Calibration Using the Finite Element Approach", *PERS* 52, No. 3 (1986).

Kenefick, John F., M. S. Gyer and B. F. Harp; "Analytical Self-Calibration", *PE* 38, No. 11 (1972).

Kupfer, G.; "Improvement of Analytical Aerial Triangulation by Field Calibration"; *Proceedings of the Conference of Working Group on Image Geometry,* ISP Commission I; Ottawa, Canada (1975).

Light, Donald L.; "Altimeter Observations as Orbital Constraints", *PE* 38, No. 4 (1972).

Maarek, A.; "New Math Model for Independent-Model Triangulation", *PE* 39, No. 10 (1973).

Maune, David F.; *Photogrammetric Self-Calibration of a Scanning Electron Microscope* (Ph.D Dessertation, The Ohio State Univ., Columbus, Ohio: 1973).

Mikhail, Edward M.; "Paremeter Constraints in Least Squares", *PE* 36, No. 12 (1970).

Mikhail, Edward M.; *Observations and Least Squares* (IEP-A Dun-Donnelly Publishers, New York: 1976).

Moritz, Helmut; "Least-Squares Collocation", *Deutsche Geodatische Kommission, Reihe A*, Heft 75 (1973).

Moritz, Helmut; "Statistical Foundations of Collocation", *US Air Force Geophysics Laboratory Document* No. AFGL-TR-78-0182 (1978).

Schmid, H. H. and E. Schmid; "A Generalized Least Squares Solution for Hybrid Measuring Systems", *The Canadian Surveyor* 9, No. 1 (1965).

Schöler, H.; "Zur Selbstkalibrierung von Aufnahmekammern, insbesondere bei der photogrammetrischen Vermessungim Nahbereich", *Vermessungstechnik 34*; Heft 8 (1986).

10

UNCONVENTIONAL CASES

The purpose of this chapter is to present selected unconventional photogrammetric (Remote Sensing, Close-range and Micro-range) systems, to evaluate these systems through the application of the unifying concept of "projective equations" used in conventional photogrammetry and to establish mathematical models capable of data handling in practice.

In view of the fundamental conditions used in analytical photogrammetry (e.g., the condition of collinearity, see Chap. 4), synoptic geometric relationships pertinent to the sensing systems are presented. The approaches are not always rigorous. It is, however, intended to summarize various analytical techniques that have been developed and may be suggested to overcome problems associated with imagery which do not possess conventional metric qualities. Such techniques involve appropriate modifications of the condition equations for the more complex situations as well as modest simplifications for simple situations where lower order accuracies are acceptable. The use of the concept of Instantaneous Equivalent Frame Photography (IEFP) will be presented. With these, then, operations such as resection, absolute orientation, simultaneous multi-photo adjustment, etc. may be performed by utilizing the existing conventional (frame) photography programs.

The use of CRT, RBV and MSS could be extended by use of purely digital or analog-digital systems provided sufficient knowledge is acquired and maintained to properly correct for image distortions created by factors both internal and external to the sensing systems (e.g., Clerici, 1977).

The first two, strip and panoramic photographic systems (Figs 10.1 and 10.2),have already been used in reconnaissance mapping. Their obvious difference from the frame (conventional) photography pose interesting challenges. On the other hand, the innovative treatments utilized in using such systems can be fruitfully extended to other systems with similar imaging geometrics.

The last two, electron micrography and X-ray (radiography), are presented not only in view of their special imaging procedures and geometries but also in view of their ever increasing use in numerous fields of science and technology.

10.1 STRIP PHOTOGRAPHY

The Sonne Camera, better known as the continuous strip camera (see Kistler, 1946) was first used in 1932 and was further developed during World War II. One typical modern camera is the US Air Force's KA-71 Strip Camera (Fig. 10.3) developed during the 1960's. First used for low-altitude and high-speed military reconnnaissance, these cameras have been used in highway planning, etc. They have also been used for night photography with mercury arc-lamp illumination.

Side-looking radas and certain infrared recording systems are in reality strip cameras with optics looking at a CRT or other modulated light source (rather than the ground directly). A study of such an imaging system would, therefore, help in understanding numerous other systems in use now-a-days.

A strip camera records a continuous strip of ground as the aircraft flies over it. In its simplest form, the camera consists of a fixed lens with open shutter, the exposure being controlled by a slit of variable width. During exposure, the film is advanced in the direction of flight at a rate equivalent to the rate of image motion due to the aircraft flight. The exposure time depends on the velocity of the film and the width of the slit such that

$$t_e = w / v_F \tag{10.1}$$

where t_e is the exposure time in seconds;

          w is the slit width in mm;

and v_F is the film velocity (mm per second).

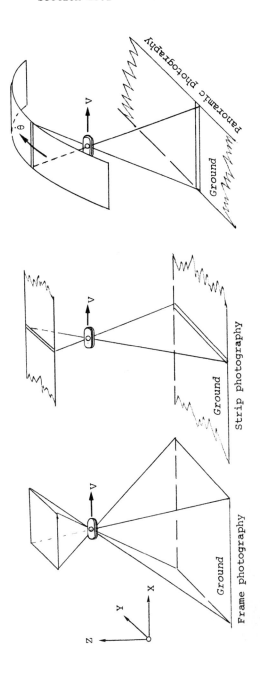

Fig. 10.1

Design concept of frame,
strip and panoramic photographies

In practice, the slit width varies between 0.25 mm and 0.51 mm. This tends to expose a narrow strip (or line) of terrain at any instant on the film, As the airplane moves forward, a long continous photograph originates by successive integration of these narrow lines. Two conditions are essential for obtaining good

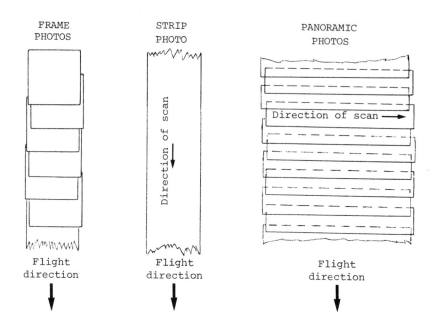

Fig. 10.2 Comparative ground coverage
with frame, strip and panoramic photographs

Fig. 10.3

Strip camera, type KA-71
(Courtesy, alan gordon enterprises, Inc.)

and continous strip photos: (i) Close synchronization between film velocity and image velocity; and (ii) Some means for stabilizing the camera in the roll axis (primary) and pitch and yaw axes (secondary). The cameras may be used in two ways, viz., (a) Mono or non-stereoscopic mode, with a single lens cone; or (b) Stereo mode, with a dual lens cone.

With a dual lens cone, the stereo base is obtained by displacing the two lenses forward and aft (Fig. 10.4). The lens offset is adjustable and may be calibrated in the *parallax angle* (2α in Fig. 10.4), which is related to the base-height ratio in the *Normal-case* by

$$b/h \;=\; 2\cdot\tan\alpha \qquad\qquad (10.2)$$

Operationally, these cameras have the simplest Image Motion Compensation (IMC) devices. The most common problem in a strip camera is *Banding* (due to cyclic changes of exposure) on the photograph. This may be due to unsteady film velocity, worn gear teeth or excessive vibration in the camera. These cameras may be used for side oblique photography, although it is not possible to have such a photo to be correctly synchronized to allow for image motion on film throughout the entire width. In order to minimize this adverse oblique effect, the camera slits can be set at the cant angle when side oblique photos are taken.

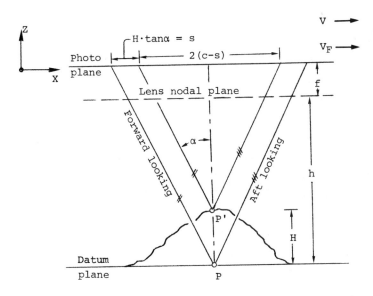

Fig. 10.4   Strip photography, schematic of stereoscopic
situation on X-Z plane

In the simplest case, i.e., when the aircraft is flying straight and level, the time (t) between recording two images of the ground point (P) is given by Eq. 10.3, V being the ground speed of aircraft (Fig. 10.4):

$$t = \frac{2h \cdot \tan\alpha}{V} \qquad (10.3)$$

The distance between the images on film is

$$2c = v_F \cdot t = \frac{v_F}{V} 2h \cdot \tan\alpha \qquad (10.4)$$

If the film speed is adjusted correctly for IMC, $v_F/V = f/h$. This gives

$$c = f \cdot \tan\alpha \qquad (10.5)$$

Next (see Fig. 10.4), the distance between the two images of a point (P') at an elevation H above the datum (elevation of point P) is

$$2(c - s) = \frac{2v_F}{V}(h - H) \cdot \tan\alpha \qquad (10.6)$$

This gives an expression for the elevation (by substitution from above),

$$H = \frac{V \cdot f \cdot s}{v_F \cdot c} = \frac{h \cdot s}{c} \qquad (10.7)$$

X, Y (positional) coordinates in such simple cases may be obtained directly from the photographs by considering the appropriate scale factor and also assuming the terrain to be flat. This approach would be appropriate in a simple analytical plotter like the Zeiss Stereocord.

10.1.1 Collinearity Condition in Strip Photography

Figure 10.5 illustrates the projection geometry of a strip photograph. The photographic exposure is made through a slit. Thus, although the projection is perspective, it takes place along a plane which contains the perspective center and the slit.

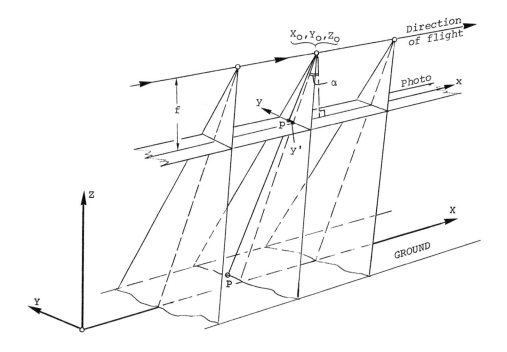

Fig. 10.5 Geometry of a strip photograph

(here with an aft-looking lens)

The basic projective equation for frame photography (Eq. 4.6) reduces to the following form in this case (see Case, 1967):

$$
\begin{bmatrix} 0 \\ y \\ -f \end{bmatrix} = k \cdot M \cdot \begin{bmatrix} X - X_o \\ Y - Y_o \\ Z - Z_o \end{bmatrix}
\tag{10.8}
$$

In this expression, k represents the scale factor (as in Eq. 4.6). Further, the photo coordinate x does not appear directly and is considered zero because it is in a direction at right angles to the narrow slit in the camera which moves with the perspective center. The perspective (projection) center here follows a line instead of being instantaneous points (as in the conventional, frame, photography case). The x-coordinate can be used here to determine the instant of time (tp) for the exposure of the photo point. The time is used to compute the perspective center coordinates (X_o, Y_o, X_o) and the orientation (M matrix) for the instant of exposure.   The determination of time is, therefore, critical. The film velocity V_F being known, the time t_p is given by

$$tp = t_o + \frac{x}{V_F} = t_o + \Delta t \tag{10.9}$$

where x is the x-photocoordinate of the point p from a preselected origin
              (e.g., a time mark at the beginning of the strip);

          t_o is the time of exposure of that origin;

and Δt is the difference in time from that origin.

   It may be noted also that the lens distortion is restricted to only the y direction (i.e. along the slit through which the exposure is made for each line scan).

   In view of Eq. 10.8, the collinearity condition equations in this case will be (cf. Eqs 4.8, for the case of frame photography)

$$0 = -f \left\{ \frac{m_{11}(Xp-X_o) + m_{12}(Yp-Y_o) + m_{13}(Zp-Z_o)}{m_{31}(Xp-X_o) + m_{32}(Yp-Y_o) + m_{33}(Zp-Z_o)} \right\}$$

$$y = -f \left\{ \frac{m_{21}(Xp-X_o) + m_{22}(Yp-Y_o) + m_{23}(Zp-Z_o)}{m_{31}(Xp-X_o) + m_{32}(Yp-Y_o) + m_{33}(Zp-Z_o)} \right\} \tag{10.10}$$

With these basic considerations, further modification in the collinearity equations become simple and fall in the model for frame photography.

   In order to provide a means for performing computational operations in such non-conventional cases, particularly when the position and attitude of the camera are unknown, Case (1967) suggested the use of *Instantaneous Equivalent Frame Photos* *(IEFP)*. All measured points are transformed from the strip (or, panoramic, etc.) photograph of interest to a fictitious frame photo having the same focal length but limited to a single instantaneous position and attitude. The positions and attitudes may be selected at such intervals as would permit good geometry without introducing the deteriorating effects of a constantly changing position and attitude. The idea of Derenyi (1973) of using "Line by line orientation" also follows similar concepts. The inverse of the collinearity equations is employed to project the strip down to the ground, for the jth point:

$$X_j = X_{o_j} + \left\{ Z_j - Z_{o_j} \right\} \left\{ \frac{m_{11_j} x_j + m_{21_j} y_j - m_{31_j} f}{m_{13_j} x_j + m_{23_j} y_j - m_{33_j} f} \right\}$$

$$Y_j = Y_{o_j} + \left\{ Z_j - Z_{o_j} \right\} \left\{ \frac{m_{12_j} x_j + m_{22_j} y_j - m_{32_j} f}{m_{13_j} x_j + m_{23_j} y_j - m_{33_j} f} \right\} \qquad (10.11)$$

Here, for the strip photograph, $x_j = 0$. The remaining terms are as in Chap. 4 (see Eqs 4.1 through 4.7). Assuming that the aircraft is flying straight and level, the X, Y, Z ground coordinate system is in agreement with the photo and the camera station coordinates are

$$X_{o_j} = V \cdot \Delta t$$

$$Y_{o_j} = 0 \qquad (10.12)$$

$$Z_{o_j} = h$$

while, $Z_j = H_j$ (i.e., ground elevation of the jth ground point).

After the measured strip photo coordinates have been projected to ground, the resulting ground points are projected back upto the IEFP. For this operation, the collinearity equations are used directly:

$$x_{Fj} = -f_F \left\{ \frac{m_{11_F}(X_j - X_{o_F}) + m_{12_F}(Y_j - Y_{o_F}) + m_{13_F}(Z_j - Z_{o_F})}{m_{31_F}(X_j - X_{o_F}) + m_{32_F}(Y_j - Y_{o_F}) + m_{33_F}(Z_j - Z_{o_F})} \right\}$$

$$y_{Fj} = -f_F \left\{ \frac{m_{21_F}(X_j - X_{o_F}) + m_{22_F}(Y_j - Y_{o_F}) + m_{23_F}(Z_j - Z_{o_F})}{m_{31_F}(X_j - X_{o_F}) + m_{32_F}(Y_j - Y_{o_F}) + m_{33_F}(Z_j - Z_{o_F})} \right\} \qquad (10.13)$$

where x_{Fj} and y_{Fj} are the IEFP coordinates of the jth point, the subscript (F) refers to this IEFP;

and X_j, Y_j, Z_j are the coordinates of the ground point corresponding to the jth point imaged on the strip photograph as obtained from Eqs 10.11 and 10.12.

The IEFP thus produced can then be utilized in any computer program which normally handles 'frame' photo coordinates (e.g., resection, relative orientation, and other related solutions).   This, however, requires some additional data processing.   This is from the fact that the exterior orientation elements and ground point coordinates are initially unknown or known only approximately; whereas they should be known in order to correctly transform the points to the IEFP.   An iterative procedure would solve this computational problem.   Case (1967) reported that such data are expected to converge rapidly, usually within three iterations. In case cemera position and attitude are known, or if these parameters can be constrained to some function of time, Eqs 10.10 can be used direclty without using IEFP.   The manner of utilizing such constraints has been discussed in Chap. 9.

10.1.2 Coplanarity Condition in Strip Photography

This condition with respect to relative orientation applies to stereostrip photographs.   Consider subscripts 1 and 2 to differentiate between the parameters related to the two strips (see Figs 10.6 and 10.7), each having a x, y, z   system of coordinates with regard to the perspective center (C).   Because the attitude and position (exterior orientation parameters) of the strip camera continuously change during photography, the x, y, z   strip systems will be variable relative to an arbitrarily fixed system X, Y, Z (say, ground or model).   The perspective centers move along space (three dimensional) curves (C_1O_1 and C_2O_2 in Fig. 10.6).

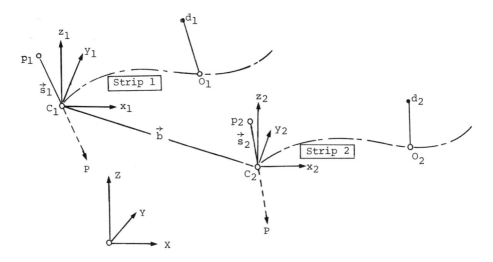

Fig. 10.6   Relative orientation of stereo-strip photographs

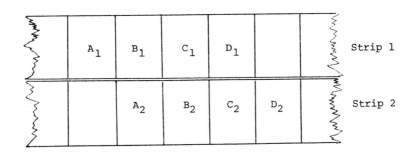

Fig. 10.7

Stereo-strip photographs divided in sections

Consider p_1 and p_2 as the two image points appearing in strips 1 and 2, respectively, corresponding to the same model location (P). The condition that the vectors $\vec{s}_1(C_1p_1)$, $\vec{b}(C_1C_2)$ and $\vec{s}_2(C_2p_2)$ are coplanar, can be written (as Masry, 1969, derived):

$$\begin{pmatrix} x_1 & y_1 & f_1 \end{pmatrix} M_1^T \begin{bmatrix} 0 & -Bz' & By' \\ Bz' & 0 & -Bx' \\ -By' & Bx' & 0 \end{bmatrix} M_2 \begin{bmatrix} x_2 \\ y_2 \\ f_2 \end{bmatrix} = 0 \qquad (10.14)$$

where $\left.\begin{array}{l} x_1, \ y_1, \ f_1 \\ x_2, \ y_2, \ f_2 \end{array}\right\}$ are image coordinates of the same point (i.e., p_1 and p_2) in photo 1 and photo 2 systems, respectively.

$M_1, \ M_2$ are the corresponding rotation matrices;

and   Bx', By', Bz'   are the components of C_1C_2 (i.e., base components in the model X, Y, Z system. They are related to the ground X, Y, Z system through a scale factor k, such that Bx = k·Bx', etc.

Assuming that the perspective centers move along straight lines (i.e., corresponding to perfect flight), good rigid connection between the two strip cameras, and considering a dependent relative orientation, Eq. 10.14 would reduce to the following form (containing the base components in terms of the ground coordinate system):

$$\begin{pmatrix} x_1 & y_1 & f_1 \end{pmatrix} \begin{bmatrix} 0 & -Bz & By \\ Bz & 0 & -Bx \\ -By & Bx & 0 \end{bmatrix} M_2 \begin{bmatrix} x_2 \\ y_2 \\ f_2 \end{bmatrix} = 0 \qquad (10.15)$$

The number of unknown in Eq. 10.15 is six (i.e., the three components of base and the three parameters defining the orientation matrix M_2). The method of determining the unknowns will be similar to that in the case of conventional photography (see Chap. 4). Equation 10.15 may be linearized and an iterative solution may be obtained. On the other hand, if the two space curves (of the perspective centers) are parallel and level, and if the terrain is flat, M_2 will reduce to a unit matrix. It then follows that only the ratios between Bx, By and Bz can be determined. This means that, as one approaches this situation, the problem becomes less stable. This is aggravated due to the very large magnitude of Bx as compared to By and Bz.

Derenyi (1973) studied three schemes for the relative orientation: (a) *Line-by-line* orientation, in which two of the orientation elements are assumed to be zero or to have known values; (b) *Section-by-section* orientation; in which the strip is subdivided into sections and it is assumed that the orientation elements remain constant within a section (Fig. 10.7); and (c) *Triple Channel* method of orientation, which presupposes three sets of recorded images, one being vertical and the other two being at diverging angles.

The section-by-section method seems to be the only feasible method for continuous mapping, computationally or analogically. It is a compromise solution in terms of accuracy and convenience in operation. It is practical in view of automated instruments like Analytical Plotters. After the relative orientation of the section is determined, the models thus formed can be joined together to form the strip in a way similar to an aeropolygon strip triangulation (Ghosh, 1975). The coordinates of all the points in such a strip can next be adjusted by an appropriate method.

10.2 PANORAMIC PHOTOGRAPHY

Panoramic cameras have been used since the 19th century. However, it was during the 1950's and later that serious efforts have been made towards their

development and application to mapping. The Perkin-Elmer Corporation, Itek
Corporation, Fairchild Corporation and Chicago Aerial Industries are some of the
well known manufacturers of panoramic cameras. Tafel (1962) evaluated the
characteristics of several airborne panoramic cameras. The Manual of
Photogrammetry (1980) and the Manual of Remote Sensing (1983), both published by
the American Society of Photogrammetry and Remote Sensing, give listings of such
cameras. The Optical Bar Camera of Itek Corp., is an example (see Figs. 10.8 and
10.9).

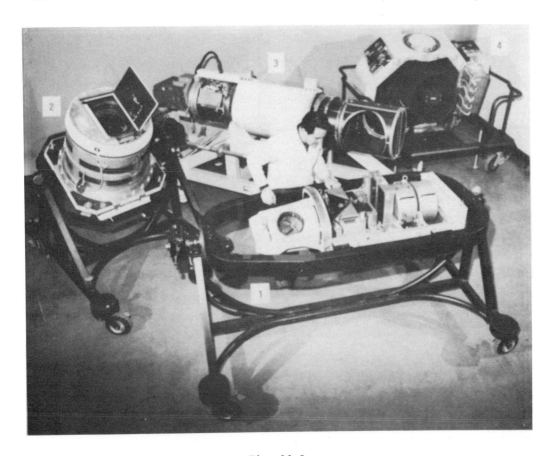

Fig. 10.8

Some cameras used in NASA-USA space programs

(1) Foreground: KA 80, 61cm (21 in) Optical Bar Camera; (2) Left rear: Large Format Camera; (3) Center rear: KA 102 LOROP (stand off) Camera, Effective Focal
length: 168 cm (66 in); Film framing system: 12.7 cm (5 in); (4) Right rear:
LOROP Pan Camera, Effective Focal length: 183 cm (72 in); Gyro stabilized; Film
framing system: 70 mm (2.75 in). [Courtesy, Itek Optical System]

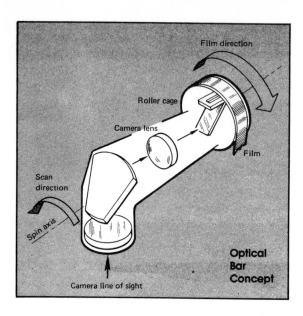

Fig. 10.9

Optical bar camera design concept
[Courtesy, Itek Optical System]

A panoramic camera is of the scanning type. It sweeps the ground from side to side across the direction of flight (see Figs 10.1 and 10.2 for camparative ideas). This permits the panoramic camera to record a much wider ground area per flight than either the frame or the strip camera. Continuous ground coverage is obtained by properly spaced exposures timed to give sufficient overlap between frames. This method of exposure creates an inter-dependence amongst aircraft speed, altitude, camera (field) angle and the cycling rate of the lens. The basic types are catagorized into two groups: (a) *Direct-scanning* type, with rotating or swinging lens; (b) *Indirect-scanning* type, by means of rotating mirrors or prisms (not the lens).

The common characteristics of these cameras are: (i) The film (negative) surface is cylindrical, the width of film being parallel to the axis of the cylinder; (ii) The instantaneous field of view is almost a line, through a narrow slit in front of the film; (iii) The slit length is equal to the width of the photo format; (iv) The slit width is usually variable to control the exposure; and (v) Compensation for image motion (IMC) is necessary, being performed by moving either the film or the slit or lens.

The panoramic camera is more dynamic than the frame or the strip camera. Various movements contained in the imaging system tend to create distortions and image smear, both. Accordingly, corrective procedures are necessary.

The imaging system involves the following internal sources of distortion:

(1) *Optical*: Lens distortion and focal length determination. Both these can be established through calibration.

(2) *Optico-mechanical*: Irregular and wobbling motions of various optical and mechanical components, generally of systemetic nature; and

(3) *Mechanical*: Film or IMC irregularities, also of systematic nature generally.

The effect of these on the photo-coordinates can be considered in terms of refinement of such data as obtained from prior calibration. In the working of the system (in the aircraft or in the space vehicle), however, one gets three basic types of image displacements, viz., *Panoramic, Scan-positional* and *IMC distortions*. The resultant distortion, due to these three factors are given by (considering subscripts p, s and m, respectively):

$$
\begin{aligned}
x &= x_p + x_s + x_m \\
&= \frac{f \cdot X \cdot \cos\theta}{h} + \frac{\theta \cdot f \cdot V \cdot \cos\theta}{h \cdot \varsigma} + \frac{f \cdot v \cdot \sin\theta}{h \cdot \varsigma} \\
y &= y_p = f \cdot \arctan \frac{Y}{h}
\end{aligned}
\qquad (10.16)
$$

where   x, y   are the photo coordinates;
         f   is the camera focal length;
         h   is the flying height above datum;
         ς is the angular velocity of camera scan arm;
         θ is the camera scan angle;
         V   is the aircraft velocity'
         v   is the velocity of image in the focal plane;
and   X, Y   are the coordinates of the point on the ground datum plane.

Figure 10.10 gives an idea of the combined effects of all the distortions. See the paper by Itek Laboratories (1961, 1962) for the derivations and further explanations of these expressions.

AP-Q

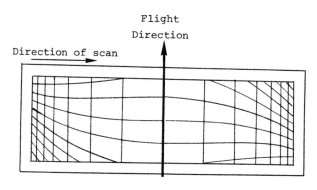

Fig. 10.10

Combined effect of all distortions on a panoramic photograph

10.2.1 Collinearity Condition in Panoramic Photography

While exposing the image, the camera lens scans through an angle θ. This may be considered as a constantly changing additional tilt (ω) of the camera axis. In order to account for this in the projective equation, the orientation matrix M can be premultiplied by a rotation matrix representing the scan angle (see Case, 1967). Furthermore, the y photo coordinate being in the direction perpendicular to the slit (cf. x in strip photography) becomes zero. However, the y coordinate of a point can be used to determine the time t_p and thus the position and the attitude of camera at that instant of time. Considering the midpoint of exposure as the origin of the photo coordinate system (which corresponds to the nadir direction), the scan angle is θ_p = y/f (Fig. 10.11).

The projective equation for panoramic photograpphy then becomes:

$$
\begin{bmatrix} x \\ 0 \\ -f \end{bmatrix} = k \begin{bmatrix} 1 & 0 & 0 \\ 0 & \cos\theta p & \sin\theta p \\ 0 & -\sin\theta p & \cos\theta p \end{bmatrix} M \begin{bmatrix} Xp - X_o \\ Yp - Y_o \\ Zp - Z_o \end{bmatrix}
\tag{10.17}
$$

The time during the exposure is rather critical. If the scan rate $\dot{\theta}$ is given, the time t_p for the photo point (p) is given by

$$
t_p = t_o + \frac{\theta_p}{\dot{\theta}}
\tag{10.18}
$$

where t_o is the time of exposure of the origin of y coordinates.

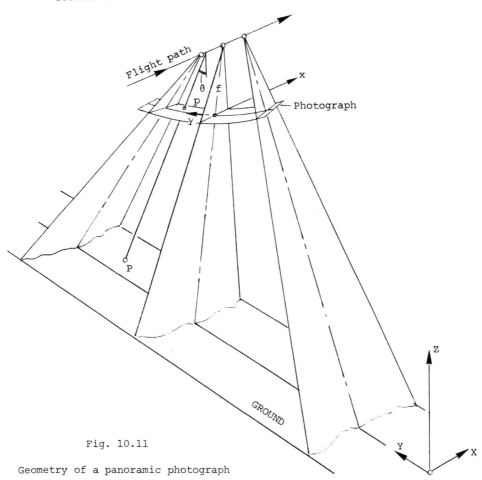

Fig. 10.11

Geometry of a panoramic photograph

It may be noted that Eq. 10.18 does not consiter second and third order effects of acceleration ($\ddot{\theta}$) and jerk ($\dddot{\theta}$) which could occur in the system.

The time marks are of great help here as in the case of strip photography. Also some modifications of Eq. 10.17 can be made in order to obtain this collinearity equation in a form where the right hand side is identical with that for frame or strip photography. If both sides are multiplied by the transpose of the scan-angle rotation matrix, one gets:

$$
\begin{bmatrix} x \\ f \cdot \sin\theta_p \\ -f \cdot \cos\theta_p \end{bmatrix} = \begin{bmatrix} x \cdot \sec\theta_p \\ f \cdot \tan\theta_p \\ -f \end{bmatrix} \frac{1}{\sec\theta_p} = k\, M \begin{bmatrix} Xp - X_o \\ Yp - Y_o \\ Zp - Z_o \end{bmatrix} \tag{10.19}
$$

Here, the scale factor k is the ratio of the absolute values of the location vectors, i.e., $k = |s|/|S|$.

Furthermore,

$$|s| = (x^2 + f^2)^{1/2} \quad \text{and} \quad |S| = \left[(Xp - X_o)^2 + (Yp - Y_o)^2 + (Zp - Z_o)^2 \right]^{1/2}$$

This will finally give the collinearity condition equations in this case in the following familiar forms:

$$\left. \begin{array}{l} x' = x \cdot \sec\theta_p = -f \left\{ \dfrac{m_{11}(Xp - X_o) + m_{12}(Yp - Y_o) + m_{13}(Zp - Z_o)}{m_{31}(Xp - X_o) + m_{32}(Yp - Y_o) + m_{33}(Zp - Z_o)} \right\} \\[4mm] y' = f \cdot \tan\theta_p = -f \left\{ \dfrac{m_{21}(Xp - X_o) + m_{22}(Yp - Y_o) + m_{23}(Zp - Z_o)}{m_{31}(Xp - X_o) + m_{32}(Yp - Y_o) + m_{33}(Zp - Z_o)} \right\} \end{array} \right\} \quad (10.20)$$

The basic similarity of Eqs 4.8 (frame photography), 10.10 (strip photography) and 10.20 (panoramic photography) brings out the essential idea that the computer program for frame photography can be used in other cases with only slight changes. In each case, however, various constraints (functional or geometric) may be utilized (see Chap. 9). In the event the positions or attitudes of the camera are known or can be constrained by some function of time, one can easily use IEFP, whereby the inverse of the collinearity equation is first employed to project the photo coordinates to the ground system. The resulting ground coordinates are projected back upto IEFP by using the collinearity equations directly. The expressions 10.11 and 10.12 apply in the case of panoramic photography also. The value for Δtj is $\dot{\theta}j/\dot{\theta}$.

10.2.2 Relative Orientation With Panoramic Photographs

Stereomodels are formed in the panoramic system with convergent pairs (using forward or rear looking oblique panoramic photographs, sometimes in conjunction with vertical, normal photographs). The main advantage of convergent photography is that the ground points appearing in the areas common to both cameras can be located with accuracy somewhat higher than a normal pair. However, in such cases, the panoramic distortion should first be rectified appropriately. The operation of relative orientation also means the imposition of the condition of coplanarity (see Ghosh, 1972 and Kratky, 1983).

In spite of a clear understanding of the deformations in the panoramic photographs, their use in conventional stereoplotters is not practicable. The panoramic photographs have formats which exceed the limitations permitted in such instruments. This prompted scientists to take the sections approach (similar to the strip photography). However, even this compromises perspective geometry by introducing undesirable model-deformations, which are difficult to compensate during the map compilation process. This would, consequently, lead into the use of the analytical plotters.

An operational procedure of relative orientation developed at the US Air Force's Aeronautical Chart and Information Center (ACIC, St. Louis, presently known as DMA, Aerospace Center) has been described by Gill (1964).

This idea divides the photography into sections (or segments) which appear on the 23 cm × 23 cm diapositives in such a manner as to permit overlaps with succeeding models (stereo-pairs) of other segments (Fig. 10.12). As long as the correct parameters are set into the computer of the Analytical Plotter, there is no limitation on the location of the section.

Relative orientation of these section-models cannot be easily performed by using conventional techniques associated with conventional (frame) photography. This is primarily because of high correlation between orientation elements affecting Y-parallaxes.

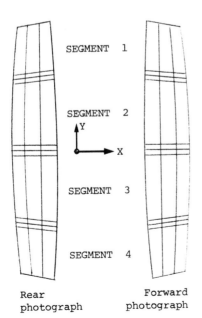

SEGMENT 1

SEGMENT 2

SEGMENT 3

SEGMENT 4

Rear photograph

Forward photograph

Fig. 10.12

Segmentation of panoramic stereo-photographs (schematic indicating overlaps)

The method considers Y-parallax observations at preselected locations as shown in Fig. 10.13. Points 1, 2, 3 and 4 indicate the four corners of a segment-model. 2-3 and 1-4 correspond to the width of the strip. The system of coordinates correspond directly to the conventional (frame) photography (see Ghosh, 1972). I, II are the nadir points for the forward and rear photographs, respectively. Their separation gives the base.

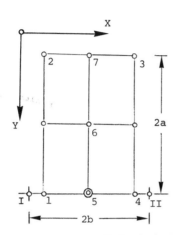

Fig. 10.13

Location of points

for relative orientation

(stereo-model of Segment 2)

The Y-parallax formulas for frame photography may be considered here. However, model coordinates of each point with respect to each segment should be carefully considered. Consider the following notations:

$2b$ = Model base: distance I-II

$2a$ = Model length in y distance

P_i = Model Y-parallax at point i

X, Y, Z = Model coordinates, in the International System, i.e. right handed with positive X in the direction of flight and Z pointing downwards from model air-base, origin at left side perspective center

and $2c$ = Model width in X-direction.

With the above considerations, if the model has a scale equal to that of the average photo: $f = Z$ = constant; the coordinates of points are as given below in Table 10.1.

Model points in segments 3 and 4 as also their coordinates can be obtained directly in the same system.

Table 10.1

Model coordinates of points indicated in Fig. 10.13

Segment 1					Segment 2			
Pt	X	Y	Z		Pt	X	Y	Z
1	(b-c)	-2a	Z		1	(b-c)	0	Z
2	(b-c)	-4a	Z		2	(b-c)	-2a	Z
3	(b+c)	-4a	Z		3	(b+c)	-2a	Z
4	(b+c)	-2a	Z		4	(b+c)	0	Z
5	b	-2a	Z		5	b	0	Z
6	b	-3a	Z		6	b	-a	Z
7	b	-4a	Z		7	b	-2a	Z

Consider a dependent relative orientation using the elements of the right side camera (camera II, see Ghosh, 1972) and considering flat terrain, the Y-parallax equation is (correction equation):

$$-Py = -dby + \frac{Y}{Z} dbz + Z(1+\frac{Y^2}{Z^2})d\omega - \frac{(X-2b)Y}{Z} d\varphi - (X-2b)d\kappa \qquad (10.21)$$

Application of the Least Squares principle and solution of normal equations would yield the solutions for the elements. It may be noted here that κ and φ are the weakest elements from the geometric standpoint. Therefore, the use of points having maximum spread in X (note the coefficients in Eq. 10.21) and in a number more than the minimum is recommended. Points 1, 2, 3 and 4 may, thus, be used for solving $d\kappa$ and $d\varphi$. This gives, for segment 2 (P_i being Y-parallaxes):

$$d\varphi = \frac{Z}{4ac} (P_1 - P_2 + P_3 - P_4)$$

$$d\kappa = -\frac{1}{2c} (P_1 - P_4) \qquad (10.22)$$

For segment 1, they are:

$$d\varphi = \frac{Z}{4ac} (P_1 - P_2 + P_3 - P_4)$$

$$d\kappa = -\frac{1}{2c} (2P_1 - P_2 + P_3 - 2P_4) \qquad (10.23)$$

For the other elements, for Segment 2:

$$d\omega = \frac{Z}{2a^2} (P_5 - 2P_6 + P_7)$$

$$dbz = \frac{Z}{2a} (3P_5 - 4P_6 + P_7)$$

$$dby = -\frac{Z^2}{2a^2} (P_5 - 2P_6 + P_7) + P_5$$

$$(10.24)$$

For segment 1:

$$d\omega = \frac{Z}{2a^2} (P_5 - 2P_6 + P_7)$$

$$dbz = \frac{Z}{2a} (7P_5 - 12P_6 + 5P_7)$$

$$dby = 6P_5 - 8P_6 + 3P_7 - \frac{Z^2}{2a^2} (P_5 - 2P_6 + P_7)$$

$$(10.25)$$

Note: The signs in the formulas would be according to the distance "a" being negative or positive with respect to the base-nadir plane of the model (X-Z plane).

The elimination of Y-parallax (i.e. imposing the coplanarity condition analogically at the analytical plotter) can be accomplished within the viewing accuracy of the instrument, and is limited only by the resolution of the original material.

The segmented models can next be absolutaly oriented (scaled, levelled and translated) like conventional (frame photography) models.

Kratky (1983) has discussed some salient points to be noted in particular when using panoramic photographs in an analytical plotter. He has presented several two-way transformation formulas which could permit direct conversions between panoramic, equivalent frame and stereo-model coordinates. The effect of such transformation solutions on real-time control of image positioning at an analytical plotter in various phases of orientaiton and map compilation would simplify the work in practice.

Steps to be taken with regard to model orientation at an analytical plotter are discussed earlier in Chap.2, pp 33-35.

The ACIC at St. Louis, Mo. has performed stereo-photogrammetric reduction of Apollo 15 panoramic photographs using the Analytical AS-11 plotter system in a large scale topographic compilation: 1:25,000 scale, 20 m. contour interval (see Peterson, 1973). In this production process they considered three segments instead of four as discussed above. An off-line computational technique was used for adjusting the stereomodel to selected selenodetic control. As statistical method used to evaluate the topographic information (without the benefit of the ability to perform a field check) indicates:

$$
\begin{array}{lll}
\text{Pointing precision:} & & \text{5 to 7 m on lunar surface} \\
m_H \ (\sigma_{CE}) & : & \pm \ 10 \text{ m at 90\% confidence} \\
m_p \ (\sigma_p) & : & \pm \ 20 \text{ m at 90\% confidence}
\end{array}
$$

The above with f = 609.608 mm

$$h = 105.127 \text{ km}$$

$$\varphi = \pm 12.5 \text{ degrees (i.e. } \gamma = 25°)$$

Another example may be quoted from the NASA (1978) publication No. SP-427, with regard to the U-2 Aircraft capabilities: The nominal resolution at a flying height of 65,000 ft with the Itek Optical Bar camera is between 0.3 and 2 m. It may be noted that the U-2 has been used extensively to collect underflight (or "ground truth") data to support LANDSAT investigations in forestry, water management, coastal zone processing, etc.

10.2.3 Recent Innovations With Frame Cameras

A horizon to horizon coverage of 180° in the direction perpendicular to the line of flight (as found to be well suited for low altitude aerial reconnaissance) can be performed also with special arrangements of frame cameras. One such system, developped in the late 1970s, is the Zeiss KRb 8/24E camera, with which a three-lens array covers an angle of 144° perpendicular to the line of flight. Prisms in front of the two lateral lenses deflect the optical axes by 47.5°. As opposed to the pure panoramic system, the photographs are so arranged on the film that stereo-viewing is possible directly without cutting the film. The deformation schematic is presented in Fig. 10.14. It may be of interest to compare this pattern with the one shown in Fig. 10.10 for a pure panoramic photograph.

Modern technology permits a shutter speed of between 1/150 and 1/2000 second of

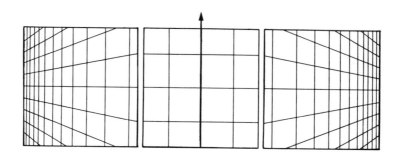

Fig. 10.14

Deformation schematic

in the form of projected square grid for KRb 8/24E photography

(Courtesy, Carl Zeiss, Oberkochen, FR Germany)

time, a cycling speed of seven exposures per second, automatic aperture and shutter settings within ±1/2 f-stop and a maximum v/h rate of 5 $\sec^{-1}$. The photogrammetric data processing for this system would be as for frame cameras.

Similar other multilens cameras for high velocity and/or low altitude photogrammetric operations like the Carl Zeiss camera KS-153A (Dreyer, 1986) offer very satisfactory performance.

10.3 ELECTRON MICROGRAPHY

Electron microscopes have enabled scientists to have a wide variety of application and detection capabilities which make them indispensable in the fields of microbiology, metallurgy, microelectronics, criminology and many other physical and biological sciences. Single, two-dimensional, micrographs are generally satisfactory for many uses. There is, however, a growing demand for three-dimensional information. The geometry of such imaging systems being different, conventional approaches to such problems are usually unsatisfactory.

There are basically two types of electron microscopes: Transmission Electron Microscope (TEM) and Scanning Electron Microscope (SEM). Both of them, however differ fundamentally from the Optical Light Microscope (OLM) and from each other in many ways (see Table 10.2). An electron beam is used for the illumination (in both

Table 10.2

Comparison of OLM, TEM and SEM characteristics (after Black, 1970; with updated data)

Characteristics	OLM	TEM	SEM
Lens system	Glass or Quartz	Electromagnetic	Electromagnetic
Image display	Eye retina, Film or Frosted glass	Fluorescent viewing plate or film	CRT for viewing and photography
Energy	Radiation from UV through visible spectrum to IR	Thermonic emission of electrons accelerated by 50 to 1000 KV	Thermonic emission of electrons by 1 to 30 KV
Wave lengths	200 to 700 nm	> 0.1 nm	> 0.1 nm
Resolution	100 nm	0.3 nm	3.0 nm
Depth of field	Poor; 250 μm at 15x to 0.08 μm at 1200x	Good; 500 μm at 4000x to 0.2 μm at 500,000x	Excellent; 1000 μm at 100x to 10 μm at 10,000x
Magnification	15x to 3000x	100x to 500,000x (Stepped)	10x to 200,000x (Continuous)
Sample requirements	Thin sections only	0.1 to 1 μm thin section or only replica; 2 to 3 mm diameter	No thickness limit; non-metals are better metal coated (Au, Pd or Al); to 25 mm dia.

TEM and SEM) and this beam is allowed to impimge upon the specimen. In the TEM,
the image is formed by the objective lens (not to be confused with the lens in a
conventional photographic camera) and is a measure of the scattering power of each
point in the specimen as the electron beam passes through the sample (specimen),
which is an ultra-thin section. The image is further magnified and finally
displayed on a fluorescent screen. The photograph is obtained by inserting a
sensitized film in place of this screen. In the SEM, the focussed beam is allowed
to impinge upon the surface of the specimen. Interaction with the specimen
(object) produces a variety of signals, one of which, the secondary electron
signal, is drawn to a collector at positive voltage. The electron radiation is
used for two synchronous scanning beams, viz., (i) a point source of radiation
sweeping over the specimen in a well defined pattern of lines with a well defined
velocity; and (ii) a corresponding second point source of radiation over a

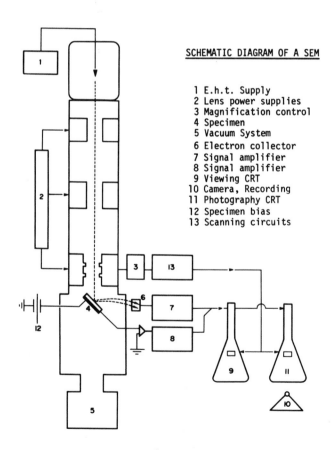

SCHEMATIC DIAGRAM OF A SEM

1 E.h.t. Supply
2 Lens power supplies
3 Magnification control
4 Specimen
5 Vacuum System
6 Electron collector
7 Signal amplifier
8 Signal amplifier
9 Viewing CRT
10 Camera, Recording
11 Photography CRT
12 Specimen bias
13 Scanning circuits

Fig. 10.15

Schematic diagram of a Scanning Electron Microscope

fluorescent screen, which is recorded with a camera (e.g., Polaroid Land Camera). During the recent years, electron microscope systems have been developed in which the features of both TEM and SEM (and even more) are combined. One such example is the TEMSCAN System manufactured by the Japan Electro Optical Laboratories (JEOL), Ltd. The typical features of a SEM and a TEM are illustrated in Figs. 10.15 and 10.16, respectively.

While the SEM micrographs depict the surface details of the object (sample), the TEM system penetrates through the sample giving micrographs of nature somewhat similar to X-ray radiographs. Therefore, three dimensional surface mapping

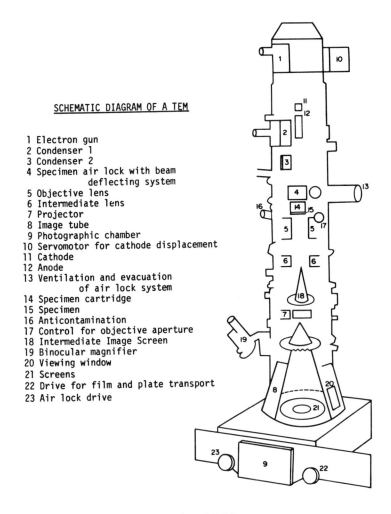

SCHEMATIC DIAGRAM OF A TEM

1 Electron gun
2 Condenser 1
3 Condenser 2
4 Specimen air lock with beam
            deflecting system
5 Objective lens
6 Intermediate lens
7 Projector
8 Image tube
9 Photographic chamber
10 Servomotor for cathode displacement
11 Cathode
12 Anode
13 Ventilation and evacuation
            of air lock system
14 Specimen cartridge
15 Specimen
16 Anticontamination
17 Control for objective aperture
18 Intermediate Image Screen
19 Binocular magnifier
20 Viewing window
21 Screens
22 Drive for film and plate transport
23 Air lock drive

Fig. 10.16

Schematic diagram of a Transmission Electron Microscope

potential with SEM stereo-micrographs is great. On the other hand, since the TEM has a much better resolving power as compared with the SEM, it offers larger magnification capabilities..

The features of SEM and TEM being so different, from the point of view of information extraction, a combination of stereo micrographs of the same sample obtained from both SEM and TEM would supplement each other, the equal of which is not possible with any other system in the field of microscopic measurements. Interesting applications in this regard (see Ghosh and ElGhazali, 1977) would open up new areas of quantitative research with electron microscopy.

A one-to-one correspondence exists between the object points and the corresponding image points. The resolving power is dictated by electron optics and the information content is dictated by the interaction of visible light in the matter. Oatley (1972) listed the primary factors causing the intensity variation in SEM imagery: (a) Factors which depend on the local angle of incidence of the electron probe; (b) Factors which cause variations in the fraction of secondary electrons collected by the detector; and (c) Factors which depend on the nature of the material of the object (specimen). The first two are largely determined by the "topographic" features and are similar to the angular relationship of the Sun to the surface features of the earth's terrain in aerial photograpphy. The third one is analogous to color in a visual image. A stereogram of a familiar object taken with a SEM (Fig. 10.17) will illustrate the above facts.

The stage plate containing the specimen (object) in both TEM and SEM has, generally, four degrees of freedom, viz., (1) Tilt, uniaxial, around the X- or Y-axis (corresponding to Ω or Φ tilt in conventional photogrammetry); (2) Rotation about the general direction of the principal electron axis (similar to K rotation in conventional photogrammetry); (3) X-translation; and (4) Y-translation. In a relative sense, assuming no movement of the object, these correspond to the following exterior orientation parameters, respectively: (1) ω or φ; (2) κ; (3) Bx; and (4) By. There are, however, limitations in each of these elements peculiar to the various TEMs and SEMs.

In the mensural evaluation of the electron micrographs, a major role is played by the resolution capability. Very high magnification giving comparatively unsharp images may yield unreliable results, whereas a low magnification giving sharp micrographs would demand precision measuring instrument, stable photographic material, etc. The choice of instrument must also depend on the geometry of

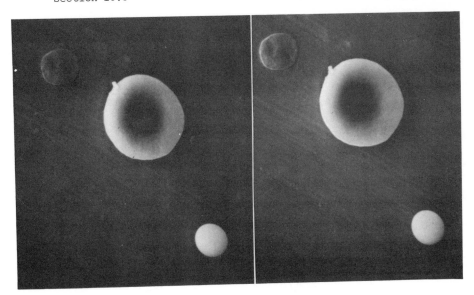

Fig. 10.17

Stereo-micrograph with a SEM

Showing a platelet (top), a human blood-cell (middle), and a latex par-
ticle (bottom, used for dimensional comparison). Note : The left photo
is untilted while the right one has 10° tilt. Magnification : ~4000x

projection inherent in the system. In this respect, continous mapping can be
performed with instruments in which near parallel projection is adaptable as in an
analytical plotter or the Zeiss Stereotope (Ghosh, 1971; Wood, 1972).

10.3.1 Geometric Aspects in an EM System

An understanding of the particular EM system is essential for precision
measurements with micrographs therefrom. The implied systems of coordinates,
transformation concepts and consideration of various distortions, although in many
respects similar to conventional photogrammetry, are uniquely special in both, SEM
and TEM.

With regard to the various phases of EM applications, one may refer to photo-
(micrograph), model- or object- coordinate systems. These being mutually
associated (Fig. 10.18), their relationship to one another may be establish through
transformation of coordinates.

By using rigorous and statistically controlled self-calibration procedures, it has been observed (see Ghosh, 1975; Maune, 1973; Nordberg, 1972; Ghosh and Nagaraja, 1976; Adiguzel, 1985) that

1. An electron micrograph system is better respresented by a mathematical model for an effective central (perspective) projection (see Fig. 10.19) rather than for a parallel projection (see Fig. 10.20), although it is not generally significant statistically at magnifications above 2000x. The difference between the two types of projections can be mathematically modelled for convenient uses at a computer;

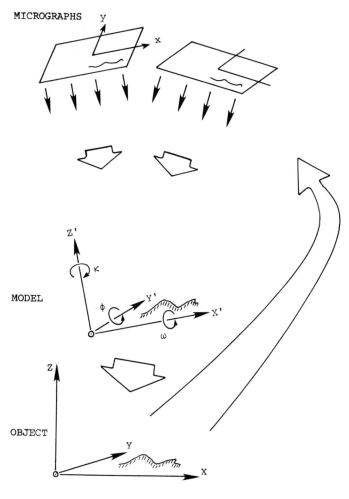

Fig. 10.18

Systems of coordinates involved in EM applications

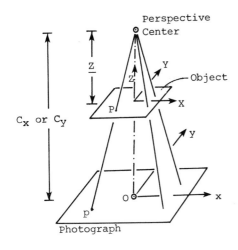

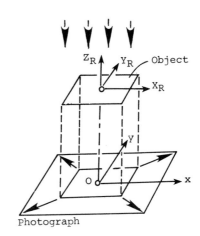

Fig. 10.19

Perspective projection

and the condition of collinearity

Fig. 10.20

Parallel projection

and magnification

2. Strict collinearity condition is disturbed by four types of systematic distortions, viz., Scale (differential), Radial, Tangential and Spiral (see Fig. 10.21). In most applications, however, the tangential distortion part can be effectively contained in the mathematical model of the spiral distortion;

3. The scale distortion can be contained directly in the mathematical model for the projection (parallel or perspective); and

4. The effects of such distortions are best corrected by use of polynomials if applied sequentially.

With the above considerations, the basic interior and exterior orientation parameters as understood in conventional photogrammetry will be suitably applicable in electron micrography utilization.

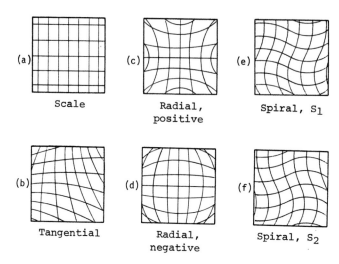

(a) Scale

(c) Radial, positive

(e) Spiral, S_1

(b) Tangential

(d) Radial, negative

(f) Spiral, S_2

Fig. 10.21

Typical distortion patterns in electron micrography

A. *Parallel projection* (Fig. 10.20)

The parallel projection can be expressd by:

$$\begin{bmatrix} x \\ y \\ 0 \end{bmatrix} = \begin{bmatrix} K_1 & 0 & 0 \\ 0 & K_2 & 0 \\ 0 & 0 & 0 \end{bmatrix} \begin{bmatrix} X_R \\ Y_R \\ Z_R \end{bmatrix} \qquad (10.26)$$

where   x, y   are the photo coordinates;

K_1, K_2 are the scale factors along X_R, Y_R directions, respectively;

and X_R, Y_R, Z_R are the object-space coordinates (considering rotations).

In view of rotations and translations to a selected origin the last term in Eq. 10.26 becomes:

$$\begin{bmatrix} X_R \\ Y_R \\ Z_R \end{bmatrix} = M \begin{bmatrix} X - X_o \\ Y - Y_o \\ Z - Z_o \end{bmatrix} \qquad (10.27)$$

where X_o, Y_o, Z_o are the coordinates of the selected origin in the object system; and M is the orientation matrix.

If the height datum (level reference) is defined by setting $Z_o = 0$, ofter substitutions and simplifications, one obtains the following projective equations in the case of parallel projection:

$$
\left.
\begin{aligned}
x &= K_1(X - X_o)(c\varphi c\kappa + s\omega s\varphi s\kappa) + K_1(Y - Y_o)c\omega s\kappa + K_1 Z(s\omega c\varphi s\kappa - s\varphi c\kappa) \\
\\
y &= K_2(X - X_o)(s\omega s\varphi c\kappa - c\varphi s\kappa) + K_2(Y - Y_o)c\omega s\kappa + K_2 Z(s\varphi s\kappa + s\omega s\varphi c\kappa)
\end{aligned}
\right\} \quad (10.28)
$$

where c and s prefixes mean cosine and sine functions, respectively, of the rotation angles as indicated.

B. *Perspective Projection* (Fig. 10.19)

The principal characteristics of a perspective projection are that, (1) there exists a perspective center from where the rays appear to diverge, and (2) the projection distance, in view of possible affine scale deformation, may be considered in terms of C_x and C_y, with regard to x and y coordinates respectively. The following relationships hold:

$$
x = X_R \frac{C_x}{Z - Z_R} \qquad\qquad y = Y_R \frac{C_y}{Z - Z_R} \qquad (10.29)
$$

where $\underline{Z}$ in the projection distance to the reference datum of the object, and the rest of the terms are as defined previously.

By substituting the expansion for Z_R from Eq. (10.27) into Eq. (10.29), after rearranging,

$$
\left.
\begin{aligned}
x &= \frac{(C_x/\underline{Z})\ X_R}{1 - \dfrac{1}{\underline{Z}}\left[(X - X_o)c\omega s\varphi - (Y - Y_o)s\omega + (Z - Z_o)c\omega c\varphi\right]} \\
\\
y &= \frac{(C_y/\underline{Z})\ Y_R}{1 - \dfrac{1}{\underline{Z}}\left[(X - X_o)c\omega s\varphi - (Y - Y_o)s\omega + (Z - Z_o)c\omega c\varphi\right]}
\end{aligned}
\right\} \quad (10.30)
$$

One can substitute K_1 for $C_x/\underline{Z}$ and K_2 for $C_y/\underline{Z}$. Furthermore, the second term in the denominator being smaller than unity, the expression can be expanded in a series (cf. $1/\{1-q\} = 1 + q + q^2 + q^3 + \ldots$). This gives the final expressions for a perspective projection:

$$\left.\begin{array}{l} x = K_1 X_R \{ 1 + \nabla + \nabla^2 + \ldots \} \\[3mm] y = K_2 Y_R \{ 1 + \nabla + \nabla^2 + \ldots \} \end{array}\right\} \qquad (10.31)$$

where ∇ is the second term in the denominators of Eqs. (10.30). Details of this derivation and the validity of the various approximations are credited to Nagaraja (1974).

C. *Distortions*

In consideration of working convenience, without compromising accuracy, one may consider the deviations form parallel projection as distortions. The various distortions and their mathematical models as applicable to electron micrography are presented below in accordance with their relative magnitudes (as established from research studies reported by Nordberg, 1972; Maune, 1973; Nagaraja, 1974; Ghosh and ElGhazali, 1977 and Adiguzel, 1985).

1. *Projective distortion*: This defines the departure of the perspective projection from the parallel projection, in view of Eqs. 10.31, without considering the effect of any other distortion:

$$\left.\begin{array}{l} x_{parallel} = x_{pers} - x_{pers} \{\nabla + \nabla^2 + \ldots \} \\[3mm] y_{parallel} = y_{pers} - y_{pers} \{\nabla + \nabla^2 + \ldots \} \end{array}\right\} \qquad (10.32)$$

The representative values of ∇, ∇^2 etc. can be obtained from calibration studies of the specific EM imaging system.

2. *Scale distortion* or affinity in view of different scale factors in different directions is contained in Eqs. 10.27 through 10.31. It is best dealt with directly in the mathematical model for the specific projection used.

3. *Radial distortion*: Similar to conventional photogrammetry, considering a

polynomial, the radial distortion can be expressed by

$$\Delta r = k_o r + k_1 r^3 + k_2 r^5 + \ldots \qquad (10.33)$$

where r is the radial image distance from the photo center and the k's are certain constants. The first term (k_o) is equivalent to a scale factor and, in a sequential application of the corrections, may be considered contained in the terms K_1 or K_2 (see Eqs. 10.28 and 10.31) for the respective coordinates. From actual studies it has been found that terms of 5 and higher order in r can be neglected in practice. For the components of this distortion, then,

$$\left.\begin{array}{l} \Delta x = \Delta r \dfrac{x}{r} = k_1 \cdot r^3 \cdot \dfrac{x}{r} = k_1 (x^3 + xy^2) = D_1 x^3 + D_2 xy^2 \\[4mm] \Delta y = \Delta r \dfrac{y}{r} = k_1 \cdot r^3 \cdot \dfrac{y}{r} = k_1 (x^2 y + y^3) = D_3 y^3 + D_4 x^2 y \end{array}\right\} \qquad (10.34)$$

where the D's are certain constants.

4. *Spiral distortion*: Klemperer and Barnett (1971) expressed the spiral or rotational twist of the electron beam by

$$\Delta d = C(y_o'/y) r^3 \qquad (10.35)$$

where Δd is the lateral (to the radial direction on micrograph) displacement; C is the spiral distortion coefficient; y_o'/y is the magnification; and r is the radial distance of the point from the principal electron axis. Magnification being already contained in the K's, a substitution, $S = C(y_o'/y)$, will give the components of the spiral distortion as follows:

$$\left.\begin{array}{l} \Delta x = \Delta d \cdot \sin\Theta = S\dfrac{y}{r} r^3 = S(x^2 y + y^3) \\[4mm] \Delta y = \Delta d \cdot \cos\Theta = S\dfrac{x}{r} r^3 = S(x^3 + xy^2) \end{array}\right\} \qquad (10.36)$$

Here Θ is the angle the radial direction makes with the photo (micrograph) x-axis and, in view of the possible affine deformation, the above expressions can be modified for practical applications as below:

$$\left.\begin{array}{l} \Delta x = S_1 (x^2 y + y^3) \\[4mm] \Delta y = S_2 (x^3 + xy^2) \end{array}\right\} \qquad (10.37)$$

where S_1 and S_2 are the spiral constants.

5. *Tangential distortion*: Although the tangential distortion of the conventional photogrammetric camera is different from this, Maune (1973) modelled it in accordance with Eq. 5.7 and got satisfactory results. It was found (see also Ghosh, 1975) that this mathematical model is solvable only when non-zero estimates for the P_1 and P_2 terms are used. Nagaraja (1974) found subsequently that this type of distortion can be effectively contained in the mathematical model for spiral distortion. Adiguzel, (1985) found some very minor improvement in the mensural accuracy by considering this distortion.

The degree of stability of the electron microscope has a very significant influence on the distortions, as would be expected of any working system. The reliability of the mathematical models, therefore, would depend on the calibration and evaluation of such an electron microscope system performed under the specific working conditions.

10.3.2 Stereoscopic Model and Final Accuracies

After the photo coordinates are corrected for the appropriate distortions, the refined data can be used for all photogrammetric operations in ways similar to the conventional systems. Electron micrographs do not pose any further complications in analytical solutions. It may be pertinent, however, to mention that considering the near parallel or parallel projection involved here, use of a conventional stereo plotter for continuous mapping should be ruled out. Analytical plotters of any type or simple instruments that do not operate on the principles of central projection (e.g., Zeiss Stereotope) are found to be of successful use. See Ghosh (1971, 1986) and Boyde et al (1974) for further ideas on plotting instruments usable with electron micrographs. Oshima et al (1970) contributed valuable ideas on the mapping problems with conventional stereo plotting instruments.

As in conventional photogrammetry, a stereo model of the object can be oriented by means of intersection of conjugate rays established by using two micrographs of the same object. In conventional photogrammetry, photo orientations are defined by "exterior" orientation elements consisting of translations along, and rotations around, the X, Y and Z axes. In EM imaging systems, however, there is no "exterior space" and the elements of orientations obtained with regard to the specimen plate are of prime importance. There are, however, limitations and yet simplifications in these "elements" as have been discussed earlier.

The orientations and data acquisition are simplified if the first micrograph is taken with a tilt angle amounting to half of the parallactic angle ($\theta = \gamma/2$ in Fig. 10.22 and the second micrograph is taken with the same angle of tilt in the opposite direction ($\theta' = -\theta$). The pretilt (θ_o), if any, would then contribute to tilting the stereo-model, i.e., levelling of the elevation datum as necessary in the absolute orientation.

If parallel projection is assumed, the 3-D data of a point P with regard to a reference point B are:

$$
\left.
\begin{aligned}
Z' &= \Delta p. \frac{1}{2\sin\theta} = (x' - x'')\frac{1}{2}\cosec\frac{\gamma}{2} \\[2mm]
X' &= x'\sec\theta - Z'\tan\theta \\[2mm]
\text{and} \quad Y' &= y' = y''
\end{aligned}
\right\} \qquad (10.38)
$$

where x', y'   are the photo coordinates with regard to the reference B in the first (left) photo;

x", y"   are the photo coordinates with regard to the same reference in the second (right) photo;

and $\Delta p = x' - x''$ is the parallax difference between the observed point P and the reference B.

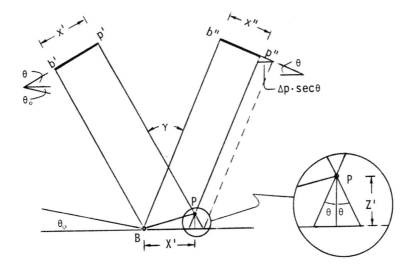

Fig. 10.22   Intersection geometry

Considering affinity, i.e., different magnifications, M_x and M_y in x and y directions, respectively, on the micrographs, Eq. 10.38 can be expressed as follows:

$$
\begin{bmatrix} X' \\ Y' \\ Z' \end{bmatrix} =
\begin{bmatrix} \sec\theta/M_x & 0 & 0 \\ 0 & 1/My & 0 \\ 0 & 0 & \csc\theta/2M_x \end{bmatrix}
\begin{bmatrix} x' \\ y' \\ \Delta p \end{bmatrix}
\tag{10.39}
$$

The final data in the object space is then subject to a simple transformation from the X', Y', Z' (Model) system into the X, Y, Z (object) system. However, this step is not often necessary at all.

With regard to the *accuracy* of the mensural data, one must consider several salient points:

1) *Stability* of the imaging and the measuring equipment systems. Studies made by Adiguzel (1985), ElGhazali (1978), Nagaraja (1974) and Maune (1973) indicate that most EM systems are stable for practically all applications. Modern photogrammetric equipment are undoubtedly capable of all related tasks.

2) *Resolution capacity* of the EM imaging system against the *mensuration capability* of the measuring instrument. Empirical studies in this regard would indicate the optimum capacity of the total system. Ghosh and ElGhazali (1977), for example, reported the following pointing accuracies, which would typify the situations: (Note, in each case the precision stereocomparator PSK of Zeiss was used):

> a) SEM at magnification 6 k: ± 4.2 nm
> b) SEM at magnification 17 k: ± 7.4 nm
> c) TEM at magnification 17 k: ± 2.0 nm
> d) TEM at magnification 91 k: ± 3.3 nm

It may be noted that the pointing accuracy is a function of the type of point (involving the image quality also) observed.

3) *The parallactic angle* would influence the quality of the intersection geometry. Theoretically, the best intersection is when the angle is 90°. However, very large angles would create stereoscopic gaps and other related problems, while very small angles would give comparatively unreliable heights. For a given object, a practical compromise between the two extremes is, therefore, necessary. Ghosh and ElGhazali (1977) reported that a parallactic angle between 8° and 20° would generally give adequate results, the optimum being usually between 10° and 15°.

4) *Provision of control* as necessary for absolute orientation in the conventional sense is impossible in EM applications. On the other hand, problems concerning multiple models (strips or blocks) are not necessary in practice. One should, however, use a "standard" for dimensional control.

Scale correction (or scaling) can be performed by making measurements against dimensions of known values. Ghosh (1971) used latex particles as "standards" in mapping human blood cells with SEM micrographs. The best available usable stantards are carbon replicas made from master diffraction gratings for the TEM and metal coated colabration specimens for the SEM. These are cross-ruled grids of fine grooves in a plane surface. The replica grids used for high magnification (e.g., manufactured by the SIRA, i.e., Scientific and Industrial Research Association, or by Ernest F. Fullam, Inc.) give 2160 line per mm. The line frequencies are generally guaranteed to be within 1 per cent of the stated figure by the manufacturer. The grids made from diffraction gratings are two-dimensional. However, certain configurations of convergent photography (see Ghosh, 1975) can be used to generate the third demension and thus the stereo-model can be fully controlled for assuring precision measurements.

The levelling of a model being generally arbitrary and with regard to an assumed reference datum plane decided by the user, control is no problem.

Note: To an EM user, comparative or relative results from different specimens are often more important than the absolute results in accuracy. Sometimes, the variability between specimens far outweighs the importance of some inaccuracies in individual results, which cause a general reluctance to consider accuracy related aspects. Nevertheless, these are important considerations.

10.4 X-RAY PHOTOGRAMMETRY

The term X-ray (Roentgen) photogrammetry is used when 'roentgen' radiation is utilized for the photography. Its use in recording and studying anatomical or physiological data of the human body is well established. There is a growing demand for three-dimensional information in such cases. In this respect, several techniques such as Kymography, Tomography, X-ray scanning, Biplane Angiocardiography, etc. have been developed and utilized. But, these either involve a much greater exposure of the subject (patient) to the X-ray than usually desirable and time-consuming cumbersome operations, or are too inaccurate for routine clinical practices. X-ray stereo-photogrammetry is a very logical technique in most such applications.

The basic geometric property of an X-ray photograph (radiograph) is the central (perspective) projection. The perspective center is the *focus* of the roentgen tube. Generally, the focus is assumed to be a point. This, however, is not true in physical reality. The focus is a small surface area (see Fig. 10.23) the size of which differs from one tube to another. For limited accuracy, therefore, the mensural evaluation can generally follow established stereo photogrammetric procedures with simple computations based on parallax measurements (see also Hallert, 1970).

Three dimensional mapping has been successfully attempted with stereo-plotting instruments like Kelsh or Wild B8 plotters (see Schernhorst, 1969). These however,

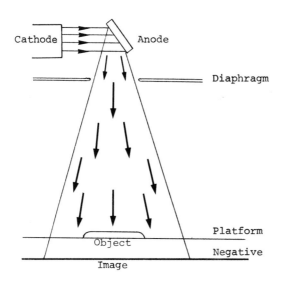

Fig. 10.23

Schematic diagram
of an X-ray system

do not give very high precision because of poor photographic resolution which is inherent in X-ray and of somewhat undesirable geometry. In spite of these, more than satisfactory results have been reported in some cases. Jonason and Hindmarsh (1975) reported obtaining a standard error of unit weight ±0.4 mm in the scale of the object. Such successful results have prompted many to pursue analytical photogrammetric solutions based on precision comparator measurements. These in turn, have yielded successful and extremely satisfactory results (see Takamoto, 1976 or Kratky, 1975).

In the imaging system, one should consider an *effective principal distance* (but not the focal length) and orientation elements, which correspond to the exterior orientation of conventional photogrammetry. Inherent in this is the collinearity condition of the rays. In reality, there is no exterior space in an X-ray imaging system, the object being placed between the source of energy (focus) and the film. The focal length would correspond directly to the projection distance.

Stereo radiograms can be produced under various combinations of the positions of the X-ray tube and the object. Some basic configurations (drawn after McNeil, 1966) are given in Fig. 10.24. Configuration (a) indicates the use of two X-ray tubes. The other configurations are obtainable with one tube by translating (case b) or rotating either the tube (case c) or the object (platform, case d).

10.4.1 Distortions in an X-ray System.

The object being always very close to the emulsion, radial or tangential or other projection system related distortions have no appreciable effect on the image. This has been established with certainty through recent research studies (see Boulianne, 1986). However, certain other distortions peculiar to a radiograph are discussed below (see also Hallert, 1970 and Takamoto, 1976).

A. *Film Deformation*:

This could be due to (a) lack of film flatness; (b) film deformation occurring during the time lapsed between the exposure and the measurement; and (c) possible variation in the thickness of film. The total effect of these is expected to be of irregular nature, However, with modern films and good handling procedures, these are seldom any cause of real concern.

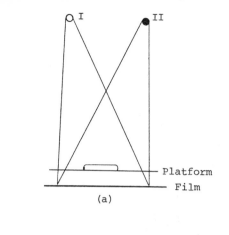

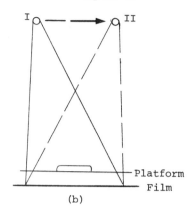

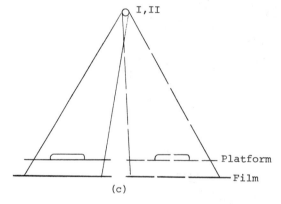

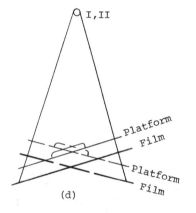

Fig. 10.24

Basic configurations for stereo-radiographs (after McNeil,
1966).   Note: I and II are X-ray tube locations.

B.   *Double Emulsion Effect*:

     The standard X-ray film has emulsion on both sides of the film as shown in
schematic in Fig. 10.25. The two layers of emulsion can cause a blurry stereo
image, images being registered in both the layers. This effect can be avoided by
using films having single layer of emulsion.   In the case of two layers, as an
example, while the emulsion thickness is between 5 and 10 μm, the average thickness
of a polyester base film is around 175 μm. For images with wide field angle, this
may cause considerable image separation, this resulting in blurs.   This is
illustrated in Fig. 10.26. Point P is imaged on both emulsions at locations R and
S. The thickness of film being T, the resulting separation of the point being in a
radial direction, can be formulated in two components:

$$\Delta x = T(x - x_o)/Z_o$$

$$\Delta y = T(y - y_o)/Z_o$$

(10.40)

where Δx, Δy are the x, y components of the radial separation (Δr);

x, y are the image coordinates at the first surface (R);

x_o, y_o are the image coordinates of the principal point;

and Z_o is the principal distance.

In measuring the image coordinates, the point is mostly defined at the middle of R and S, which accounts for the dislocation in amounts of one-half of these expressed in Eqs. 10.40. Alternately, if the principal distance is considered to be referred to the middle of the two planes of emulsion, from the mensural point of view, this effect can be mostly ignored in practice.

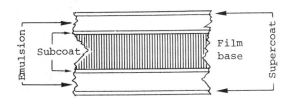

Fig. 10.25

Cross-section

of a standard X-ray film

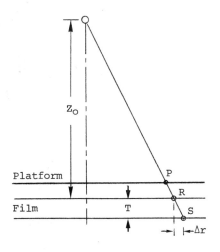

Fig. 10.26

Deformation due to double emulsion

C. *Refraction Effect*:

The displacement (d) of the ray due to X-ray refraction (Fig. 10.27), in the material medium in front of the emulsion is expressed by

$$d = W(\tan r - \tan i) \tag{10.41}$$

where   i and r are the angles of incidence and refraction, respectively;

and   W   is the thickness of the material.

D. *Focal Region Effect*:

This is due to the radiation source being of finite size instead of being a point. Its size and shape can vary from one apparatus to another. The emitted radiation would cause image blur, its nature depending also on the size and location of the object with respect to the focal region and the film. This is illustrated in Fig. 10.28, where the focus is assumed to be a circular area of diameter a. Assuming a circular object of diameter b placed at a distance C from the focus, one can consider three typical images formed at principal distances Z_1, Z_2 and Z_3. The image at Z_1 consists of a "umbra" and a "penumbra"; at Z_2 the image would consist of only a penumbra; whereas at Z_3 it would consist of an annular shaped penumbra around an unexposed central area. From simple geometry, one would find the following expressions:

$$\left. \begin{aligned} d &= \frac{Z}{C} b + \left\{ \frac{Z}{C} - 1 \right\} a \\ d' &= \frac{Z}{C} b - \left\{ \frac{Z}{C} - 1 \right\} a \end{aligned} \right\} \tag{10.42}$$

where d and d' are the diameters of the penumbra and umbra regions, respectively.

Note: In Fig. 10.28, b is smaller than a. In other cases, therefore, Eqs 10.42 are to be appropriately modified.

An individual X-ray photographic system may have other distortion patterns of systematic nature, which can be ascertained only after an adequate calibration of the system. With increasing applications of X-ray mensurations, it is expected that more research in this direction would give us more insight into such systems.

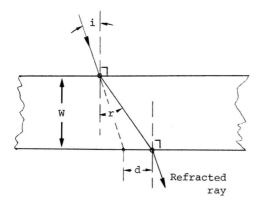

Fig. 10.27

X-ray refraction effect

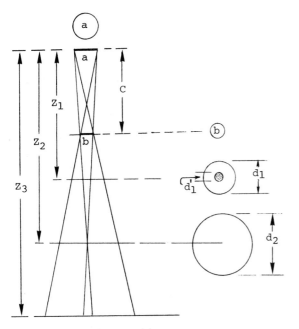

Fig. 10.28

Effect of extended focal region

(after Köhnle, 1967)

10.4.2 Orientations of Models

All standard photogrammetric operations like relative and obsolute orientations, space intersection, etc. can follow after the image coordinates data are 'refined' in regard to the aforementioned distortions and are treated like the conventional (frame photography) cases.

The growing interest of stereo X-ray (see Fig. 10.29 for example) photogrammetry will be also apparent from the fact that instrument manufacturers are introducing newer stereo plotting systems. One such system, introduced in 1976 by Carl Zeiss, is the StR Instruments, models 1-3 (see Fig. 10.30). These are meant for both interpreting and plotting from X-ray stereograms. The design of the

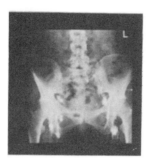

Fig. 10.29 Stereo-radiograph showing a female pelvis for the localization of isolated metastases in a lymph node (Taken by Dr. Hans Greuel, Düsseldorf University; Courtesy, Carl Zeiss, Oberkochen, FR Germany)

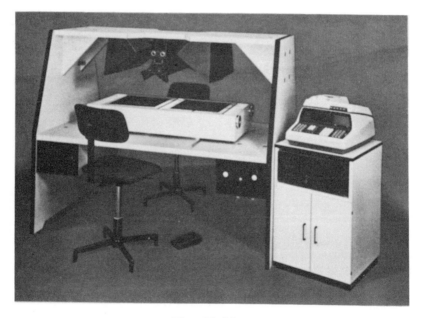

Fig. 10.30

Zeiss StR Instrument system

(Courtesy, Carl Zeiss, Oberkochen, FR Germany)

basic unit is based on the comparator principles. The model StR-3 uses electrical pulse generators for measuring x and y photo coordinates and the corresponding x-parallaxes (px). These are fed to a process computer via interface, which permits automatic computation of spatial coordinates, distances and angles. Best results, however, would be obtained at an analytical plotter where a large focal length (corresponding to the projection distance) can be introduced along with all relevant distortion effects.

BIBLIOGRAPHY

Strip and Panoramic Photography

Abraham, Victor; "Relative Geometric Strength of Frame, Strip and Panoramic
    Cameras", *PE* 27, No. 5 (1961).

American Society of Photogrammetry; *Manuel of Remote Sensing (two volumes) (2nd
    Ed.)* (ASP, Falls Church, Virginia: 1983).

Case, James B.; "The Utilization of Constraints in Analytical Photogrammetry", *PE*
    27, No. 5 (1961).

Case, James B.; "The Analytical Reduction of Panoramic and Strip Photography",
    Photogrammetria 22, No. 4 (1967).

Clerici, Enrico; *Über die Anwendbarkeit von Side Scan Sonar zur Erstellung von
    topographischen Karten des Meeresbodens* (Tech. Univ. Hannover, Fr Germany; No.
    74: 1977).

Derenyi, Eugene E.; "Orientation of Continuous Strip Imagery", *PE* 39, No. 12
    (1973).

Dreyer, Günther; "Multilens cameras for high velocity/low altitude photo-
    reconnaissance". *Optical Engineering* 25, No. 11 (1986).

Elms, David G.; "Mapping with a Strip Camera", *PE* 28, No. 4 (1962).

Ghosh, Sanjib K.; *Phototriangulation* (Lexington Books, Lexington, Mass: 1975).

Ghosh, Sanjib K.; *Strip Photography* (Notes de cours, photogrammétrie-télédétection
    série no. 179-82; Laval University, Québec: 1982).

Ghosh, Sanjib K.; *Panoramic Photography* (Notes de cours, photogrammétrie-
    télédétection série no. 181-84; Laval University, Québec: 1984).

Gill, Charlene; "Relative Orientation of Segmented, Panoramic Grid Models on the
    AP-II", *PE* 30, No. 6 (1964).

Gullicksen, Spencer O.; "Continuous Strip Photography", *PE* 33, No. 3 (1967).

Itek Laboratories; "Panoramic Progress – Parts I and II", *PE* 27, No. 5 (1961) and
     28, No. 1 (1962).

Kawachi, Donald A.; "Image Geometry of Vertical and Oblique Panoramic Photography",
     PE 32, No. 2 (1966).

Kistler, Phillips S.; "Continuous Strip Aerial Photography", *PE* 12, No. 2 (1946).

Kratky, V.; "Simple Panoramic Camera Formulation for Analytical Plotters",
     Proceedings of ASPRS Annual Convention (1983).

Masry, S. E.; "Analytical Treatment of Stereo Strip Photos", *PE* 35, No. 12 (1969).

McCash, Donald K.; "Apollo 15 Panoramic Photography", *PE* 39, No. 1 (1973).

NASA–USA; *High Altitude Perspective* (NASA Ames Center Publication No. SP–427.   US
     Govt Printing Office No. 0–266–639: 1978).

Peterson, Charles G.; "Compilation of Lunar Pan Photos", *PE* 39, No. 1 (1973).

Shmutter, B. and U. Etrog; "Analysis of Panoramic Photographs", *PE* 40, No. 4
     (1974).

Tafel, R. W.; *Comparative Evaluation of Panoramic Camera Reconnaissance Systems* (US
     Bureau of Naval Weapons: VAPEL Report No. NADC AP–6204 DDC Document 277908:
     1962).

Trachsel, Arnold F.; "Electro–Optical Rectifier", *PE* 33, No. 5 (1967).

Electron Micrography

Adiguzel, M,; *Problems Related to Three Dimensional Mapping with Electron
     Micrographs* (Ph.D. Thesis, Laval University, Québec: 1984).

Black, T. J.; "SEM: Scanning Electron Microscope", *Photographic Applications in
     Science, Technology and Medecine* (1970).

Boyde, A. and H. F. Ross; "Photogrammetry and the Scanning Electron Microscope", *PR*
     8, No. 46 (1975).

Boyde, A., H. F. Ross and W. B. Bucknall; "Plotting Instruments for Use with Images
     produced by SEM", *Biostereometrics* '74; Symposium of ISP Commsission V;
     Washington, D.C. (1974).

ElGhazali, M. Shawki; *Some Photogrammetric Investigations of Scanning and
     Transmission Electron Micrography and their applications* (Ph.D. Dissertation,
     The Ohio State University, Columbus, Ohio: 1978).

Ghosh, Sanjib K.; "Volume Determination with an Electron Microscope:, *PE* 37, No. 2
     (1971).

Ghosh, Sanjib K.; "Photogrammetric Calibration of a Scanning Electron Microscope",
     Phorogrammetria 31, No. 3 (1975).

Ghosh, Sanjib K. and Hebbur Nagaraja; "Scanning Electron Micrography and
     Photogrammetry", *PERS* 42, No. 5 (1976).

Ghosh, Sanjib K. and M. Shawki ElGhazali; *Stereo Electron Micrography Studies of Carbon Black* (Report No. 261, the Ohio State Univ. Dept. of Geodetic Sci.; Columbus, Ohio: 1977).

Ghosh, Sanjib K. and M. S. ElGhazali, M. L. Deviney and H. N. Mercer; "Three Dimensional Mapping by Combining Transmission and Scanning Electron Microscopes", *Proceedings of ISP Commission V Symposium*; Stockholm, Sweden (1978).

Ghosh, Sanjib K.; *Electron Microscopy, Systems and Applications* (Notes de cours, Photogrammétrie-télédétection série no. 189-86; Laval University, Québec: 1986).

Helmcke, J. G.; W. Kleinn and R. Burkhardt; "Quantitative Electron Microscopy", *PE* 31, No. 5 (1965).

Howell, P. G. T. and A. Boyde; "Comparison of Various Methods of Reducing Measurements from Stereopair Scanning Electron Micrographs to Real 3-D Data", *Scanning Electron Microscopy/*1972 (Ed: O. Johari and I. Corvin); Illinois Inst. of Tech. Res. Inst., Chicago, Illinois (1972).

Klemperer, O. and M. E. Barnett; *Electron Optics* (3rd Ed.) (Cambridge Univ. Press, Cambridge, U.K.: 1971).

Maune, David F.; *Photogrammetric Self-Calibration of Scanning Electron Microscope* (Ph.D. Dissertation, The Ohio State Univ., Columbus, Ohio: 1973).

Nagaraja, Hebbur; *Application Studies of Scanning Electron Microscope Photographs for Micro-Measurements and 3-D Mapping* (Ph.D. Dissertation, The Ohio State Univ., Columbus, Ohio: 1974).

Nordberg, John A.; *A Procedure for Photogrammetric Calibration of Electron Microscopes* (M.Sc. Thesis, The Ohio State Univ., Columbus, Ohio: 1972).

Oatley, C. W.; *The Scanning Electron Microscope* (Cambridge Univ. Press, Cambridge, U.K.: 1972).

Oshima, T., S. Kimoto and T. Suganuma; "Stereomicrography With a Scanning Electron Microscope", *PE* 36, No. 8 (1970).

Wood, R.; "The Modification of a Topographic Plotter and Its Application in Three Dimensional Plotting of Stereomicrographs", *PR* 7, No. 40 (1972).

X-ray Photogrammetry

Boulianne, Michel; *Les Rayons-X, l'Auto-calibrage et la Ligne-flottante Utilisés dans un Nouvel Appareil Photogrammétrique* (Ph.D. Thesis, Laval University, Québec: 1986).

Ghosh, S. K. and M. Boulianne; "Adaptation and Utilization of a Conventional System of Radiography (X-Ray) for Precision Measurements", *Proceedings of ASP Annual Convention* (1984).

Hallert, Bertil; *X-Ray Photogrammetry* (Elsevier Publishing Co.: 1970).

Jonason, C. and J. Hindmarsh; "Stereo X-ray Photogrammetry as a Tool in Studying Scoliosis," *Proceedings of ASP Symposium on "Close-Range Photogrammetric Systems"*, Urbana, Illinois (1975).

Köhnle, H.; *Röntgenstereoverfahren* (Handbuch der Medizinischen Radiologie, Band. III; Allegmeine Röntgendiagnostische Methodik; Springer-Verlag, Berlin 3: 1967).

Kratky, V.; "Analytical X-ray Photogrammetry in Scoliosis," *Proceedings of ASP Symposium on "Close-range Photogrammetric Systems"*; Urbana, Illinois, (1975).

Krusos, G. A.; "Restoration of Radiologic Images by Optical Spatial Filtering" *Opticial Engineering* 13, No. 3 (1974).

Lippert, F. G., T. Takamoto ans S. A, Veress; "Determination of Pateller Tracking Patterns by X-ray Photogrammetry", *Proceedings of ASP Fall Convention*; Seattle, Washington (1976).

McNeil, G. T.; "X-ray Stereophotogrammetry", *PE* 32, No. 6 (1966).

Moffitt, F. H.; "Stereo X-ray Photogrammetry Applied to Orthodontic Measurements", *Proceedings of Commission II, ISP Congress;* Ottawa, Canada (1972).

Patel, M. V.; *The Joint Space in Normal and Osteoarthretic Knees* (Department of Orthopeadic Surgery, Stockholm, Sweden: 1973).

Schernhorst, J. N.; "A Feasibility Study of Medical X-ray Stereophotogrammetry with Second Order Plotters", *Proceedings of ASP Fall Convention*; Portland, Oregon (1969).

Takamoto, T.; *X-ray Photogrammetric Analysis of Skeletal Spatial Motions* (Ph.D. Dissertation, Univ. of Washington, Seattle, Washington: 1976).

APPENDIX

PARTIAL DERIVATIVES, COLLINEARITY CONDITION EQUATIONS

The collinearity condition equations as given in Chapter 4 are:

$$x = -f \frac{M_1\overline{X}}{M_3\overline{X}} \quad \text{and} \quad y = -f \frac{M_2\overline{X}}{M_3\overline{X}} \tag{4.9}$$

For reasons of clarity and operational ease, symbolize the first one as function one (F_1) and the second one as function two (F_2). Due to the rather complicated nature of the derivations, determinant notations are utilized here. We obtain:

$$\frac{\partial F_1}{\partial \omega} = \frac{f}{(M_3\overline{X})^2} \begin{vmatrix} M_3\overline{X} & M_1\overline{X} \\ \dfrac{\partial (M_3\overline{X})}{\partial \omega} & \dfrac{\partial (M_1\overline{X})}{\partial \omega} \end{vmatrix} = \frac{f}{(M_3\overline{X})^2} (M_3\overline{X} \cdot M_{\omega_1}\overline{X} - M_1\overline{X} \cdot M_{\omega_3}\overline{X})$$

$$= \frac{f}{M_3\overline{X}} (M_{\omega_1}\overline{X} - \frac{x}{f} M_{\omega_3}\overline{X}) \tag{A.1}$$

Similarly,

$$\frac{\partial F_1}{\partial \phi} = \frac{f}{M_3\overline{X}} (M_{\phi_1}\overline{X} - \frac{x}{f} M_{\phi_3}\overline{X}) \tag{A.2}$$

$$\frac{\partial F_1}{\partial \kappa} = \frac{f}{M_3\overline{X}} (M_{\kappa_1}\overline{X} - \frac{x}{f} M_{\kappa_3}\overline{X}) \tag{A.3}$$

$$\frac{\partial F_1}{\partial X} = \frac{f}{M_3\overline{X}} (m_{11} - m_{31} \frac{x}{f}) \tag{A.4}$$

$$\frac{\partial F_1}{\partial Y} = \frac{f}{M_3 \overline{X}} \left(m_{12} - m_{32} \frac{x}{f} \right) \tag{A.5}$$

$$\frac{\partial F_1}{\partial Z} = \frac{f}{M_3 \overline{X}} \left(m_{13} - m_{33} \frac{x}{f} \right) \tag{A.6}$$

$$\frac{\partial F_1}{\partial X_o} = - \frac{f}{M_3 \overline{X}} \left(m_{11} - m_{31} \frac{x}{f} \right) \tag{A.7}$$

$$\frac{\partial F_1}{\partial Y_o} = - \frac{f}{M_3 \overline{X}} \left(m_{12} - m_{32} \frac{x}{f} \right) \tag{A.8}$$

$$\frac{\partial F_1}{\partial Z_o} = - \frac{f}{M_3 \overline{X}} \left(m_{13} - m_{33} \frac{x}{f} \right) \tag{A.9}$$

and

$$\frac{\partial F_2}{\partial \omega} = \frac{f}{M_3 \overline{X}} \left(M_{\omega 2} \overline{X} - \frac{y}{f} M_{\omega 3} \overline{X} \right) \tag{A.10}$$

$$\frac{\partial F_2}{\partial \phi} = \frac{f}{M_3 \overline{X}} \left(M_{\phi 2} \overline{X} - \frac{y}{f} M_{\phi 3} \overline{X} \right) \tag{A.11}$$

$$\frac{\partial F_2}{\partial \kappa} = \frac{f}{M_3 \overline{X}} \left(M_{\kappa 2} \overline{X} - \frac{y}{f} M_{\kappa 3} \overline{X} \right) \tag{A.12}$$

$$\frac{\partial F_2}{\partial X} = \frac{f}{M_3 \overline{X}} \left(m_{21} - m_{31} \frac{y}{f} \right) \tag{A.13}$$

$$\frac{\partial F_2}{\partial Y} = \frac{f}{M_3 \overline{X}} \left(m_{22} - m_{32} \frac{y}{f} \right) \tag{A.14}$$

$$\frac{\partial F_2}{\partial Z} = \frac{f}{M_3 \overline{X}} \left(m_{23} - m_{33} \frac{y}{f} \right) \tag{A.15}$$

$$\frac{\partial F_2}{\partial X_o} = - \frac{f}{M_3 \overline{X}} \left(m_{21} - m_{31} \frac{y}{f} \right) \tag{A.16}$$

$$\frac{\partial F_2}{\partial Y_o} = - \frac{f}{M_3 \overline{X}} \left(m_{22} - m_{32} \frac{y}{f} \right) \tag{A.17}$$

$$\frac{\partial F_2}{\partial Z_o} = - \frac{f}{M_3 \overline{X}} \left(m_{23} - m_{33} \frac{y}{f} \right) \tag{A.18}$$

It may be noted that the above derivatives are given in general terms and some expressions in these equations are equal to zero, e.g., $M_{\omega 3} = 0$, which would then modify equations (A.1) and (A.10) into the following forms:

$$\frac{\partial F_1}{\partial \omega} = \frac{f}{M_3 \overline{X}} \left(M_{\omega_1} \overline{X} \right) , \qquad \frac{\partial F_2}{\partial \omega} = \frac{f}{M_3 \overline{X}} \left(M_{\omega_2} \overline{X} \right)$$

Further simplifications may also be possible, e.g., when $M_{K=0}$ or $M_{K=\omega=0}$ matrices are used instead of the M matrix.

APPENDIX

B

PARTIAL DERIVATIVES, COPLANARITY CONDITION EQUATION

The coplanarity condition equation as given in Chapter 4 is:

$$F_i = \begin{vmatrix} b_X & b_Y & b_Z \\ X_{1i} & Y_{1i} & Z_{1i} \\ X_{2i} & Y_{2i} & Z_{2i} \end{vmatrix} = 0 \tag{4.17}$$

Equation 4.22 defines $[A_i]$:

$$[A_i] = \begin{bmatrix} \dfrac{\partial F_i}{\partial x_{1i}} & \dfrac{\partial F_i}{\partial y_{1i}} & \dfrac{\partial F_i}{\partial x_{2i}} & \dfrac{\partial F_i}{\partial y_{2i}} \end{bmatrix} \tag{4.22}$$

From corresponding equations in Chapter 4,

$$\frac{\partial F_i}{\partial x_{1i}} = \begin{vmatrix} bx & by & bz \\ m_{11}^1 & m_{12}^1 & m_{13}^1 \\ X_{2i} & Y_{2i} & Z_{2i} \end{vmatrix} = \begin{vmatrix} bx & by & bz \\ 1 & 0 & 0 \\ X_{2i} & Y_{2i} & Z_{2i} \end{vmatrix} = (bz \cdot Y_{2i} - by \cdot Z_{2i}) \tag{B.1}$$

$$\frac{\partial F_i}{\partial y_{1i}} = \begin{bmatrix} bx & by & bz \\ m_{21}^1 & m_{22}^1 & m_{23}^1 \\ X_{2i} & Y_{2i} & Z_{2i} \end{bmatrix} = \begin{bmatrix} bx & by & bz \\ 0 & 1 & 0 \\ X_{2i} & Y_{2i} & Z_{2i} \end{bmatrix} = (bx \cdot Z_{2i} - bz \cdot X_{2i}) \qquad (B.2)$$

$$\frac{\partial F_i}{\partial x_{2i}} = \begin{bmatrix} bx & by & bz \\ X_{1i} & Y_{1i} & Z_{1i} \\ m_{11}^2 & m_{12}^2 & m_{13}^2 \end{bmatrix} = \begin{bmatrix} bx & by & bz \\ x_{1i} & y_{1i} & -f \\ \cos\phi\,\cos\kappa & \cos\omega\,\sin\kappa & \sin\omega\,\sin\kappa \\ & +\sin\omega\,\sin\phi\,\cos\kappa & -\cos\omega\,\sin\phi\,\cos\kappa \end{bmatrix}$$

$$(B.3)$$

$$\frac{\partial F_i}{\partial y_{2i}} = \begin{bmatrix} bx & by & bz \\ X_{1i} & Y_{1i} & Z_{1i} \\ m_{21}^2 & m_{22}^2 & m_{23}^2 \end{bmatrix} = \begin{bmatrix} bx & by & bz \\ x_{1i} & y_{1i} & -f \\ -\cos\phi\,\cos\kappa & \cos\omega\,\sin\kappa & \sin\omega\,\sin\kappa \\ & -\sin\omega\,\sin\phi\,\sin\kappa & +\cos\omega\,\sin\phi\,\sin\kappa \end{bmatrix}$$

$$(B.4)$$

Equation 4.23 defines $[B_i]$:

$$[B_i] = \begin{bmatrix} \dfrac{\partial F_i}{\partial by_2} & \dfrac{\partial F_i}{\partial bz_2} & \dfrac{\partial F_i}{\partial \omega_2} & \dfrac{\partial F_i}{\partial \phi_2} & \dfrac{\partial F_i}{\partial \kappa_2} \end{bmatrix} \qquad (4.23)$$

$$\frac{\partial F_i}{\partial by_2} = -\begin{bmatrix} X_{1i} & Z_{1i} \\ X_{2i} & Z_{2i} \end{bmatrix} \qquad (B.5)$$

$$\frac{\partial F_i}{\partial bz_2} = \begin{bmatrix} X_{1i} & Y_{1i} \\ X_{2i} & Y_{2i} \end{bmatrix} \qquad (B.6)$$

$$\frac{\partial F_i}{\partial \omega_2} = \begin{bmatrix} bx & by & bz \\ X_{1i} & Y_{1i} & Z_{1i} \\ \dfrac{\partial X_{2i}}{\partial \omega_2} & \dfrac{\partial Y_{2i}}{\partial \omega_2} & \dfrac{\partial Z_{2i}}{\partial \omega_2} \end{bmatrix} = \begin{bmatrix} bx & by & bz \\ X_{1i} & Y_{1i} & -f \\ \dfrac{\partial X_{2i}}{\partial \omega_2} & \dfrac{\partial Y_{2i}}{\partial \omega_2} & \dfrac{\partial Z_{2i}}{\partial \omega_2} \end{bmatrix} \qquad (B.7)$$

From Eq. 4.19, for the above,

$$\frac{\partial X_{2i}}{\partial \omega_2} = 0$$

$$\frac{\partial Y_{2i}}{\partial \omega_{2i}} = x_{2i}(\cos\omega \ \sin\phi \ \cos\kappa - \sin\omega \ \sin\kappa)$$
$$\left. - y_{2i}(\sin\omega \ \cos\kappa + \cos\omega \ \sin\phi \ \sin\kappa) + f \ \cos\omega \ \cos\phi \right\}$$

and
$$\frac{\partial Z_{2i}}{\partial \omega_2} = x_{2i}(\cos\omega \ \sin\kappa + \sin\omega \ \sin\phi \ \cos\kappa)$$
$$\left. + y_{2i}(\cos\omega \ \cos\kappa - \sin\omega \ \sin\phi \ \sin\kappa) + f \ \sin\omega \ \cos\phi \right\}$$

$$\frac{\partial F_i}{\partial \phi_2} = \begin{bmatrix} bx & by & bz \\ X_{1i} & Y_{1i} & Z_{1i} \\ \dfrac{\partial X_{2i}}{\partial \phi_2} & \dfrac{\partial Y_{2i}}{\partial \phi_2} & \dfrac{\partial Z_{2i}}{\partial \phi_2} \end{bmatrix} = \begin{bmatrix} bx & by & bz \\ X_{1i} & Y_{1i} & -f \\ \dfrac{\partial X_{2i}}{\partial \phi_2} & \dfrac{\partial Y_{2i}}{\partial \phi_2} & \dfrac{\partial Z_{2i}}{\partial \phi_2} \end{bmatrix} \qquad (B.8)$$

Here, for the above, from Eq. 4.19,

$$\frac{\partial X_{2i}}{\partial \phi_2} = - x_{2i} \ \sin\phi \ \cos\kappa + y_{2i} \ \sin\phi \ \sin\kappa - f \ \cos\phi$$

$$\frac{\partial Y_{2i}}{\partial \phi_2} = x_{2i} \ \sin\omega \ \cos\phi \ \cos\kappa - y_{2i} \ \sin\omega \ \cos\phi \ \sin\kappa - f \ \sin\omega \ \sin\phi$$

and
$$\frac{\partial Z_{2i}}{\partial \phi_2} = - x_{2i} \ \cos\omega \ \cos\phi \ \cos\kappa + y_{2i} \ \cos\omega \ \cos\phi \ \sin\kappa + f \ \cos\omega \ \sin\phi.$$

Finally,

$$\frac{\partial F_i}{\partial \kappa_2} = \begin{bmatrix} bx & by & bz \\ X_{1i} & Y_{1i} & Z_{1i} \\ \dfrac{\partial X_{2i}}{\partial \kappa_2} & \dfrac{\partial Y_{2i}}{\partial \kappa_2} & \dfrac{\partial Z_{2i}}{\partial \kappa_2} \end{bmatrix} = \begin{bmatrix} bx & by & bz \\ x_{1i} & y_{1i} & -f \\ \dfrac{\partial X_{2i}}{\partial \kappa_2} & \dfrac{\partial Y_{2i}}{\partial \kappa_2} & \dfrac{\partial Z_{2i}}{\partial \kappa_2} \end{bmatrix} \qquad (B.9)$$

where, from Eq. 4.19,

$$\frac{\partial X_{2i}}{\partial \kappa_2} = -x_{2i} \cos\phi \sin\kappa - y_{2i} \cos\phi \cos\kappa$$

$$\frac{\partial Y_{2i}}{\partial \kappa_2} = \left. \begin{array}{l} x_{2i}(\cos\omega \cos\kappa - \sin\omega \sin\phi \sin\kappa) \\[4pt] - y_{2i}(\cos\omega \sin\kappa + \sin\omega \sin\phi \cos\kappa) \end{array} \right\}$$

$$\frac{\partial Z_{2i}}{\partial \kappa_2} = \left. \begin{array}{l} x_{2i}(\sin\omega \cos\kappa + \cos\omega \sin\phi \sin\kappa) \\[4pt] - y_{2i}(\sin\omega \sin\kappa - \cos\omega \sin\phi \cos\kappa) \end{array} \right\}$$

Forms and sizes of the matrices :

Let   n = Number of observed values of observable quantities

   u = Number of unknown quantities (= 5, here, being the elements of

      relative orientation)

   r = Number of condition equations where both observed and unknown

      quantities are present

Here, n = 4r, since there are four coordinate readings for each point.   The

sizes of the matrices in Eq. 4.21 are, therefore,

$$_r[A]_n \, _n(V)_1 + \, _r[B]_u \, _u(\Delta)_1 + \, _r(F_o)_1 = \, _r0_1 \qquad (4.21)$$

$$
{}_r A_n = \begin{bmatrix} A_1 & 0 & 0 \cdots & 0 \\ 0 & A_2 & 0 \cdots & 0 \\ 0 & 0 & A_3 \cdots & 0 \\ \vdots & \vdots & \vdots & \vdots \\ 0 & 0 & 0 \cdots & A_r \end{bmatrix} = \begin{bmatrix} XXX & & & \\ & XXX & & \\ & & XXX & \\ & & & \ddots \\ & & & XXX \end{bmatrix}
$$

r x n

$$
{}_r B_u = \begin{bmatrix} B_1 \\ B_2 \\ B_3 \\ \vdots \\ B_r \end{bmatrix} = \begin{bmatrix} X & X & X & X & X \\ X & X & X & X & X \\ X & X & X & X & X \\ \vdots & \vdots & \vdots & \vdots & \vdots \\ X & X & X & X & X \end{bmatrix} \qquad \text{Full matrix}
$$

r x 5

$$
{}_r F_{o1} = \begin{bmatrix} F_{o1} \\ F_{o2} \\ F_{o3} \\ \vdots \\ F_{or} \end{bmatrix} \qquad {}_u \Delta_1 = \begin{bmatrix} \delta by \\ \delta bz \\ \delta \omega \\ \delta \phi \\ \delta \kappa \end{bmatrix} \qquad {}_n V_1 = \begin{bmatrix} V_1 \\ 4 \times 1 \\ V_2 \\ 4 \times 1 \\ V_3 \\ 4 \times 1 \\ \vdots \\ V_r \\ 4 \times 1 \end{bmatrix}
$$

r x 1   5 x 1   n x 1

APPENDIX

PROGRAM FOR ANALYTICAL SELF-CALIBRATION [Including an example]

```
      IMPLICIT REAL*8 (A-H,O-Z)
      DIMENSION EX(6),WE(6,6),WS(3,3),STDEX(6),ITITLE(7)

C     ******************************************************************
C     NO CARD MUST BE INSERTED AFTER PHOTO COORD.
C     ******************************************************************

C     IP=TOTAL NO. OF POINTS
C     N=NO.OF PHOTOS
C     K1=3*IP
C     J1=6*N+9
C     JA11=J1*(J1+1)/2
C     THE DIMENSIONS ARE THE FOLLOWING
C     A11(JA11),A12(J1,K1),STANAM(K1,3),B12T(J1,K1),A22T(K1,J1)
C     X(K1),Y(K1),Z(K1),STDX(K1),STDY(K1),STDZ(K1)
C     PHOTO(N,49),POINT(N,IP,22),IST(IP),ISTA(IP)
C     DATA  ISTA/IP*0/
C     THE 3 FOLLOWING CARDS CAN BE CHANGED
C     **********************************************************

      DIMENSION A11(561),A12(33,30),STANAM(30,3),B12T(33,30),
     k  A22T(30,33),X(30),Y(30),Z(30),STDX(30),STDY(30),STDZ(30),
     k  PHOTO(4,49),POINT(4,10,22),IST(10),ISTA(10)
      DATA ISTA/10*0/
      INTEGER CYCLE
      EQUVALENCE (X,DE),(Y,DS),(Z,KEY),(STDX,U1),(STDY,U2),(STDZ,AW),
     *(STANAM,A22)
      COMMON IRD,IPU,IWT,IDK

C     **********************************************************
C...          IRD=READ
C...          IPU=PUNCH
C...          IWT=WRITE
C...          IDK=READ AND WRITE FROM A DISC
C     **********************************************************
```

```
      IRD = 1
      IPU = 2
      IWT = 3
      IDK = 4


C     *************************************************************
C     READ TITLE AND NO. OF ITERATIONS
C     *************************************************************

      READ(IRD,137)ITITLE,CYCLE
  137 FORMAT(7A4,2X,I5)

C     *************************************************************
C     READ CAMERA CONSTANT,STD ERRORS ON EXT PARAM,NO. OF PHOTOS,
C     NO. OF POINTS,PHOTO COORD. WEIGHTS
C     *************************************************************

      READ(IRD,20)CC,STDPX,N,IP,WTPX
   20 FORMAT(2F10.3,2I5,F10.3)
      WRITE(IWT,19)WTPX
   19 FORMAT(' WEIGHTS OF PHOTO COORD',E15.5)
      DO 11 I=1,3
      DO 11 J=1,3
   11 WS(I,J)=0.0
      DO 21 I=1,6
      DO 21 J=1,6
   21 WE(I,J)=0.0
      WRITE(IWT,13)
   13 FORMAT(1H0,'SURVEY COORD. AND THERE STD.ERRORS',//
     *'   PT NO',5X,'NAME OF STATION',T36,'X',T46,'Y',T56,'Z',T66,
     *'STDX',T76,'STDY',T86,'STDZ',//)
      DO 1 I=1,IP

C     *************************************************************
C     READ POINT NUMBER,X,Y,Z,STD.ERRORS ON X,Y,Z
C     *************************************************************

      READ(IRD,2) IST(I),X(I),Y(I),Z(I),STDX(I),STDY(I),STDZ(I)
    2 FORMAT(I5,3F10.3,3F10.4)
C
    1 WRITE(IWT,3)IST(I),X(I),Y(I),Z(I),STDX(I),STDY(I),STDZ(I)
    3 FORMAT(I8,22X,6F10.4)
      REWIND IDK
      WRITE(IWT,6)
    6 FORMAT(' DATA FOR CALIB')
      DO 4 I=1,N

C     *************************************************************
C     READ NO.OF POINT PER PHOTO
C     *************************************************************

      READ(IRD,30)K
   30 FORMAT(10X,I10,2F10.4)
      WRITE(IWT,30)K
      WRITE(IDK)K

C     *************************************************************
C     READ THE EXT,ORIENT.ELEMENTS:XO,YO,ZO,KAPPA,PHI,OMEG
C     *************************************************************
```

```
      READ(IRD,5) EX
    5 FORMAT(5X,3E10.3,3E10.4)

C     ************************************************************
C     READ THE STD ERRORS OF EXT. ORIENT.ELEMENTS
C     ************************************************************

      READ(IRD,9) STDEX
    9 FORMAT(6E10.4)
      DO 7 J=1,6
      IF(STDEX(J).EQ.0.0)STDEX(J)=10.0D25
      WE(J,J)=(STDPX/STDEX(J))**2
      WRITE(IWT,8) EX(J)
    8 FORMAT(2F10.3)
    7 WRITE(IDK) EX(J),EX(J)
      WRITE(IWT,5) WE
      DO 22 J=1,6
   22 WRITE(IDK) (WE(J,JJ),JJ=1,6)
C     ************************************************************
C     READ COORD.OF PRINCIPAL POINT
C     ************************************************************

      READ(IRD,8)OX,OY
C
C     ************************************************************
C     READ POINT NUMBER POINT,AND PHOTO COORD.X,Y
C     ************************************************************

      DO 4 IJK=1,K
      READ(IRD,9989) ID1,PX,PY
 9989 FORMAT(4X,I6,2F10.4)
      DO 100 ID=1,IP
      IF(ID1.EQ.IST(ID)) GOTO 101
  100 CONTINUE
      WRITE(IWT,102) ID1,I
  102 FORMAT(/,5X,'NO OBJECT COORD.FOR POINT',I4,4X,'PHOTO NO',
     *I4)
      STOP
  101 PX=PX-OX
      PY=PY-OY
      WRITE(IWT,10) IST(ID),PX,PY
   10 FORMAT(I5,2F10.3)
      WRITE(IDK) PX,PY
      WRITE(IDK) ID
      WRITE(IDK)X(ID),X(ID)
      WRITE(IDK)Y(ID),Y(ID)
      WRITE(IDK)Z(ID),Z(ID)
      IF(STDX(ID).EQ.0.0)STDX(ID)=0.02D0
      WS(1,1)=(STDPX/STDX(ID))**2

      IF(STDY(ID).EQ.0.0)STDY(ID)=0.02D0
      WS(2,2)=(STDPX/STDY(ID))**2
      IF(STDZ(ID).EQ.0.0) STDZ(ID)=0.02D0
      WS(3,3)=(STDPX/STDZ(ID))**2
      DO 4 IJ=1,3
    4 WRITE(IDK   )(WS(IJ,JJ),JJ=1,3)
      K1=3*IP
      J1=6*N+9
      JA11=J1*(J1+1)/2
```

```
      CALL CALIBA(A11,A12,STANAM,B12T,A22T,X,Y,Z,STDX,STDY,STDZ,PHOTO,
     *POINT,CC,N,IP,WTPX,K1,J1,ITITLE,CYCLE,EX,WE,WS,JA11,IST,ISTA)
      STOP
      END
      SUBROUTINE CALIBA(A11,A12,A22,B12T,A22T,DE,DS,KEY,U1,U2,AW,PHOTO,
     *POINT,CF,N,IP,WM,K1,J1,ITITLE,CYCLE,EE,WE,WS,JA11,IST ,ISTA)
C
C
      IMPLICIT REAL*8(A-H,O-Z)
      DIMENSION A11(JA11) ,A12(J1,K1),A22(K1,3),IST(IP),ISTA(IP)
      DIMENSION B12T(J1,K1),A22T(K1,J1),DE(J1),DS(K1),KEY(IP)
      DIMENSION U1(J1),U2(K1),AW(K1),PHOTO(N,49),POINT(N,IP,22)
      DIMENSION XO(6),EE(6),WE(6,6),B1(2),C(2)
      DIMENSION DATA(2),W(2,2),X(3),ES(3),WS(3,3)
      DIMENSION E(2),ATEMP(9,2),B(2,18),R(6),Q(2),EI(9),XI(9),WI(9,9),RD
     *C(2),ITITLE(7)
      REAL *8 KI,K2,K3
      INTEGER PP,P,T,CYCLE
      EQUIVALENCE (CC,XI(3)),(KI,XI(4)),(K2,XI(5)),(K3,XI(6)),(P1,XI(7))
     *,(P2,XI(8)),(P3,XI(9))
      COMMON IRD,IPU,IWT,IDK
C
C
      CC=CF
      DO 133 I=1,9
C
C     ****************************************************************
C     XI - CURRENT APPROX.OF INTERI.ORIENT.
C     EI - INITIAL ESTIMATES OF INTER.ORIENT.
C     ORDER OF IO IS;X0,Y0,C,K1,K2,K3,P1,P2,P3
C     ****************************************************************
C
  133 READ(IRD,134) XI(I),EI(I)
  134 FORMAT(2D11.4)
      DO 135 I=1,9
C
C     ****************************************************************
C     READ WEIGHT MATRIX FOR INTERIOR ORIENT.
C     ****************************************************************
C
  135 READ(IRD,136)(WI(I,J),J=1,9)
  136 FORMAT(9F8.3)
      WU=1.0D-25
      F1=1.0D6
      F2=F1*F1
      IOUT=0
      ICYCLE=0
      REWIND IDK
      DO 200 I=1,N
      READ(IDK  )P
      PHOTO(I,1)=P
      DO 201 J=2,7
      READ(IDK   ) PHOTO(I,J),PHOTO(I,J+6)
  201 PHOTO(I,J+6)=PHOTO(I,J)
      L2=13
      DO 202 J=1,6
      L1=L2+1
      L2=L2+6
  202 READ(IDK  ) (PHOTO(I,K),K=L1,L2)
      DO 200 J=1,P
```

```
      READ(IDK  ) POINT(I,J,1),POINT(I,J,2)
      READ(IDK  )IDPT
      POINT(I,J,3)=IDPT
      POINT(I,J,4)=WM
      POINT(I,J,5)=0.0
      POINT(I,J,6)=0.0
      POINT(I,J,7)=WM
      DO 204 K=17,19
      READ(IDK  ) POINT(I,J,K),POINT(I,J,K+3)
  204 POINT(I,J,K+3)=POINT(I,J,K)
      L2=7
      DO 205 K=1,3
      L1=L2+1
      L2=L2+3
  205 READ(IDK  ) (POINT(I,J,L),L=L1,L2)
  200 CONTINUE
C
C     ************************************************************
C     CLEAR NORMALS
C     ************************************************************

      WRITE(IWT,512)
  512 FORMAT(1H1,'RESIDUALS AND EQUAT.OF OBSERVATION BEFOR THE 1ST CYC
     *LE',///,' PHOTO PT',3X,'RES.EN X',3X,'RES.EN Y')
    4 ICYCLE=ICYCLE+1
      NDF=0
      VPV=0.0
      IK=0
      IF(ICYCLE.GT.1) GOTO 516
      GOTO 515
  516 WI(1,1) = 0.D0
      WI(2,2) = 0.D0
      WI(3,3) = 0.00D0
      WI(4,4) = 0.D0
      WI(5,5) = 0.D0
      WI(6,6) = 0.D0
      WI(7,7) = 00.D00
      WI(8,8) = 0.D0
      WI(9,9) = 00.D00

  515 CONTINUE
  514 DO 5 I=1,IP
    5 KEY(I)=0
    1 DO 2 I=1,J1
      U1(I)=0.0
      DO 2 J=1,K1
    2 A12(I,J)=0.0
      DO 7 I=1,JA11
    7 A11(I)=0.0
      DO 3 I=1,K1
      U2(I)=0.0
      DO 3 J=1,3
    3 A22(I,J)=0.0
C
C     ************************************************************
C     CALL PHOTO DATA
C     ************************************************************

      IPC=1
      DO 100 J=1,N
      LOC=13
```

AP-T

```
      K=PHOTO(J,1)
      DO 210 II=2,7

C     ****************************************************************
C     XO - CURRENT APPROXI.OF EXT.ORIENT.
C     EE - INITAL APPROX. OF EXT. ORIENT.
C     ****************************************************************

      XO(II-1)=PHOTO(J,II)
      EE(II-1)=PHOTO(J,II+6)
      DO 210 JJ=1,6
      LOC=LOC+1
  210 WE(II-1,JJ)=PHOTO(J,LOC)

C     ****************************************************************
C     SIN OF K,P,O AND COS OF K,P,O
C     ****************************************************************

      R(1)=DSIN(XO(4))
      R(2)=DSIN(XO(5))
      R(3)=DSIN(XO(6))
      R(4)=DCOS(XO(4))
      R(5)=DCOS(XO(5))
      R(6)=DCOS(XO(6))

C     ****************************************************************
C     ADDING TERMS DUE TO CONSTRAINTS ON EXT.ORIENT.ELEMENTS
C     ****************************************************************

      L=6*(J-1)+9
      IA11=L*(L+1)/2
      DO 10 II=1,6
      IA11=IA11+L
      IF (WE(II,II).GT.WU)NDF=NDF+1
      VPV=VPV+WE(II,II)*((EE(II)-XO(II))**2)
      DO 41 JJ=1,6

C     ****************************************************************
C     CARDS PERTAINING TO FORMATION OF MATRIX WILL HAVE 5C'S
C        -W(E)*E(E)
C     ****************************************************************

   41 U1(L+II)=U1(L+II)-WE(II,JJ)*(EE(JJ)-XO(JJ))
      DO 10 JJ=1,II
      IA11=IA11+1

C     ****************************************************************
C        W(E)
C     ****************************************************************

   10 A11(IA11)    =A11(IA11)    +WE(II,JJ)
C
C     ****************************************************************
C     CALL POINT DATA
C     ****************************************************************

      DO 100 I=1,K
      DATA(1)=POINT(J,I,1)
      DATA(2)=POINT(J,I,2)
      P=POINT(J,I,3)
```

```
      LOC=3
      DO 215 II=1,2
      DO 215 JJ=1,2
      LOC=LOC+1
  215 W(II,JJ)=POINT(J,I,LOC)
      DO 216 II=1,3
      DO 216 JJ=1,3
      LOC=LOC+1
  216 WS(II,JJ)=POINT(J,I,LOC)
      DO 217 II=17,19

C     ****************************************************************
C     X - CURRENT APPROX.OF SURVEY COORD.
C     ES - INITIAL ESTIMATES OF SURVEY COORD.
C     ****************************************************************

      X(II-16)=POINT(J,I,II)
  217 ES(II-16)=POINT(J,I,II+3)
      LL=3*(P-1)

C     ****************************************************************
C     CALL PARTIALS
C     ****************************************************************

      CALL COFEI(X,R,B,XO,CC,XC,YC)
C     ****************************************************************
C     COMPUTE NORMALS
C     TERMS DUE TO INTERNAL ORIENT. PARAMETERS
C     ****************************************************************

      R2=(DATA(1)-XI(1))**2+(DATA(2)-XI(2))**2
      R4=(R2*R2)/F2
      R6=(R4*R2)/F1
      RPF=1.0+KI*R2/F1+K2*R4+K3*R6
      CP1=R2+2*((DATA(1)-XI(1))**2)
      CP2=R2+2*((DATA(2)-XI(2))**2)
      CP3=2*(DATA(1)-XI(1))*(DATA(2)-XI(2))
      CP4=1+P3*R2/(F1*F2)
      RDC(1)=P1*CP1/F1+P2*CP3/F2
      RDC(2)=P1*CP3/F1+P2*CP2/F2
      XC=XC/RPF
      YC=YC/RPF
      E(1)=DATA(1)-XI(1)-XC+RDC(1)*CP4/RPF
      E(2)=DATA(2)-XI(2)-YC+RDC(2)*CP4/RPF
      IF(ICYCLE.GT.1)GO TO 300
      WRITE(IWT,511)J,IST(P),E(1),E(2)
  511 FORMAT(2I5,2F10.3)
  300 NDF=NDF+2
      VPV=VPV+W(1,1)*E(1)**2
      VPV=VPV+W(2,2)*E(2)**2
      B(2,12)=YC/CC
      B(1,12)=XC/CC
      Q(1)=XC/RPF-RDC(1)*CP4/RPF
      Q(2)=YC/RPF-RDC(2)*CP4/RPF
      DO 122 II=1,2
      DO 121 JJ=1,9
  121 B(II,JJ)=B(II,JJ)/RPF
      B(II,13)=Q(II)*R2/F1
      B(II,14)=Q(II)*R4
      B(II,15)=Q(II)*R6
```

```
  122 B(II,II+9)= 1.0
      B(1,16)=(CP1*CP4/F1)/RPF
      B(1,17)=(CP3*CP4/F2)/RPF
      B(2,16)=(CP3*CP4/F1)/RPF
      B(2,17)=(CP2*CP4/F2)/RPF
      B(2,18)=(RDC(2)*R2/(F1*F2))/RPF
      B(1,18)=(RDC(1)*R2/(F1*F2))/RPF
      B(1,11)=0.0
      B(2,10)=0.0
      DO 148 II=1,2
      DO 148 JJ=10,12
  148 B(II,JJ)=-B(II,JJ)

C     **************************************************************
C     FORMING A11 DUE TO INTERIOR ORIENT.
C     **************************************************************

      KA11=0

      DO 123 II=1,9
      DO 123 JJ=1,2
      TEMP=0.0
      DO 123 KK=1,2


C     **************************************************************
C         B(I)T*W
C     **************************************************************

      TEMP=TEMP+B(KK,II+9)*W(KK,JJ)
  123 ATEMP(II,JJ)=TEMP
      DO 128 II=1,9
      IA11=KA11
      DO 124 JJ=1,II
      IA11=IA11+1
      KA11=IA11
      TEMP=0.0
      DO 125 KK=1,2

C     **************************************************************
C         B(I)T*W*B(I)
C     **************************************************************

  125 TEMP=TEMP+ATEMP(II,KK)*B(KK,JJ+9)

C     **************************************************************
C     TERMS DUE TO CONSTRAINT ON EXTERIOR ELEMENTS
C     **************************************************************

      IF(IK.EQ.1) GO TO 124

C     **************************************************************
C         B(I)TWB(I)+W(I)
C     **************************************************************

      A11(IA11) =A11(IA11) +WI(II,JJ)
  124 A11(IA11) =A11(IA11) +TEMP
      IA11=L*(L+1)/2+II
      DO 126 JJ=1,6
      TEMP=0.0
      DO 146 KK=1,2
```

```
C     ************************************************************
C           B(I)TW*B(E)
C     ************************************************************

 146  TEMP=TEMP+ATEMP(II,KK)*B(KK,JJ)
      A11(IA11)=A11(IA11)+TEMP
 126  IA11=IA11+L+JJ
      DO 127 JJ=7,9
      TEMP=0.0
      DO 147 KK=1,2

C     ************************************************************
C           B(I)TW*B(S)
C     ************************************************************

 147  TEMP=TEMP+ATEMP(II,KK)*B(KK,JJ)
 127  A12(II,LL+JJ-6)=A12(II,LL+JJ-6)+TEMP
      DO 128 KK=1,2

C     ************************************************************
C     TERMS DUE TO CONSTRAINTS ON INTERIOR ORIENT.
C     ************************************************************

      TEMP=0.0
      IF (IK.EQ.1) GO TO 128
      IF(WI(II,II).GT.WU.AND.KK.EQ.1)NDF=NDF+1
      VPV=VPV+WI(II,II)*((EI(II)-XI(II))**2)
      DO 129 JJ=1,9

C     ************************************************************
C           W(I)*E(I)
C     ************************************************************

 129  TEMP=TEMP+WI(II,JJ)*(EI(JJ)-XI(JJ))
      U1(II)=U1(II)-TEMP

C     ************************************************************
C           B(I)TW*E
C     ************************************************************

 128  U1(II)=U1(II)+ATEMP(II,KK)*E(KK)
      IK=1
      ITEST=1
      IF(IPC.GT.IP) GO TO 12
      DO 11 II=1,IPC
      IF(P.EQ.KEY(II)) GO TO 12
 11   CONTINUE
      KEY(IPC)=P
      IPC=IPC+1
      ITEST=0
 12   DO 15 II=1,6
      DO 15 JJ=1,2
      ATEMP(II,JJ)=0.0
      DO 15 KK=1,2

C     ************************************************************
C           B(E)T*W
C     ************************************************************

 15   ATEMP(II,JJ)=ATEMP(II,JJ)+B(KK,II)*W(KK,JJ)
```

```
C     ****************************************************************
C     COMPUTE OF A11
C     ****************************************************************

      IA11=L*(L+1)/2
      DO 17 II=1,6
      IA11=IA11+L
      IIL=II+L
      DO 16 KK=1,2

C     ****************************************************************
C          B(E)TW*E
C     ****************************************************************

   16 U1(IIL)=U1(IIL)+ATEMP(II,KK)*E(KK)
      DO 17 JJ=1,II
      IA11=IA11+1
      DO 17 KK=1,2

C     ****************************************************************
C          B(E)TW*B(E)+W(E)
C     ****************************************************************

   17 A11(IA11)=A11(IA11)+ATEMP(II,KK)*B(KK,JJ)

C     ****************************************************************
C     COMPUTE OF A12
C     ****************************************************************

      DO 19 II=1,6
      DO 19 JJ=7,9
      DO 19 KK=1,2

C     ****************************************************************
C          B(E)TW*B(S)
C     ****************************************************************

   19 A12(L+II,LL+JJ-6)=A12(L+II,LL+JJ-6)+ATEMP(II,KK)*B(KK,JJ)

C     ****************************************************************
C     COMPUTE OF A21
C     COMPUTE OF A22
C     ****************************************************************

      DO 23 II=7,9
      DO 23 JJ=1,2
      ATEMP(II-6,JJ)=0.0
      DO 23 KK=1,2

C     ****************************************************************
C          B(S)T*W
C     ****************************************************************

   23 ATEMP(II-6,JJ)=ATEMP(II-6,JJ)+B(KK,II)*W(KK,JJ)
      DO 27 II=1,3
      M=LL+II
      DO 26 KK=1,2
```

```
C     **********************************************************
C         B(S)TW*E
C     **********************************************************

      U2(M)=U2(M)+ATEMP(II,KK)*E(KK)
      DO 26 JJ=7,9

C     **********************************************************
C         B(S)TW*B(S)
C     **********************************************************

   26 A22(M,JJ-6)=A22(M,JJ-6)+ATEMP(II,KK)*B(KK,JJ)
      IF(ITEST.EQ.1) GO TO 27

C     **********************************************************
C     ADDING TERMS DUE TO CONSTRAINT ON SURVEY COORD.
C     **********************************************************

      IF(WS(II,II).GT.WU)NDF=NDF+1
      VPV=VPV+WS(II,II)*((ES(II)-X(II))**2)
      DO 28 JJ=1,3

C     **********************************************************
C         B(S)TWB(S)+W(S)
C     **********************************************************

      A22(M,JJ)=A22(M,JJ)+WS(II,JJ)

C     **********************************************************
CCCCC     W(S)*E
C     **********************************************************

   28 U2(M)=U2(M)-WS(II,JJ)*(ES(JJ)-X(JJ))
   27 CONTINUE
  100 CONTINUE
C
  143 CONTINUE

C     **********************************************************
C     FORMING B11
C     INVERTING  A22-SUBROUTINE MATINV
C     **********************************************************

      DO 34 II=1,IP
      II3=3*(II-1)
      A22(II3+1,1)=1.0/A22(II3+1,1)
      DO 34 JJ=1,2
      LI=JJ+1
      L=II3+LI
      DO 48 I=1,2

      B1(I)=0.0
   48 C(I)=0.0
      DO 49 J=1,JJ
      DO 49 K=1,JJ
      II3K=II3+K
      B1(J)=B1(J)-A22(II3K,J)*A22(L,K)
   49 C(K)=C(K)-A22(II3K,J)*A22(II3+J,LI)
      D=A22(L,LI)
      DO 30 J=1,JJ
   30 D=D+C(J)*A22(L,J)
```

```
      D=1.0/D
      DO 31 J=1,JJ
      II3K=II3+J
      A22(II3K,LI)=C(J)*D
      A22(L,J)=B1(J)*D
      DO 31 K=1,JJ
   31 A22(II3K,K)=A22(II3K,K)+B1(K)*C(J)*D
   34 A22(L,LI)=D

C     ****************************************************************
C     FORMING B11
C     ****************************************************************

      DO 35 I=1,IP
      M=3*(I-1)
      DO 35 J=1,3
      II=M+J
      DO 35 K=1,J1
      A22T(II,K)=0.0
      DO 35 L=1,3
   35 A22T(II,K)=A22T(II,K)+A22(II,L)*A12(K,M+L)
      DO 36 I=1,J1
      DO 36 L=1,IP
      M=3*(L-1)
      DO 36 J=1,3
      JJ=M+J
      B12T(I,JJ)=0.0
      DO 36 K=1,3
      KK=M+K
   36 B12T(I,JJ)=B12T(I,JJ)+A12(I,KK)*A22(KK,J)
C
      IA11=0
      DO 37 I=1,J1
      DO 37 J=1,I
      IA11=IA11+1
      DO 37 K=1,K1
   37 A11(IA11)=A11(IA11)-A12(I,K)*A22T(K,J)

C     ****************************************************************
C     INVERTING A11
C     ****************************************************************

      CALL LINV3P(A11,C,1,J1,IER)
C     ****************************************************************
C     IER =0 --- NO ERROR
C     IER =-1 ----MATRIX IS NOT POSITIVE DEFINITE
C     IER =K ---- LOSS OF SIGNIFICANCE
C     ****************************************************************

      IF(IER) 139,138,140
  139 WRITE(IWT,3013)
 3013 FORMAT('0A11 IS NOT A POSITIVE DEFINE SYMETRIC MATRIX',
     *'-- EXECUTION TERMINATED')
      STOP
  140 WRITE(IWT,3014)
 3014 FORMAT('   LOSS OF SIGNIFICANCE OCCURED IN A11')
  138 IF(IOUT.EQ.1)GO TO 302
      DO 38 I=1,J1
      KA11=I*(I-1)/2
      DO 38 J=1,K1
```

```
        A12(I,J)=0.0
        IA11=KA11
        DO 38 K=1,J1
        IA11=IA11+1
        IF(K.GT.I) IA11=IA11+K-2
     38 A12(I,J)=A12(I,J)-A11(IA11)*B12T(K,J)
        DO 40 I=1,J1
        DE(I)=0.0
        IA11=I*(I-1)/2
        DO 39 J=1,J1
        IA11=IA11+1
        IF(J.GT.I) IA11=IA11+J-2

C       ************************************************************
C       SOLVING FOR DELTA(I) AND DELTA(E)
C       ************************************************************

     39 DE(I)=DE(I)-A11(IA11)*U1(J)
        DO 40 J=1,K1
     40 DE(I)=DE(I)-A12(I,J)*U2(J)
        DO 42 I=1,K1
        DO 45 J=1,K1
        DS(J)=0.0
        DO 45 K=1,J1

C       ************************************************************
C       SOLVING FOR DELTA(S)
C       ************************************************************

     45 DS(J)=DS(J)+A22T(I,K)*A12(K,J)
        A22T(I,1)=0
        DO 42 J=1,K1
     42 A22T(I,1)=A22T(I,1)+DS(J)*U2(J)
        DO 43 I=1,IP
        M=3*(I-1)
        DO 43 J=1,3
        JJ=M+J

        DS(JJ)=0.0
        DO 43 K=1,3
     43 DS(JJ)=DS(JJ)+A22(JJ,K)*U2(M+K)
        DO 44 I=1,K1
        DS(I)=A22T(I,1)-DS(I)
        DO 44 J=1,J1
     44 DS(I)=DS(I)-A12(J,I)*U1(J)

C       ************************************************************
C       APPLY ALTERATIONS
C       ************************************************************

        WRITE(IWT,132)
    132 FORMAT('INTERIOR ORIENTATION PARAMETERS')
        DO 130 I=1,9

C       ************************************************************
C       UPDATING CURRENT APPROX. OF INTERI.ORIENT.
C       ************************************************************

    130 XI(I)=XI(I)+DE(I)
        WRITE(IWT,131) (XI(J),J=1,9)
    131 FORMAT(' ',9E12.5)
```

```
C
  302  NDF=NDF-K1-J1
       VAR=VPV/NDF
       WRITE(IWT,604) ICYCLE,VAR,NDF
  604  FORMAT('0ICYCLE=',I5,5X,'VARIANCE=',D14.6,5X,'NDF=',I5)
       IF(ICYCLE.EQ.CYCLE) IOUT = 1
       DO 306 I=1,J1
       KA11=I*(I-1)/2
       DO 306 K=1,J1
       KA11=KA11+1
       IF(K.GT.I) KA11=KA11+K-2

C     ***************************************************************
C     FORMING  VARIANCE -COVARIANCE MATRIX
C     ***************************************************************

  306  A12(I,K)=A11(KA11)*VAR
       DO 66 I=1,9
   66  ATEMP(I,1)=DSQRT(A12(I,I))
       WRITE(IWT,3000)ITITLE,N,IP,NDF,ICYCLE,VAR
 3000  FORMAT('1',T42,'CALIBRATION OF THE CAMERA',7A4           ,/T52,'
      *NUMBER OF PHOTOS:',I5,/T48,'NUMBER OF CONTROL POINTS:',I5,/T49
      *,'DEGREES OF FREEDOM:',I5,/T52,'NUMBER OF CYCLES:',I5,/T42,
      *'VARIANCE OF UNIT WEIGHT=',E12.5,///T58,'RESULTS',/T51,'INTERIOR
      *ORIENTATION',//T18,'X',T31,'Y',T44,'F',T56,'K1*10**-6',T68,
      *'K2*10**-12',T80,'K3*10**-18',T92,'P1*10**-6',T104,'P2*10**-12',
      *T116,'P3*10**-18')
       WRITE(IPU,3015) XI
 3015  FORMAT(3D15.7)
       WRITE(IWT,3001) XI,(ATEMP(I,1),I=1,9),(WI(I,I),I=1,9)
 3001  FORMAT('0',T12,3F13.6,1X,6E13.5,//,T3,'STD ERROR',T12,3F13.6,1X,
      *   6E13.5,//,T3,'POIDS ',T13,9E13.6,////)
   67  DO 115 I=1,N
       K=PHOTO(I,1)
       LL=6*(I-1)
       DO 101 IZ=2,7
       KK=LL+IZ+8

C     ***************************************************************
C     EE = EXTERIOR ORIENTATION STD. ERROR
C     ***************************************************************

       EE(IZ-1)=DSQRT(A12(KK,KK))

C     ***************************************************************
C     UPDATING EXT.ORIENT.
C     ***************************************************************

  101  PHOTO(I,IZ)=PHOTO(I,IZ)+DE(6*(I-1)+IZ+8)

C     ***************************************************************
C     SIN DE K,P,O ET COS DE K,P,O
C     ***************************************************************

       R(1)=DSIN(PHOTO(I,5))
       R(2)=DSIN(PHOTO(I,6))
       R(3)=DSIN(PHOTO(I,7))
       R(4)=DCOS(PHOTO(I,5))
       R(5)=DCOS(PHOTO(I,6))
       R(6)=DCOS(PHOTO(I,7))
```

```
      IF(I.GT.1) GO TO 61
      WRITE(IWT,3006)
 3006 FORMAT(T34,'VARIANCE/COVARIANCE/ CORRELATION COOFFICIENT ',
     *'MATRIX')
      NVAL = 9
      IF(ICYCLE.EQ.8) NVAL = J1
      DO 60 II=1,NVAL
      TEMP = A12(II,II)
      I2 = II
      IF(ICYCLE.EQ.8) I2 = 1
      DO 55 KK=I2,J1

C     **************************************************************
C     THE CORRELATION COEFFICIENT MATRIX
C     **************************************************************

   55 A12(II,KK) = A12(II,KK) / DSQRT(TEMP * A12(KK,KK))
      WRITE(IWT,3003) II,(A12(II,J),J=1,J1)
 3003 FORMAT('0',T4,'LIGNE',I4,T16,6E15.6,/(T16,6E15.6))
   60 A12(II,II) = TEMP
   61 WRITE(IWT,3007)
 3007 FORMAT(7(/))
      WRITE(IWT,3008)
 3008 FORMAT(T51,'EXTERIOR ORIENTATION',//)
      WRITE(IWT,3002) I,(PHOTO(I,II),II=2,7),EE,(PHOTO(I,II),II=14,49,7)

 3002 FORMAT(T12,'PHOTO NO.',I4,T30,'XO',T45,'YO',T60,'ZO',T73,'KAPPA(RA
     *D.)',T89,'PHI(RAD.)',T103,'OMEGA(RAD.)',
     *    //T23,3F15.6,3E15.6,//T12,'STD.ERROR',
     *      T23,3F15.6,3E15.6,//T12,'POIDS ',T23,6E15.6,////)
      WRITE(IWT,3004)
 3004 FORMAT('0',T43,'RESIDUALS ON CONTROL POINTS',/T55,'(IN
     * MICROMETRE)',///T37,'POINT NO.',T55,'RESIDUALS ON X',T77,'RESID
     *UALS ON Y')
         RMSX= 0.0
         RMSY=0.0
   68 DO 116 J = 1,K
      P=POINT(I,J,3)
   69 DO 114 IZ=17,19

C     **************************************************************
C     UPDATING CURRENT APPROX. OF SURVEY COORD.
C     **************************************************************

  114 POINT(I,J,IZ)=POINT(I,J,IZ)+DS(3*(P-1)+IZ-16)
      DX=POINT(I,J,17)-PHOTO(I,2)
      DY=POINT(I,J,18)-PHOTO(I,3)
      DZ=POINT(I,J,19)-PHOTO(I,4)

C     **************************************************************
C     SUBSTITUING  IN GENERAL PROJECTIVE EQUATIONS
C     **************************************************************

      XT=DX*R(5)*R(4)+DY*(R(6)*R(1)+R(3)*R(2)*R(4))+DZ*(R(3)*R(1)-R(6)*R
     *(2)*R(4))
      YT=-DX*R(5)*R(1)+DY*(R(6)*R(4)-R(3)*R(2)*R(1))+DZ*(R(3)*R(4)+R(6)*
     *R(2)*R(1))
      ZT=DX*R(2)-DY*R(3)*R(5)+DZ*R(6)*R(5)
      TEMP1=POINT(I,J,1)-XI(1)
      TEMP2=POINT(I,J,2)-XI(2)
      R2=TEMP1**2+TEMP2**2
```

```
      R4=(R2*R2)/F2
      R6=(R4*R2)/F1
      RPF=1.0+KI*R2/F1+K2*R4+K3*R6
      CP1=R2+2*TEMP1**2
      CP2=R2+2*TEMP2**2
      CP3=2*TEMP1*TEMP2
      CP4=1+P3*R2/(F1*F2)
      RDC(1)=P1*CP1/F1+P2*CP3/F2
      RDC(2)=P1*CP3/F1+P2*CP2/F2
      XC=(CC*XT/ZT)/RPF
      YC=(CC*YT/ZT)/RPF

C     **************************************************************
C     COMPUTING  RESIDUALS
C     **************************************************************

      E(1)=TEMP1-XC+RDC(1)*CP4/RPF
      E(2)=TEMP2-YC+RDC(2)*CP4/RPF
      WRITE(IWT,3005) IST(P),E(1),E(2)
 3005 FORMAT('0',T37,I5,T46,3P2F20.1)
      RMSX = RMSX + E(1)*E(1)
 116  RMSY = RMSY + E(2)*E(2)
      RMSX=DSQRT(RMSX/K)
      RMSY=DSQRT(RMSY/K)
 115     WRITE(IWT,6500) RMSX,RMSY
 6500    FORMAT('0',T40,'RMS = ',T46,3P2F20.1)
      IF(IOUT.EQ.1) GOTO 5000
      IF(ICYCLE.LT.CYCLE) GO TO 4
 5000 WRITE(IWT,5001)
 5001 FORMAT('1',40X,'ADJUSTED SURVEY COORDINATES',//,33X,'POINT',
     k    8X,'X',14X,'Y',15X,'Z')


C     **************************************************************
C     POINT(K,I,J) TO BE AS CONTAINING PHOTO K
C     ALL CONTROLE POINTS USED (IF POSSIBLE)
C     **************************************************************

      DO 5007 I = 1,N
      DO 5007 K = 1,IP
      P = POINT(I,K,3)
      DO 5008 L = 1,IP
      IF(IST(L).EQ.P.AND.ISTA(L).EQ.0) GO TO 5002
 5008 CONTINUE
      GO TO 5007
 5002 ISTA(L) = IST(L)

C     **************************************************************
C     ADJUSTED SURVEY COORDINATES
C     **************************************************************

      WRITE(IWT,5003) IST(L),(POINT(I,K,J),J=17,19)
 5003 FORMAT(/,31X,I5,3F15.4)
      WRITE(IPU,5006) IST(L),(POINT(I,J,K),J=17,19)
 5006 FORMAT(6X,I3,3F15.4)
 5007 CONTINUE
      WRITE(IWT,5004)
 5004 FORMAT('1',30X,'STANDARD DEVIATIONS OF SURVEY COORDINATES (CM)',
     k//,30X,'POINT',10X,'X',15X,'Y',15X,'Z')
      DO 5005 I=1,IP
```

```
       I3 = I * 3
       I2 = I3 - 1
       I1 = I3 - 2
       XSTD = DSQRT(A22(I1,1))
       YSTD = DSQRT(A22(I2,2))
       ZSTD = DSQRT(A22(I3,3))

C      ************************************************************
C      PRINTING THE STD DEVIATION OF SURVEY COORD.
C      ************************************************************

       WRITE(IPU,5006) IST(I),XSTD,YSTD,ZSTD
 5005  WRITE(IWT,5009) IST(I),XSTD,YSTD,ZSTD
 5009  FORMAT(/,32X,I3,2P3F15.4)
       WRITE(IWT,5010)
 5010  FORMAT('1')
  145  FORMAT(' ',21F5.2)
  500  FORMAT(2F10.5)
  501  FORMAT(6D10.5)
  502  FORMAT(2F10.3)
  503  FORMAT(I5)
  504   FORMAT(3D10.3)
  505  FORMAT('1PHOTO NUMBER',I3)
  506  FORMAT('0POINT NUMBER',I4,/)
  508   FORMAT( 1H0,15E8.1)
  509  FORMAT(1H1,'VARIANCE/COVARIANCE MATRIX/COEFFICIENTS OF ',
      k--'CORRELATION')
  510   FORMAT(2F10.6)
  603  FORMAT(F5.0)
       RETURN
       END
```

```
      SUBROUTINE COFEI(D,R,B,XO,CC,XC,YC)
C     **********************************************************************
C     COMPUTE B FOR EXTERIOR AND INTERIOR ORIENTATION ELEMENTS  INCLUDING CC
C     ORDER REQUIRED (X,Y,Z,K,P,O)
C     N=NUMBER OF POINTS WHERE THE COEFFICIENTS ARE COMPUTED
C     NEGATIVE VALUE OF THE  FOCAL LENGTH
C     R=MATRIX(SK,SP,SW,CK,CP,CW)
C     DATA=MATRIX(PT,X,Y,Z,MX,MY,X,Y,Z)
C     **********************************************************************
      IMPLICIT REAL*8(A-H,O-Z)
      DIMENSION R(6),D(3),XO(6),B(2,9)
      SK=R(1)
      SP=R(2)
      SW=R(3)
      CK=R(4)
      CP=R(5)
      CW=R(6)
      DX=D(1)-XO(1)
      DY=D(2)-XO(2)
      DZ=D(3)-XO(3)
      DO 110 L=1,6
      B(1,L)=0.0
  110 B(2,L)=0.0
      XT=DX*CP*CK+DY*(CW*SK+SW*SP*CK)+DZ*(SW*SK-CW*SP*CK)
      YT=-DX*CP*SK+DY*(CW*CK-SW*SP*SK)+DZ*(SW*CK+CW*SP*SK)
      ZT=DX*SP-DY*SW*CP+DZ*CW*CP
      COZ=CC*(1.0éZT**2)
      B(1,1)  =-COZ*(ZT*CP*CK-XT*SP)
      B(1,2)  =-COZ*(ZT*(CW*SK+SW*SP*CK)+XT*SW*CP)
      B(1,3)  =-COZ*(ZT*(SW*SK-CW*SP*CK)-XT*CW*CP)
      B(1,4)  =COZ*(-DX*CP*SK+DY*(CW*CK-SW*SP*SK)+DZ*(SW*CK+CW*SP*SK)
     1)*ZT
      B(1,5)  =COZ*(ZT*(-DX*SP*CK+DY*SW*CP*CK-DZ*CW*CP*CK)-XT*(DX*
     1CP+DY*SW*SP-DZ*CW*SP))
      B(1,6)  =COZ*(ZT*(DY*(CW*SP*CK-SW*SK)+DZ*(CW*SK+SW*SP*CK))+
     1XT*(DY*CW*CP+DZ*SW*CP))
      XC=CC*XT*(1.0éZT)
      B(2,1)  =COZ*(ZT*CP*SK+YT*SP)
      B(2,2)  =-COZ*(ZT*(CW*CK-SW*SP*SK)+YT*SW*CP)
      B(2,3)  =-COZ*(ZT*(SW*CK+CW*SP*SK)-YT*CW*CP)
      B(2,4)  =COZ*(ZT*(-DX*CP*CK-DY*(CW*SK+SW*SP*CK)+DZ*(CW*SP*CK-SW*SK)))
      B(2,5)  =COZ*(ZT*(DX*SP*SK-DY*SW*CP*SK+DZ*CW*CP*
     1SK)-YT*(DX*CP+DY*SW*SP-DZ*CW*SP))
      B(2,6)   =COZ*(ZT*(-DY*(SW*CK+CW*SP*SK)+DZ*(CW*CK-SW*SP*SK))+
     1YT*(DY*CW*CP+DZ*SW*CP))
      YC=CC*YT*(1.0éZT)
      DO 126 I=1,3
      B(1,I+6)=B(1,I)
  126 B(2,I+6)=B(2,I)
      DO 125 I=1,2
      DO 125 J=1,6
  125 B(I,J)=-B(I,J)
      RETURN
      END
```

INPUT DATA FOR CALIB

```
   PHOTO    2 [subsequently #1]
  1.0000      1.5050     1.9040      .0000       .0000     -.5094
1.00E+04   1.00E+04   1.00E+04   1.00E+04   1.00E+04   1.00E+04
   9     -9.825      8.838
  11       .500      8.904
  13     10.845      8.910
  23     -8.841      -.181
  27      9.945      -.156
  37     -8.012     -7.684
  39       .546     -7.706
  41      9.164     -7.685

   PHOTO    4 [subsequently #2]
   .4950      1.0000      1.9040     1.5708     -.5094      .0000
1.00E+04   1.00E+04   1.00E+04   1.00E+04   1.00E+04   1.00E+04
   9     11.311      9.060
  11     10.394      -.040
  13      9.595     -7.576
  23       .923      9.033
  27       .971     -7.584
  37     -9.417      8.967
  39     -8.447      -.070
  41     -7.611     -7.585

   PHOTO    5 [subsequently #3]
  1.0000       .4950      1.9040     3.1416      .0000      .5094
1.00E+04   1.00E+04   1.00E+04   1.00E+04   1.00E+04   1.00E+04
   9      9.576     -7.615
  11       .967     -7.626
  13     -7.591     -7.584
  23     10.369      -.057
  27     -8.438      -.072
  37     11.304      9.033
  39       .919      9.028
  41     -9.426      8.946

   PHOTO    7 [subsequently #4]
  1.5050      1.0000      1.9040    -1.5708      .5094      .0000
1.00E+04   1.00E+04   1.00E+04   1.00E+04   1.00E+04   1.00E+04
   9     -7.628     -7.704
  11     -8.452      -.232
  13     -9.399      8.757
  23       .938     -7.732
  27       .906      8.838
  37      9.541     -7.733
  39     10.350      -.214
  41     11.272      8.863
```

ESTIMATES OF INTERIOR ORIENTATIONELEMENTS AND THEIR WEIGHTS

```
                .000E+00          .000E+00      -5.809E+01
   .000E+00          .000E+00          .000E+00
   .000E+00          .000E+00          .000E+00
            1.000E+00       1.000E+00       1.000E+00
   1.000E+08       1.000E+08       1.000E+08
   1.000E+08       1.000E+08       1.000E+08
```

WT ON PHOTO COORD. =   .40000E+05

SURVEY COORD. AND STD ERROR

PT NO	X	Y	Z	WX	WY	WZ
9	.8004	1.2004	1.0000	.5000E-04	.5000E-04	.1000E-03
11	1.0004	1.2002	1.0000	.5000E-04	.5000E-04	.1000E-03
13	1.2002	1.2001	1.0000	.5000E-04	.5000E-04	.1000E-03
23	.8006	1.0003	1.0000	.5000E-04	.5000E-04	.1000E-03
27	1.2002	1.0000	1.0000	.5000E-04	.5000E-04	.1000E-03
37	.8002	.8001	1.0000	.5000E-04	.5000E-04	.1000E-03
39	1.0002	.7999	1.0000	.5000E-04	.5000E-04	.1000E-03
41	1.2006	.7999	1.0000	.5000E-04	.5000E-04	.1000E-03

RESIDUAL AND OBSERVATION EQUATION BEFORE 1ST CYCLE

PHOTO	PT	RES.IN X	RES.IN Y
1	9	2.541	-1.994
1	11	.474	-1.921
1	13	-1.553	-1.904
1	23	2.347	-.193
1	27	-1.287	-.153
1	37	2.231	1.266
1	39	.533	1.252
1	41	-1.119	1.274
2	9	-1.095	-1.729
2	11	-.837	-.016
2	13	-.661	1.387
2	23	.906	-1.744
2	27	.971	1.379
2	37	2.960	-1.831
2	39	2.778	-.056
2	41	2.646	1.393
3	9	-.658	1.354
3	11	.989	1.338
3	13	2.672	1.373
3	23	-.817	-.041
3	27	2.794	-.070
3	37	-1.068	-1.770
3	39	.934	-1.789
3	41	2.996	-1.871
4	9	2.646	1.235
4	11	2.783	-.251
4	13	2.991	-2.065
4	23	.952	1.199
4	27	.905	-1.986
4	37	-.707	1.212
4	39	-.877	-.223
4	41	-1.125	-1.982

ICYCLE=   3   VARIANCE= 4.173861D+00   NDF=   64

CALIBRATION OF A 35 mm CAMERA

NO. OF PHOTOS: 4

NO. OF CONTROL POINTS: 8

DEGREES OF FREEDOM: 64

NO. OF CYCLES: 3

VARIANCE OF UNIT WEIGHT =   4.17386E+00

Camera focused to an object distance 1 m

RESULTS

INTERIOR ORIENTATION

	X	Y	F
	.30	−.23	−49.15
STD ERROR	.07	.24	.41
WEIGHT	1.00E+00	1.00E+00	1.00E+00

COVARIANCE/VARIANCE/CORRELATION COEFFICIENT MATRIX

ROW   1

```
     1.000000E+00    7.469924E-02    7.917231E-02
    -9.173663E-06   -3.122617E-09   -8.387379E-13
    -1.698846E-05   -2.027027E-13   -4.914128E-32
     1.048427E-01   -7.680774E-02   -8.042404E-02
     4.653678E-02   -6.530021E-01    7.174345E-02
     7.571649E-02    9.922658E-02   -8.399174E-02
     7.757544E-01    6.624370E-02    6.533002E-01
    -9.719019E-02    7.563749E-02   -8.403568E-02
     3.592680E-02    6.529486E-01   -6.844289E-02
    -7.574491E-02   -1.040261E-01   -8.385907E-02
     7.747490E-01   -6.675023E-02   -6.519591E-01
```

ROW   2

```
     7.469924E-02    1.000000E+00    9.422777E-01
    -5.400204E-06   -1.759249E-09   -4.328698E-13
     1.090964E-07   -3.412857E-12   -3.871550E-35
    -4.698180E-02   -9.019717E-01   -9.450746E-01
    -7.379969E-02   -6.099197E-02    9.664367E-01
     9.024726E-01   -9.952879E-02   -9.451482E-01
     1.039986E-01    9.664011E-01    9.200499E-02
     1.034766E-01    9.022594E-01   -9.451647E-01
    -1.520769E-01    6.659660E-02   -9.663983E-01
    -9.016863E-01    9.407832E-02   -9.450454E-01
     9.943856E-02   -9.664023E-01   -8.845795E-02
```

ROW   3

```
     7.917231E-02    9.422777E-01    1.000000E+00
    -1.254867E-06    1.197576E-10    6.675999E-14
     1.409343E-08    9.583870E-13    1.079870E-34
    -4.620746E-02   -9.704371E-01   -9.925475E-01
    -6.975854E-02   -6.131377E-02    9.282896E-01
     9.704523E-01   -9.634306E-02   -9.925735E-01
     9.996102E-02    9.279779E-01    8.747656E-02
     9.989579E-02    9.703764E-01   -9.925644E-01
    -1.438525E-01    6.265434E-02   -9.280920E-01
    -9.703803E-01    9.057655E-02   -9.925244E-01
     9.571265E-02   -9.284607E-01   -8.411274E-02
```

ROW   4

```
        -9.173663E-06    -5.400204E-06    -1.254867E-06
         1.000000E+00    -3.359060E-13    -7.074505E-17
        -1.316595E-11    -5.507450E-17    -1.344880E-37
        -4.575735E-07    -1.354273E-06    -2.138933E-06
         2.314880E-07     6.574596E-06    -5.815918E-06
         1.331604E-06     2.511689E-07    -2.166586E-06
        -8.376403E-06    -5.837310E-06    -7.426008E-06
        -3.749736E-09     1.295122E-06    -2.184055E-06
         9.404955E-07    -7.091882E-06     5.898529E-06
        -1.335461E-06    -2.308005E-07    -2.146531E-06
        -8.326825E-06     5.809043E-06     7.397078E-06
```

ROW   5

```
        -3.122617E-09    -1.759249E-09     1.197576E-10
        -3.359060E-13     1.000000E+00    -1.967896E-20
        -5.362982E-15    -1.741566E-20    -5.415672E-41
        -2.654991E-10    -4.685425E-10    -6.182083E-10
        -2.644926E-12     2.146870E-09    -1.814353E-09
         4.597581E-10    -2.176608E-10    -6.331598E-10
        -2.681295E-09    -1.826496E-09    -2.276908E-09
         2.910010E-10     4.469495E-10    -6.390870E-10
         1.099106E-10    -2.174745E-09     1.846971E-09
        -4.590397E-10     2.046781E-10    -6.242481E-10
        -2.674337E-09     1.817746E-09     2.282347E-09
```

ROW   6

```
        -8.387379E-13    -4.328698E-13     6.675999E-14
        -7.074505E-17    -1.967896E-20     1.000000E+00
        -1.512137E-18    -4.139331E-24    -1.521726E-44
        -9.437319E-14    -1.207198E-13    -1.440430E-13
        -1.916685E-14     5.574824E-13    -4.361498E-13
         1.178372E-13    -1.226526E-13    -1.494437E-13
        -6.839406E-13    -4.409173E-13    -5.582923E-13
         1.411104E-13     1.147379E-13    -1.508006E-13
        -1.781102E-14    -5.329094E-13     4.458525E-13
        -1.172480E-13     1.141327E-13    -1.465311E-13
        -6.844934E-13     4.385868E-13     5.635885E-13
```

ROW   7

```
        -1.698846E-05     1.090964E-07     1.409343E-08
        -1.316595E-11    -5.362982E-15    -1.512137E-18
         1.000000E+00     3.617064E-20    -1.089502E-37
        -6.481866E-07     1.634803E-08    -3.674408E-08
         1.448761E-07     1.258988E-05     7.640981E-08
        -4.924218E-08    -7.477634E-07    -6.238886E-08
        -1.417719E-05     7.497494E-08    -1.246941E-05
         6.993950E-07    -5.205669E-08    -6.387764E-08
         1.456195E-07    -1.251111E-05    -2.848611E-08
         4.905015E-08     6.710459E-07    -6.228995E-08
        -1.422863E-05    -6.903514E-08     1.256583E-05
```

ROW   8

```
-2.027027E-13   -3.412857E-12    9.583870E-13
-5.507450E-17   -1.741566E-20   -4.139331E-24
 3.617064E-20    1.000000E+00   -2.449338E-45
-1.906188E-13   -1.158620E-12   -8.848827E-13
 5.438742E-14    5.930561E-14   -3.230773E-12
 1.177345E-12   -4.205348E-13   -8.780938E-13
-2.968269E-13   -3.211087E-12    1.397023E-15
 4.359107E-13    1.173673E-12   -8.796438E-13
 6.282523E-15    9.694739E-14    3.213922E-12
-1.152681E-12    4.109129E-13   -8.857175E-13
-2.830603E-13    3.234296E-12   -1.052959E-14
```

ROW   9

```
-4.914128E-32   -3.871550E-35    1.079870E-34
-1.344880E-37   -5.415672E-41   -1.521726E-44
-1.089502E-37   -2.449338E-45    1.000000E+00
-6.265358E-33   -2.818210E-35   -1.821088E-34
-1.474992E-33    3.262122E-32   -1.179361E-34
-2.029668E-34   -6.686960E-33   -3.885702E-34
-3.777869E-32   -3.296601E-34   -3.220293E-32
 6.557968E-33   -1.893039E-34   -3.797590E-34
-1.452255E-33   -3.229335E-32    4.258882E-34
 1.977773E-34    6.209451E-33   -3.866352E-34
-3.810336E-32    3.404711E-34    3.265597E-32
```

ROW   10

```
 1.048427E-01   -4.698180E-02   -4.620746E-02
-4.575735E-07   -2.654991E-10   -9.437319E-14
-6.481866E-07   -1.906188E-13   -6.265358E-33
 1.000000E+00    4.418908E-02    4.506594E-02
 6.870060E-01    6.827072E-01   -4.672296E-02
-1.998653E-02   -1.328628E-01    5.403893E-02
 1.459952E-01   -2.224895E-02    1.797835E-01
-9.130678E-02   -4.461832E-02    4.544223E-02
-1.196753E-02    1.194190E-02    4.633832E-02
 6.937402E-02    1.325027E-01    3.731417E-02
 1.406838E-01    7.107254E-02   -1.787349E-01
```

ROW   11

```
-7.680774E-02   -9.019717E-01   -9.704371E-01
-1.354273E-06   -4.685425E-10   -1.207198E-13
 1.634803E-08   -1.158620E-12   -2.818210E-35
 4.418908E-02    1.000000E+00    9.382451E-01
 6.764128E-02    5.900432E-02   -9.496128E-01
-9.379878E-01    1.170612E-01    9.652152E-01
-9.647446E-02   -8.844127E-01   -1.026342E-01
-9.598849E-02   -9.403023E-01    9.625247E-01
 1.378879E-01   -6.002577E-02    8.880050E-01
 9.380227E-01   -6.226101E-02    9.652172E-01
-8.984463E-02    8.849544E-01    6.131424E-02
```

ROW   12

-8.042404E-02	-9.450746E-01	-9.925475E-01
-2.138933E-06	-6.182083E-10	-1.440430E-13
-3.674408E-08	-8.848827E-13	-1.821088E-34
4.506594E-02	9.382451E-01	1.000000E+00
6.872333E-02	6.157784E-02	-9.019749E-01
-9.653042E-01	8.808607E-02	9.849772E-01
-1.011100E-01	-9.322198E-01	-8.261232E-02
-9.961402E-02	-9.624788E-01	9.868088E-01
1.440574E-01	-6.391061E-02	9.290960E-01
9.651205E-01	-9.901238E-02	9.849199E-01
-9.851362E-02	9.326075E-01	9.223139E-02

ROW   13

4.653678E-02	-7.379969E-02	-6.975854E-02
2.314880E-07	-2.644926E-12	-1.916685E-14
1.448761E-07	5.438742E-14	-1.474992E-33
6.870060E-01	6.764128E-02	6.872333E-02
1.000000E+00	4.861749E-01	-7.340777E-02
-3.323355E-02	-9.266823E-02	8.057575E-02
1.299152E-01	-3.876377E-02	1.082299E-01
1.175549E-02	-6.699534E-02	6.959316E-02
-1.815224E-02	5.072036E-02	7.171014E-02
1.004727E-01	9.301224E-02	5.895023E-02
1.227066E-01	1.049564E-01	-1.070363E-01

ROW   14

-6.530021E-01	-6.099197E-02	-6.131377E-02
6.574596E-06	2.146870E-09	5.574824E-13
1.258988E-05	5.930561E-14	3.262122E-32
6.827072E-01	5.900432E-02	6.157784E-02
4.861749E-01	1.000000E+00	-5.908091E-02
-3.940244E-02	-1.762800E-01	7.124918E-02
-4.567016E-01	-3.586031E-02	-3.414396E-01
6.722778E-03	-5.840529E-02	6.458363E-02
-4.270784E-02	-4.674805E-01	5.626926E-02
7.757957E-02	1.793692E-01	5.813536E-02
-4.602287E-01	7.424494E-02	3.413649E-01

ROW   15

7.174345E-02	9.664367E-01	9.282896E-01
-5.815918E-06	-1.814353E-09	-4.361498E-13
7.640981E-08	-3.230773E-12	-1.179361E-34
-4.672296E-02	-9.496128E-01	-9.019749E-01
-7.340777E-02	-5.908091E-02	1.000000E+00
8.851216E-01	-1.208550E-01	-9.325306E-01
1.000523E-01	9.301787E-01	1.064467E-01
1.007367E-01	8.884481E-01	-9.293566E-01
-1.472789E-01	6.328916E-02	-9.348051E-01
-8.845549E-01	6.684020E-02	-9.324625E-01
9.257250E-02	-9.303430E-01	-6.504005E-02

ROW   16

```
7.571649E-02     9.024726E-01      9.704523E-01
1.331604E-06     4.597581E-10      1.178372E-13
-4.924218E-08    1.177345E-12     -2.029668E-34
-1.998653E-02   -9.379878E-01     -9.653042E-01
-3.323355E-02   -3.940244E-02      8.851216E-01
1.000000E+00    -9.249279E-02     -9.383613E-01
1.018526E-01     9.498069E-01      8.451829E-02
1.207140E-01     9.378805E-01     -9.652559E-01
-1.711275E-01    7.835683E-02     -8.850105E-01
-9.403190E-01    8.717599E-02     -9.625463E-01
9.078707E-02    -8.888176E-01     -7.994054E-02
```

ROW   17

```
9.922658E-02    -9.952879E-02     -9.634306E-02
2.511689E-07    -2.176608E-10     -1.226526E-13
-7.477634E-07   -4.205348E-13     -6.686960E-33
-1.328628E-01    1.170612E-01      8.808607E-02
-9.266823E-02   -1.762800E-01     -1.208550E-01
-9.249279E-02    1.000000E+00      9.500498E-02
-3.684030E-01   -9.640545E-02     -6.858767E-01
1.273157E-01    -6.803339E-02      1.043397E-01
-8.538502E-02    1.760112E-01      7.247544E-02
9.267877E-02    -9.610127E-02      9.571596E-02
-5.818250E-03    9.724668E-02     -5.103251E-03
```

ROW   18

```
-8.399174E-02   -9.451482E-01     -9.925735E-01
-2.166586E-06   -6.331598E-10     -1.494437E-13
-6.238886E-08   -8.780938E-13     -3.885702E-34
5.403893E-02     9.652152E-01      9.849772E-01
8.057575E-02     7.124918E-02     -9.325306E-01
-9.383613E-01    9.500498E-02      1.000000E+00
-1.007081E-01   -9.017870E-01     -8.984390E-02
-9.123591E-02   -9.652255E-01      9.850249E-01
1.334428E-01    -5.999616E-02      9.323420E-01
9.624599E-01    -8.992850E-02      9.868089E-01
-9.987874E-02    9.294755E-01      8.768766E-02
```

ROW   19

```
7.757544E-01     1.039986E-01      9.996102E-02
-8.376403E-06   -2.681295E-09     -6.839406E-13
-1.417719E-05   -2.968269E-13     -3.777869E-32
1.459952E-01    -9.647446E-02     -1.011100E-01
1.299152E-01    -4.567016E-01      1.000523E-01
1.018526E-01    -3.684030E-01     -1.007081E-01
1.000000E+00     1.015991E-01      8.479340E-01
-1.316310E-01    9.298115E-02     -1.056027E-01
1.097212E-01     4.614966E-01     -9.429371E-02
-9.477731E-02    2.080692E-03     -1.040586E-01
6.740857E-01    -9.517427E-02     -5.673095E-01
```

ROW   20

6.624370E−02	9.664011E−01	9.279779E−01
−5.837310E−06	−1.826496E−09	−4.409173E−13
7.497494E−08	−3.211087E−12	−3.296601E−34
−2.224895E−02	−8.844127E−01	−9.322198E−01
−3.876377E−02	−3.586031E−02	9.301787E−01
9.498069E−01	−9.640545E−02	−9.017870E−01
1.015991E−01	1.000000E+00	8.517563E−02
1.256456E−01	8.846334E−01	−9.322157E−01
−1.803184E−01	7.870181E−02	−9.302313E−01
−8.876310E−01	9.197959E−02	−9.289413E−01
9.043276E−02	−9.348160E−01	−8.078415E−02

ROW   21

6.533002E−01	9.200499E−02	8.747656E−02
−7.426008E−06	−2.276908E−09	−5.582923E−13
−1.246941E−05	1.397023E−15	−3.220293E−32
1.797835E−01	−1.026342E−01	−8.261232E−02
1.082299E−01	−3.414396E−01	1.064467E−01
8.451829E−02	−6.858767E−01	−8.984390E−02
8.479340E−01	8.517563E−02	1.000000E+00
−1.709452E−01	6.386180E−02	−9.793088E−02
9.631247E−02	3.426067E−01	−6.631072E−02
−8.310013E−02	−8.224365E−03	−9.099673E−02
5.677494E−01	−8.449440E−02	−4.686019E−01

ROW   22

−9.719019E−02	1.034766E−01	9.989579E−02
−3.749736E−09	2.910010E−10	1.411104E−13
6.993950E−07	4.359107E−13	6.557968E−33
−9.130678E−02	−9.598849E−02	−9.961402E−02
1.175549E−02	6.722778E−03	1.007367E−01
1.207140E−01	1.273157E−01	−9.123591E−02
−1.316310E−01	1.256456E−01	−1.709452E−01
1.000000E+00	9.608099E−02	−9.830923E−02
−6.932343E−01	6.856925E−01	−1.027198E−01
−7.144376E−02	−1.270742E−01	−1.078595E−01
−1.377767E−01	−7.695283E−02	1.723059E−01

ROW   23

7.563749E−02	9.022594E−01	9.703764E−01
1.295122E−06	4.469495E−10	1.147379E−13
−5.205669E−08	1.173673E−12	−1.893039E−34
−4.461832E−02	−9.403023E−01	−9.624788E−01
−6.699534E−02	−5.840529E−02	8.884481E−01
9.378805E−01	−6.803339E−02	−9.652255E−01
9.298115E−02	8.846334E−01	6.386180E−02
9.608099E−02	1.000000E+00	−9.382256E−01
−1.387780E−01	5.930449E−02	−9.497983E−01
−9.379016E−01	1.115602E−01	−9.651551E−01
9.154205E−02	−8.851644E−01	−9.869197E−02

ROW   24

```
-8.403568E-02   -9.451647E-01   -9.925644E-01
-2.184055E-06   -6.390870E-10   -1.508006E-13
-6.387764E-08   -8.796438E-13   -3.797590E-34
 4.544223E-02    9.625247E-01    9.868088E-01
 6.959316E-02    6.458363E-02   -9.293566E-01
-9.652559E-01    1.043397E-01    9.850249E-01
-1.056027E-01   -9.322157E-01   -9.793088E-02
-9.830923E-02   -9.382256E-01    1.000000E+00
 1.427972E-01   -6.550999E-02    9.018997E-01
 9.651634E-01   -8.203301E-02    9.849630E-01
-9.964442E-02    9.326975E-01    8.162879E-02
```

ROW   25

```
 3.592680E-02   -1.520769E-01   -1.438525E-01
 9.404955E-07    1.099106E-10   -1.781102E-14
 1.456195E-07    6.282523E-15   -1.452255E-33
-1.196753E-02    1.378879E-01    1.440574E-01
-1.815224E-02   -4.270784E-02   -1.472789E-01
-1.711275E-01   -8.538502E-02    1.334428E-01
 1.097212E-01   -1.803184E-01    9.631247E-02
-6.932343E-01   -1.387780E-01    1.427972E-01
 1.000000E+00   -4.923861E-01    1.502485E-01
 1.043806E-01    8.565200E-02    1.548201E-01
 1.179804E-01    1.147271E-01   -9.817213E-02
```

ROW   26

```
 6.529486E-01    6.659660E-02    6.265434E-02
-7.091882E-06   -2.174745E-09   -5.329094E-13
-1.251111E-05    9.694739E-14   -3.229335E-32
 1.194190E-02   -6.002577E-02   -6.391061E-02
 5.072036E-02   -4.674805E-01    6.328916E-02
 7.835683E-02    1.760112E-01   -5.999616E-02
 4.614966E-01    7.870181E-02    3.426067E-01
 6.856925E-01    5.930449E-02   -6.550999E-02
-4.923861E-01    1.000000E+00   -6.247948E-02
-4.019454E-02   -1.789158E-01   -7.288353E-02
 4.562805E-01   -4.099071E-02   -3.408162E-01
```

ROW   27

```
-6.844289E-02   -9.663983E-01   -9.280920E-01
 5.898529E-06    1.846971E-09    4.458525E-13
-2.848611E-08    3.213922E-12    4.258882E-34
 4.633832E-02    8.880050E-01    9.290960E-01
 7.171014E-02    5.626926E-02   -9.348051E-01
-8.850105E-01    7.247544E-02    9.323420E-01
-9.429371E-02   -9.302313E-01   -6.631072E-02
-1.027198E-01   -9.497983E-01    9.018997E-01
 1.502485E-01   -6.247948E-02    1.000000E+00
 8.842400E-01   -1.156829E-01    9.322645E-01
-9.302467E-02    9.301937E-01    1.008045E-01
```

ROW   28

```
-7.574491E-02    -9.016863E-01    -9.703803E-01
-1.335461E-06    -4.590397E-10    -1.172480E-13
 4.905015E-08    -1.152681E-12     1.977773E-34
 6.937402E-02     9.380227E-01     9.651205E-01
 1.004727E-01     7.757957E-02    -8.845549E-01
-9.403190E-01     9.267877E-02     9.624599E-01
-9.477731E-02    -8.876310E-01    -8.310013E-02
-7.144376E-02    -9.379016E-01     9.651634E-01
 1.043806E-01    -4.019454E-02     8.842400E-01
 1.000000E+00    -8.724303E-02     9.381142E-01
-9.759933E-02     9.495724E-01     8.146322E-02
```

ROW   29

```
-1.040261E-01     9.407832E-02     9.057655E-02
-2.308005E-07     2.046781E-10     1.141327E-13
 6.710459E-07     4.109129E-13     6.209451E-33
 1.325027E-01    -6.226101E-02    -9.901238E-02
 9.301224E-02     1.793692E-01     6.684020E-02
 8.717599E-02    -9.610127E-02    -8.992850E-02
 2.080692E-03     9.197959E-02    -8.224365E-03
-1.270742E-01     1.115602E-01    -8.203301E-02
 8.565200E-02    -1.789158E-01    -1.156829E-01
-8.724303E-02     1.000000E+00    -8.922334E-02
 3.657327E-01    -9.145662E-02    -6.837122E-01
```

ROW   30

```
-8.385907E-02    -9.450454E-01    -9.925244E-01
-2.146531E-06    -6.242481E-10    -1.465311E-13
-6.228995E-08    -8.857175E-13    -3.866352E-34
 3.731417E-02     9.652172E-01     9.849199E-01
 5.895023E-02     5.813536E-02    -9.324625E-01
-9.625463E-01     9.571596E-02     9.868089E-01
-1.040586E-01    -9.289413E-01    -9.099673E-02
-1.078595E-01    -9.651551E-01     9.849630E-01
 1.548201E-01    -7.288353E-02     9.322645E-01
 9.381142E-01    -8.922334E-02     1.000000E+00
-9.645515E-02     9.020550E-01     8.639140E-02
```

ROW   31

```
 7.747490E-01     9.943856E-02     9.571265E-02
-8.326825E-06    -2.674337E-09    -6.844934E-13
-1.422863E-05    -2.830603E-13    -3.810336E-32
 1.406838E-01    -8.984463E-02    -9.851362E-02
 1.227066E-01    -4.602287E-01     9.257250E-02
 9.078707E-02    -5.818250E-03    -9.987874E-02
 6.740857E-01     9.043276E-02     5.677494E-01
-1.377767E-01     9.154205E-02    -9.964442E-02
 1.179804E-01     4.562805E-01    -9.302467E-02
-9.759933E-02     3.657327E-01    -9.645515E-02
 1.000000E+00    -9.741858E-02    -8.473891E-01
```

ROW   32

```
        -6.675023E-02   -9.664023E-01   -9.284607E-01
         5.809043E-06    1.817746E-09    4.385868E-13
        -6.903514E-08    3.234296E-12    3.404711E-34
         7.107254E-02    8.849544E-01    9.326075E-01
         1.049564E-01    7.424494E-02   -9.303430E-01
        -8.888176E-01    9.724668E-02    9.294755E-01
        -9.517427E-02   -9.348160E-01   -8.449440E-02
        -7.695283E-02   -8.851644E-01    9.326975E-01
         1.147271E-01   -4.099071E-02    9.301937E-01
         9.495724E-01   -9.145662E-02    9.020550E-01
        -9.741858E-02    1.000000E+00    8.227587E-02
```

ROW   33

```
        -6.519591E-01   -8.845795E-02   -8.411274E-02
         7.397078E-06    2.282347E-09    5.635885E-13
         1.256583E-05   -1.052959E-14    3.265597E-32
        -1.787349E-01    6.131424E-02    9.223139E-02
        -1.070363E-01    3.413649E-01   -6.504005E-02
        -7.994054E-02   -5.103251E-03    8.768766E-02
        -5.673095E-01   -8.078415E-02   -4.686019E-01
         1.723059E-01   -9.869197E-02    8.162879E-02
        -9.817213E-02   -3.408162E-01    1.008045E-01
         8.146322E-02   -6.837122E-01    8.639140E-02
        -8.473891E-01    8.227587E-02    1.000000E+00
```

EXTERIOR ORIENTATION

PHOTO NO.   1

	VALUE	STD ERROR	WEIGHT
XO	1.004030E+00	1.441743E-03	1.000000E+04
YO	1.507674E+00	4.409604E-03	1.000000E+04
ZO	1.916047E+00	7.739163E-03	1.000000E+04
KAPPA(RAD)	-1.987476E-03	5.230699E-04	1.000000E+04
PHI(RAD)	8.212977E-03	1.764687E-03	1.000000E+04
OMEGA(RAD)	-5.071542E-01	4.912047E-03	1.000000E+04

RESIDUALS ON CONTROL POINTS
(MICROMETER UNITS)

POINT NO.	RESIDUALS IN X	RESIDUALS IN Y
9	1.9	-12.2
11	.6	13.0
13	-2.0	-.7
23	-3.5	1.7
27	10.7	.3
37	7.2	5.0
39	-9.1	-7.9
41	-6.6	.7
RMS =	6.3	7.2

EXTERIOR ORIENTATION

PHOTO NO.   2

	VALUE	STD ERROR	WEIGHT
XO	4.950632E-01	4.414422E-03	1.000000E+04
YO	1.003202E+00	1.448218E-03	1.000000E+04
ZO	1.915694E+00	7.734373E-03	1.000000E+04
KAPPA(RAD)	1.559733E+00	8.615936E-04	1.000000E+04
PHI(RAD)	-5.077330E-01	4.912955E-03	1.000000E+04
OMEGA(RAD)	-1.838524E-02	2.026314E-03	1.000000E+04

RESIDUALS ON CONTROL POINTS
(MICROMETER UNITS)

POINT NO.	RESIDUALS IN X	RESIDUALS IN Y
9	-6.9	-8.0
11	4.6	-2.1
13	-1.1	1.2
23	4.5	14.6
27	3.6	-1.5
37	-1.7	-4.9
39	-1.8	-2.1
41	-.7	2.9
RMS =	3.7	6.4

EXTERIOR ORIENTATION

PHOTO NO.   3

	VALUE	STD ERROR	WEIGHT
XO	9.964466E-01	1.450882E-03	1.000000E+04
YO	4.947275E-01	4.412032E-03	1.000000E+04
ZO	1.916096E+00	7.737345E-03	1.000000E+04
KAPPA(RAD)	3.140140E+00	5.291136E-04	1.000000E+04
PHI(RAD)	-1.672892E-02	1.770089E-03	1.000000E+04
OMEGA(RAD)	5.073168E-01	4.914888E-03	1.000000E+04

RESIDUALS ON CONTROL POINTS
(MICROMETER UNITS)

POINT NO.	RESIDUALS IN X	RESIDUALS IN Y
9	-8.3	.4
11	3.7	-12.5
13	6.5	4.5
23	6.3	6.8
27	-7.8	7.0
37	-2.3	-8.7
39	3.4	13.3
41	-1.4	-10.7
RMS =	5.5	8.9

EXTERIOR ORIENTATION

PHOTO NO.   4

	VALUE	STD ERROR	WEIGHT
XO	1.508858E+00	4.410216E-03	1.000000E+04
YO	9.974985E-01	1.448132E-03	1.000000E+04
ZO	1.916602E+00	7.741267E-03	1.000000E+04
KAPPA(RAD)	-1.580470E+00	8.609583E-04	1.000000E+04
PHI(RAD)	5.066496E-01	4.913017E-03	1.000000E+04
OMEGA(RAD)	1.727583E-02	2.018983E-03	1.000000E+04

RESIDUALS ON CONTROL POINTS
(MICROMETER UNITS)

POINT NO.	RESIDUALS IN X	RESIDUALS IN Y
9	.6	8.3
11	-5.8	-1.4
13	2.1	-8.7
23	3.7	-9.9
27	1.7	14.8
37	-3.9	2.7
39	5.8	.2
41	-4.2	-6.0
RMS =	3.9	8.0

ADJUSTED SURVEY COORDINATES (M)

POINT	X	Y	Z
9	.8005	1.2003	1.0000
11	1.0004	1.2004	1.0001
13	1.2001	1.2000	1.0000
23	.8004	1.0003	1.0000
27	1.2004	1.0000	.9999
37	.8003	.8002	1.0000
39	1.0002	.7998	1.0000
41	1.2005	.8000	1.0000

STD. DEV. OF SURVEY COORDINATES (MM)

POINT	X	Y	Z
9	.0878	.0878	.1803
11	.0850	.0837	.1688
13	.0878	.0878	.1803
23	.0837	.0850	.1688
27	.0838	.0850	.1688
37	.0878	.0878	.1803
39	.0850	.0837	.1688
41	.0878	.0878	.1803

MATRIX OF VARIANCE
OBJECT COORD.

SUB-MATRIX :   1

.13810D-08   .60862D-11   .25425D-09
.60862D-11   .13817D-08   -.25731D-09
.25425D-09   -.25731D-09   .53732D-08

SUB-MATRIX :   2

.13934D-08   .76226D-12   -.19520D-11
.76226D-12   .13931D-08   -.24466D-09
-.19520D-11   -.24466D-09   .54296D-08

SUB-MATRIX :   3

.13847D-08   -.47579D-11   -.25714D-09
-.47579D-11   .13839D-08   -.25396D-09
-.25714D-09   -.25396D-09   .53756D-08

SUB-MATRIX :   4

.13917D-08   .78037D-13   .24469D-09
.78037D-13   .13928D-08   -.57087D-12
.24469D-09   -.57087D-12   .54303D-08

SUB-MATRIX :   5

.13950D-08   .10930D-12   -.24475D-09
.10930D-12   .13942D-08   .13444D-11
-.24475D-09   .13444D-11   .54329D-08

SUB-MATRIX :   6

.13812D-08   -.54988D-11   .25804D-09
-.54988D-11   .13822D-08   .25522D-09
.25804D-09   .25522D-09   .53739D-08

SUB-MATRIX :   7

.13934D-08   -.24920D-13   .92388D-12
-.24920D-13   .13930D-08   .24561D-09
.92388D-12   .24561D-09   .54313D-08

SUB-MATRIX :   8

.13842D-08   .53766D-11   -.25462D-09
.53766D-11   .13830D-08   .25795D-09
-.25462D-09   .25795D-09   .53756D-08

INDEX

THE AUTHOR:

Sanjib K. Ghosh was educated in India, the Netherlands and the U.S.A. He has had experience as a surveyor in India, as a United Nations Fellow in Europe, and as an academic at the Ohio State University (U.S.A.) as well as at Laval University (Canada).   He has served as external examiner at numerous universities in the world. He has delivered invitational lectures at various institutions and organizations in several countries. This includes visiting professorship at the Federal University of Parana (Brazil), Institute of Agronomy and Veterinary, Hassan II of Rabat (Morocco) and the Universiti Teknologi Malaysia (Malaysia) as well as a distinguished invited professorship at the Hosei University of Tokyo (Japan). Author of numerous scientific publications, two other books (*Theory of Stereophotogrammetry* and *Phototriangulation*) and a contributing author of three other books, Ghosh's research interest lies in the geometry and calibration of conventional as well as unconventional photogrammetric-geodetic systems and their applications in mensural problems. Associated with several national and international scientific and technical organizations, he has been serving the ASPRS and the ISPRS in various capacities. He continues acting as a consultant on surveying and mapping to the United Nations Organization.